The Innkeepers'
REGISTER

Country Inns of 🏮 North America

1997

INDEPENDENT INNKEEPERS' ASSOCIATION
Marshall, Michigan
Founded in 1972 by Norman T. Simpson

Photo Credits:

G. E. Arnold
   Madewood Plantation House, Napoleonville, LA
Tom Bagley
   Inn at Olde New Berlin, New Berlin, PA
   Swiss Woods, Lititz, PA
   Canyon Villa Inn, Sedona, AZ
Patricia Brabant
   Carter House, Carter Hotel, Eureka, CA
George W. Gardner; all © copyrighted
   Boulder Inn, The, New Preston, CT
   Cliff Park Inn, Milford PA
   Dan'l Webster Inn, Sandwich, MA
   Glasbern, Fogelsville, PA
   Inn at Starlight Lake, Starlight, PA
   Landgrove Inn, The, Landgrove, VT
   Oliver Loud's Inn, Pittsford, NY
   Orchard Inn, The, Saluda, NC
   Sea Crest by the Sea, Spring Lake, NJ
   Settlers Inn, The, Hawley, PA
   White Inn, The, Fredonia, NY
   White Oak Inn, The, Danville, OH
Denny Goodman
   LaCorsette Maison Inn, Newton, IA
Stewart Hopkins
   Johnson House, The, Florence, OR
Tom Liden
   Joshua Grindle Inn, Mendocino, CA
Roger Miller
   Antietam Overlook Farm, Keedysville, MD
Dave Monaghan
   Montague Inn, Saginaw, MI
Bruce Muncy
   Oak Bed & Breakfast Inn, The, Christianburg, VA
M. P. Myers Photography, Cape May, NJ
   Mainstay, The, Cape May, NJ
   Manor House, The, Cape May, NJ
   Queen Victoria, The, Cape May, NJ
John Rizzo
   Steamboat Inn, Steamboat, OR
David Schwartz
   Belle Grae Inn, The, Staunton, VA
Mort Tucker Photography, Cleveland, Ohio
   Inn at Honey Run, The, Millersburg, OH
Jim McElholm
   Dan'l Webster Inn, Sandwich, MA
   The Red Lion Inn, Stockbridge, MA
Shevaun Williams
   Montford Inn, Norman, OK

Commentary by Kathryn Kinney   Cover Photo—White Lace Inn, Sturgeon Bay, WI

1997 The Innkeepers' Register

For further information, call Independent Innkeepers' Association,
800-344-5244   FAX: 616-789-0970
616-789-0393   www.innbook.com

Contents

Introduction 7
Preface 8
Gift Certificate 11
How to Use This Book 12
Key to Symbols 13
Style, Location, Type Descriptors 14

ARIZONA
Arizona Map 15
Canyon Villa Inn, Sedona 15
Lodge on the Desert, The, Tucson 16
Tanque Verde Ranch, Tucson 16

CALIFORNIA
California Map 17
Carter House/Hotel Carter, Eureka 18
Gingerbread Mansion, The, Ferndale 18
Grey Whale Inn, Fort Bragg 19
Joshua Grindle Inn, Mendocino 19
Stanford Inn by the Sea, The, Mendocino 20
Harbor House Inn by the Sea, Elk 20
Madrona Manor, Healdsburg 21
Wine Country Inn, The, St. Helena 21
Inn at Occidental, The, Occidental 22
Groveland Hotel, Groveland 22
Babbling Brook, The, Santa Cruz 23
Inn at Depot Hill, The, Capitola-by-the-Sea 23
Martine Inn, The, Pacific Grove 24
Old Monterey Inn, Monterey 24
Sandpiper Inn at the Beach,
  Carmel-by-the-Sea 25
Vagabond's House Inn, Carmel 25
Ballard Inn, The, Ballard 26
Simpson House, Santa Barbara 26
Inn on Summer Hill, Summerland 27
Seal Beach Inn and Gardens, The, Seal
  Beach 27
Habitat for Humanity 28

COLORADO
Colorado Map 29
Romantic RiverSong, Estes Park 29
Lovelander B&B Inn, The, Loveland 30
Castle Marne - A Luxury Urban Inn, Denver .. 30
Allaire Timbers Inn, Breckenridge 31
Hearthstone Inn, Colorado Springs 31
Abriendo Inn, Pueblo 32
Inn at Zapata Ranch, Mosca 32

CONNECTICUT
Connecticut Map 33
Under Mountain Inn, Salisbury 33
Boulders Inn, The, New Preston 34
West Lane Inn, Ridgefield 34
Griswold Inn, The, Essex 35
Bee and Thistle Inn, Old Lyme 35
Homestead Inn, The, Greenwich 36

FLORIDA
Florida Map 37
Chalet Suzanne, Lake Wales 37
Marquesa Hotel, The, Key West 38

GEORGIA
Georgia Map 39
Glen-Ella Springs, Clarkesville 39
Shellmont B&B Inn, Atlanta 40

GEORGIA (Continued)
Veranda, The, Senoia 40
1842 Inn, Macon 41
Gastonian, The, Savannah 41
Little St. Simons Island, St. Simons Island 42
Greyfield Inn, Cumberland Island 42

INDIANA
Indiana Map 43
Checkerberry Inn, The, Goshen 43

IOWA
Iowa Map 44
LaCorsette Maison Inn, Newton 44

KENTUCKY
Kentucky Map 45
Beaumont Inn, Harrodsburg 45

LOUISIANA
Louisiana Map 46
Madewood Plantation House, Napoleonville 46

MAINE
Maine Map 47
Lodge at Moosehead Lake, The, Greenville 48
Country Club Inn, Rangeley 48
Rangeley Inn, Rangeley 49
Crocker House Country Inn, Hancock 51
Pentagoet Inn, The, Castine 49
Blue Hill Inn, Blue Hill 50
Inn at Canoe Point, The, Hulls Cove 50
Claremont Hotel and Cottages, Southwest
  Harbor 51
Goose Cove Lodge, Sunset 52
Pilgrim's Inn, Deer Isle 52
Whitehall Inn, Camden 53
Maine Stay, Camden 53
Newcastle Inn, The, Newcastle 54
Squire Tarbox Inn, The, Wiscasset 54
Waterford Inne, The, Waterford 55
Pomegranate Inn, Portland 55
Black Point Inn, Prouts Neck 56
Maine Stay Inn & Cottages, Kennebunkport ... 56
Captain Lord Mansion, Kennebunkport 57
Old Fort Inn, Kennebunkport 57
Hartwell House, Ogunquit 58
Dockside Guest Quarters, York 58

MARYLAND
Maryland Map 59
Antietam Overlook Farm, Keedysville 59
Tyler Spite House, Frederick 60
Inn at Buckeystown, The, Buckeystown 60
Antrim 1844, Taneytown 61
Twin Gates B&B Inn, Lutherville 61
Robert Morris Inn, The, Oxford 62

MASSACHUSETTS
Massachusetts Map 63
Village Inn, The, Lenox 64
Red Lion Inn, The, Stockbridge 64
Inn at Stockbridge, The, Stockbridge 65
Weathervane Inn, The, South Egremont 65
Deerfield Inn, Deerfield 66
Longfellow's Wayside Inn, South Sudbury 66
Hawthorne Inn, Concord 67
Harbor Light Inn, Marblehead 67

MASSACHUSETTS (Continued)

Yankee Clipper Inn, Rockport 68
Ralph Waldo Emerson Inn, Rockport 68
Isaiah Jones Homestead, Sandwich 69
Dan'l Webster Inn, Sandwich 69
Charles Hinckley House, Barnstable 70
Bramble Inn & Restaurant, The, Brewster 70
Whalewalk Inn, The, Eastham 71
Captain's House Inn, The,
    Chatham/Cape Cod 71
Queen Anne Inn, The, Chatham/Cape Cod 72
Thorncroft Inn, Vineyard Haven/Martha's
    Vineyard 72
Jared Coffin House, Nantucket 73
Seven Sea Street Inn, Nantucket 73

MICHIGAN

Michigan Map 74
Stafford's Bay View Inn, Petoskey 74
Montague Inn, Saginaw 75
Dusty's English Inn, Eaton Rapids 75
National House Inn, The, Marshall 76
Victorian Villa, The, Union City 76

MINNESOTA

Minnesota Map 77
Lowell Inn, Stillwater 77
Schumachers' Historic European Hotel, New
    Prague 78

MISSISSIPPI

Mississippi Map 79
Duff Green Mansion, The, Vicksburg 79
Fairview Inn, Jackson 80
Monmouth Plantation, Natchez 80
Father Ryan House Inn, Biloxi 81

MISSOURI

Missouri Map 82
Southmoreland On the Plaza, Kansas City 82
Boone's Lick Trail Inn, St. Charles 83
Walnut Street Inn, Springfield 83

MONTANA

Montana Map 84
Bear Creek Lodge, Victor 84

NEW HAMPSHIRE

New Hampshire Map 85
Philbrook Farm Inn, Shelburne 86
Adair, Bethlehem 86
Notchland Inn, The, Hart's Location 87
Christmas Farm Inn, Jackson 87
Darby Field Inn, The, Conway 88
Staffords-in-the-Field, Chocorua 88
Corner House Inn, Center Sandwich 89
Moose Mountain Lodge, Etna 89
Manor on Golden Pond, The,
    Holderness 90
Dexter's Inn & Tennis Club, Sunapee 90
Colby Hill Inn, Henniker 91
Inn at Crotched Mountain, Francestown 91
Hancock Inn, The, Hancock 92
Chesterfield Inn, West Chesterfield 92

NEW JERSEY

New Jersey Map 93
Whistling Swan Inn, Stanhope 93
Inn at Millrace Pond, The, Hope 94
Hamilton House Inn, Spring lake 95
Normandy Inn, Spring Lake 95

NEW JERSEY (Continued)

Sea Crest by the Sea, Spring Lake 96
Conover's Bay Head Inn, Bay Head 96
Mainstay Inn, Cape May 97
Manor House, Cape May 97
Queen Victoria, The, Cape May 98

NEW MEXICO

New Mexico Map 99
Grant Corner Inn, Sante Fe 99

NEW YORK

New York Map 101
William Seward Inn, Westfield 102
White Inn, The, Fredonia 102
Asa Ransom House, Clarence 103
Genesee Country Inn, The, Mumford 103
Oliver Loud's Inn, Pittsford 104
Morgan-Samuels B&B Inn, Canandaigua 104
Rose Inn, Ithaca 105
Benn Conger Inn, Groton 105
Sherwood Inn, The, Skaneateles 106
Lincklaen House, Cazenovia 106
Chestnut Inn at Oquaga Lake, Deposit 107
Overlook Mansion, Little Falls 107
Lake Placid Lodge, Lake Placid 108
Interlaken Inn, Lake Placid 108
Garnet Hill Lodge, North River 109
Lamplight Inn B&B, The, Lake Luzerne 109
Westchester House B&B, The,
    Saratoga Springs 110
Sedgwick Inn, The, Berlin 110
Greenville Arms 1889 Inn, Greenville 111
Simmon's Way Village Inn & Restaurant,
    Millerton 111
Beekman Arms, Rhinebeck 112
Bird and Bottle Inn, The, Garrison 112

NORTH CAROLINA

North Carolina Map 113
Snowbird Mountain Lodge, Robbinsville 114
Hemlock Inn, Bryson City 114
Swag Country Inn, The, Waynesville 115
Waverly Inn, The, Hendersonville 115
Greystone Inn, The, Lake Toxaway 116
Orchard Inn, The, Saluda 116
Pine Crest Inn, Tryon 117
Inn at Webbley, Shelby 117
Richmond Hill Inn, Asheville 118
Inn at the Taylor House, The,
    Valle Crucis 118
Mast Farm Inn, The, Valle Crucis 119
Gideon Ridge Inn, Blowing Rock 119
Fearrington House, The, Pittsboro 120
Harmony House Inn, New Bern 120
Lords Proprietor's Inn, The, Edenton 121

OHIO

Ohio Map 122
Wooster Inn, The, Wooster 122
Inn at Honey Run, The, Millersburg 123
White Oak Inn, Danville 123
Inn at Cedar Falls, The, Logan 124
Murphin Ridge Inn, West Union 124

OKLAHOMA

Oklahoma Map 125
Jarrett Farm Country Inn, Ramona 125
Montford Inn, Norman 126

OREGON

Oregon Map 127
Heron Haus, Portland 128
Channel House Inn, Depoe Bay 128
Johnson House, The, Florence 129
Campbell House, The, Eugene 129
Steamboat Inn, Steamboat 130
Tu' Tu' Tun Lodge, Gold Beach 130
Jacksonville Inn, Jacksonville 131
Winchester Country Inn, The, Ashland 131

PENNSYLVANIA

Pennsylvania Map 133
Tara - A Country Inn, Clark 134
Gateway Lodge, Cooksburg 134
Carnegie House, State College 135
Inn at Olde New Berlin, The, New Berlin 135
Crestmont Inn, Eagles Mere 136
Eagles Mere Inn, Eagles Mere 136
Inn at Starlight Lake, The, Starlight 137
Settlers Inn, The, Hawley 137
Cliff Park Inn & Golf Course, Milford 138
French Manor, The, Sterling 138
Sterling Inn, The, South Sterling 139
Glasbern, Fogelsville 139
1740 House, Lumberville 140
Whitehall Inn, The, New Hope 140
Barley Sheaf Farm, Holicong 141
Smithton Inn, Ephrata 141
Swiss Woods B&B, Lititz 142
Cameron Estate Inn, Mount Joy 142
King's Cottage, A Bed & Breakfast Inn, The,
    Lancaster 143
Fairville Inn, Mendenhall 143
Hickory Bridge Farm, Orrtanna 144

RHODE ISLAND

Rhode Island Map 145
Larchwood Inn, Wakefield 145
Cliffside Inn, Newport 146
Hotel Manisses, Block Island 146
1661 Inn, The, Block Island 147

SOUTH CAROLINA

South Carolina Map 148
John Rutledge House Inn, Charleston 148
Two Meeting Street Inn, Charleston 149
Rhett House, The, Beaufort 149

TENNESSEE

Tennessee Map 150
Adams Edgeworth Inn, Monteagle 150
Adam's Hilborne, The, Chattanooga 151
Richmont Inn, Townsend 151

TEXAS

Texas Map 152
Beckmann Inn & Carriage House,
    San Antonio 152
Oge' House on the Riverwalk,
    San Antonio 153

VERMONT

Vermont Map 155
Inn on the Common, Craftsbury Common 156
Rabbit Hill Inn, Lower Waterford 156
Inn at Montpelier, The, Montpelier 157
Shire Inn, Chelsea 157
Blueberry Hill, Goshen 158
Mountain Top Inn and Resort, Chittenden 158

VERMONT (Continued)

October Country Inn, Bridgewater
    Corners 159
Governor's Inn, The, Ludlow 159
Inn at Weathersfield, The, Weathersfield 160
Rowell's Inn, Simonsville 160
Landgrove Inn, The, Landgrove 161
Barrows House, Dorset 161
Inn at Ormsby Hill, The, Manchester Center ... 162
West Mountain Inn, Arlington 162
Three Mountain Inn, Jamaica 163
Windham Hill Inn, West Townshend 163

VIRGINIA

Virginia Map 165
Oaks Victorian Inn, The, Christiansburg 166
Alexander Withrow House/McCampbell Inn,
    Lexington 166
Maple Hall, Lexington 167
Inn at Gristmill Square, The, Warm Springs ... 167
Meadow Lane Lodge, Warm Springs 168
Fort Lewis Lodge, Millboro 168
Trillium House, Nellysford 169
Belle Grae Inn, The, Staunton 169
Frederick House, Staunton 170
Joshua Wilton House Inn & Restaurant,
    Harrisonburg 170
Jordan Hollow Farm Inn, Stanley 171
Inn at Little Washington, The, Washington 171
Inn at Narrow Passage, Woodstock 172
L'Auberge Provencale, White Post 172
Ashby Inn & Restaurant, The, Paris 173
Bailiwick Inn, The, Fairfax 173
Graves' Mountain Lodge, Syria 174
Hidden Inn, The, Orange 174
Silver Thatch Inn, Charlottesville 175
Clifton - The Country Inn, Charlottesville 175
Prospect Hill Plantation Inn, Trevilians 176
High Meadows, Scottsville 176

WASHINGTON

Washington Map 177
Turtleback Farm Inn, Orcas Island 178
Captain Whidbey Inn, The, Coupeville 178
James House, The, Port Townsend 179
Old Consulate Inn (F. W. Hastings House),
    Port Townsend 179
Willcox House Country Inn, Bremerton 180
Shelburne Inn, Seaview 180
Birchfield Manor, Yakima 181
Haus Rohrbach Pension, Leavenworth 181

WEST VIRGINIA

West Virginia Map 183
General Lewis, The, Lewisburg 183

WISCONSIN

Wisconsin Map 185
Old Rittenhouse Inn, Bayfield 186
Canoe Bay, Chetek 186
Creamery Restaurant & Inn, The, Downsville 187
White Gull Inn, The, Fish Creek 187
Inn at Cedar Crossing, Sturgeon Bay 188
White Lace Inn, Sturgeon Bay 188
Mansion Hill Inn, Madison 189

CANADA/U.S. MAP 190

INTERNATIONAL HOSPITALITY 192

CANADA

BRITISH COLUMBIA

British Columbia Map 193
Middle Beach Lodge, Tofino 193
Oceanwood Country Inn, Mayne Island 194
Aerie Resort, The, Malahat 194
Sooke Harbour House Inn, Sooke 195
Oak Bay Beach Hotel, Victoria 195
Beaconsfield Inn, Victoria 196

ONTARIO

Ontario Map 197
Sir Sam's Inn, Eagle Lake 198
Sherwood Inn, Port Carling 198
Domain of Killien, The, Haliburton 199
Briars, The, Jackson Point 199
Eganridge Inn & Country Club,
   Fenelon Falls 200
Sam Jakes Inn, Merrickville 200
Benmiller Inn, Goderich 201
Little Inn of Bayfield, The, Bayfield 201
Westover Inn, St. Marys 202
Stone Maiden Inn, Stratford 202
Jakobstettel Guest House, Inc., St. Jacobs 203
Elora Mill Inn, Elora 203
Millcroft Inn, The, Alton 204
Kettle Creek Inn, Port Stanley 204
Elm Hurst Inn, Ingersoll 205
Langdon Hall Country House Hotel,
   Cambridge 205
Woodlawn Terrace Inn, Cobourg 206
Ste. Anne's Country Inn & Spa,
   Grafton 206
Rosemount Inn, Kingston 207
Trinity House Inn, Gananoque 207

QUEBEC

Quebec Map 209
Ripplecove Inn, Ayer's Cliff 209
Hovey Manor, North Hatley 210

MARITIMES

Maritimes Map 211
Shaw's Hotel, Brackley Beach, PEI 211

UNITED KINGDOM

GREAT BRITAIN MAP 212

SCOTLAND

Philipburn House Hotel, Selkirk, Scottish
   Borders 213

ENGLAND

Mill Hotel, The, Penrith, Cumbria 213
Cottage in the Wood, The, Worcester,
   Worcestershire 214
Petty France Hotel, Badminton, Avon 214
Royal Oak Inn, The, Withypool,
   Somerset 215
Crown Hotel, The, Exford, Somerset 215
Woolley Grange Hotel, Woolley Green,
   Wiltshire 216
Somerset House, Bath, Avon 216
Kennel Holt Hotel, Cranbrook, Kent 217
Maison Talbooth, Colchester, Essex 217

Romantik Hotels 218
Scotland's Heritage 220
Index 221

SPECIAL FEATURES BY KATHRYN KINNEY

Gift Certificate 11
Habitat for Humanity 28
We Assure Quality 36
Selecting "Your" Inn 38
Rates Definitions 62
For Your Special Occasion 78
Dining at a Country Inn 81
It Looks So Easy - Like Ducks on a Pond 98
Stay a Few Days - Enjoy the Community 100
What Did You Do Before Innkeeping? 121
The Staff at a Country Inn 126
Gift Certificate to a Country Inn 132
Inn Architecture 144
I. Chef's Uniform 147
II. Chef's Hat 153
Special Events and Getaway Packages 154
Country Inn Cuisine 164
The Shining Light in Hospitality 182
Rate Definitions 189
International Hospitality 192
I Would Like to Make a Reservation
   Please 196
Hosting Your Small Group Meeting 208
Hospitality 210

Rate Definitions

In this 1996 Innkeeper's Register, rates are quoted for 2 people for 1 night and do not necessarily include service charges and state taxes. For inns offering AP and MAP, "pp" is used to indicate rates are per person. For more detailed information, ask the inns for their brochures.

AP — American Plan (3 meals included in room rate)

MAP — Modified American Plan (breakfast & dinner included in room rate)

EP — European Plan (meals not included in room rate)

B&B — Bed & Breakfast (breakfast included in room rate)

☀R☀ — Represents recreational facilities and diversions either on the premises of an inn or nearby

• — A dot before the inn name in the index indicates that it can be booked through a travel agent. Travel agents should contact the inns directly for specific rates and restrictions.

INTRODUCTION

We are exceedingly proud to present to our inn-traveling guests this full color edition of *The Innkeepers' Register*. It was only nine years ago that we printed our first *Register*, an off-shoot of Norman T. Simpson's well-read *Country Inns and Back Roads* travel book. During that time our *Register* has developed into a highly respected source for country inn accommodations across America as well as in Canada and Great Britain. With the recent addition of color, the pictures of the Inns provide a more pleasant experience for the traveler who is selecting that special destination. As further assistance for that process, we have added another *aid for identification* for all of our Inns, our *Style, Location, and Type Descriptors*. At the end of the paragraph which describes the individual Inn, you will find (in parentheses) three single-word descriptors. These words are a universal and concise *key to the Style, Location, and Type of Inn* depicted by the information about that Inn. Additionally, we have included the year in which that Inn first became a member of our Association. All of this information will hopefully help guide you to the accommodations you want.

As you peruse the information about the 315 Inns in this directory, we encourage you to take notice of the special "offerings" at the various places. Wonderful facilities for small-group meetings have been developed at some Inns. Special barrier-free and smoke-free accommodations are noted, and frequently, mention is made of area attractions and recreational facilities. The information in this guide is updated every year; we want you to know our latest and best.

Once again, we invite you to "spend a few days" when you can. Our Inns are located in beautiful and interesting villages, towns, cities, and countrysides. Many offer gastronomic adventures and delights. And, most importantly, the innkeepers at IIA Inns are delighted to welcome you and assist in every way to make your stay pleasant and memorable. We like to brag that we are "... the best at what we do."

The *1997 Innkeepers' Register* is now on the World Wide Web

http://www.innbook.com

PREFACE

We are an association of independent innkeepers dedicated to providing our guests with a unique hospitality experience by being the best at what we do . . . individually and collectively.

Through mutual involvement, we work together to educate, promote, and support each other in our continuing efforts to set standards for our profession. — IIA MISSION STATEMENT

These are the goals and objectives of the Independent Innkeepers' Association, which has evolved from the tiny group gathered together in 1966 by Norman T. Simpson. Renowned as the "father of country inns," his book, *Country Inns and Back Roads*, was the first of its kind in contemporary times. He held informal dinners for the innkeepers who were featured in the first early editions. Then, as the number of inns grew, it became clear that country innkeepers felt isolated and out of contact with like-minded people in the hospitality industry. Hotel and motel organizations offered little of value to keepers of country inns. Their appreciation and need for gathering together with other innkeepers was immediately obvious.

The opportunity to discuss mutual problems and find solutions, and the discovery that their failures and triumphs were shared by others, gave rise to the idea of a network of fine country inns in which was implicit the sense of responsibility to each other and their shared values and standards in serving the public.

At first there were annual meetings, which would take place at one or another of the inns in this book. Then, the need for smaller, more focused sessions resulted in several regional meetings in various parts of the country throughout the year.

By 1972, Norman formally established this loose collection of inns as the Independent Innkeepers' Association. The innkeepers in this group came from all walks of life, many of them having left successful careers and lucrative opportunities to experience the joys and tribulations of innkeeping. An important quality in each of them was not only a deep sense of commitment to their inns, but also an enthusiasm and desire to be involved with other innkeepers who shared their goals and standards and who wanted to work together for the common good.

The feeling of fellowship and family is a strong bond rooted in the shared purpose of maintaining what is finest and best in the true tradition and spirit of American innkeeping.

Today, nine years after Norman Simpson's death, the IIA Board of Directors and the membership are continuing and expanding the work he began. In this ever-increasingly competitive arena, we will hold to the standards of personal hospitality, which he defined and which are so important to us and our many guests who look for both professional excellence and a genuine feeling of friendly welcome.

Accreditation Program

In accordance with our stated purpose of maintaining the highest standards of innkeeping, the Independent Innkeepers' Association requires member participation in a quality assurance program. This program provides for mandatory periodic inspection of every inn by specialists who have been retained to give an impartial evaluation of each inn.

These independent specialists are personally trained to provide thorough, unbiased and honest evaluations and do so in an unobtrusive and timely manner. The evaluation visit, which includes at least one overnight stay, permits the evaluator to get a full picture of the operation of the inn. The visits, of course, are unannounced.

The evaluation begins with the first telephone call placed by the consultants who subsequently visit the facility and report on both the highlights of their stay and any areas which may be of concern. Only upon completion of the checkout procedure do they identify themselves and go over the rough draft of their findings. A formal typed report is mailed to the innkeeper and to the Independent Innkeepers' Association office for follow-up.

Following are a few of the many issues on which member inns are rated:

Basic Requirements

Warm welcome by innkeepers or staff
Architecturally attractive facility
Buildings (inside & out) well maintained
Safety of guests insured (inside & out)
Sitting room for guests only
Impeccable housekeeping throughout inn
A pleasant dining experience or fine dining available nearby
Excellent lighting in guest rooms
Bathrooms well furnished with large, quality towels and adequate shelf space, clothes hooks, etc.

Special Or Personal Touches

Fresh cut flowers or well-tended houseplants
Soft music in dining and common rooms
Quality paintings, artwork, artifacts or memorabilia
Historical references or other material of interest
Comfortable, well-maintained outdoor seating
Books, area maps, magazines, games, bulletin boards and various other materials for guests' amusement
Quality amenities, refreshments

Another important and valuable adjunct to our accreditation program involves our encouragement of guest evaluations, through card inserts in the back of our book. We are interested in hearing from our guests and will appreciate receiving evaluations of the Independent Innkeepers' Association inns you have visited.

The Independent Innkeepers' Association continues to work with members to support and encourage them in improving their properties and maintaining the high standards which make our members the leaders in their field.

Some Criteria For Membership In The Independent Innkeepers' Association

These are a few of the criteria used in evaluating the eligibility of an inn for membership in the Independent Innkeepers' Association. Other more stringent criteria are also used; however, these are the most basic requirements.

- Inn is owner-operated or the innkeeper/manager is highly committed to the spirit of personal hospitality. Staff shows genuine interest toward guests.

- The innkeeper has owned/run the inn for a minimum of three years.

- Inn building is architecturally interesting and attractive with appropriately groomed grounds, tasteful, comfortable and inviting interior furnishings and at least one common room for houseguests only. Guest rooms are attractively and completely furnished for comfort of guests.

- Housekeeping and maintenance are excellent, with immaculate guest rooms and bathrooms.

- Breakfast and dinner should be a pleasant eating experience. If the evening meal is not provided on the premises, fine dining must be readily available in the immediate area (preferably within walking distance).

- The minimum number of rooms required for membership is 6 guest rooms.

Booking Through Your Travel Agent

Most of the Inns in this guidebook can be booked through travel agents. These Inns are identified by a dot before the name in the index. Travel agents should contact the Inn directly for specific commission rates and restrictions.

The Independent Innkeepers'
Association Gift Certificate

A Lovely Gift for Someone Special

The gift of an overnight stay or a weekend at a country inn can be one of the most thoughtful and appreciated gifts you can give your parents or children, dear friends, or valued employees for Christmas, a birthday, an anniversary, or any special occasion. Innkeepers and other employers are discovering this is an excellent way of rewarding their employees, while at the same time giving them some much needed rest and relaxation.

An Independent Innkeepers' Association gift certificate means that you can give the gift of a stay at any one of over 300 member inns from Kennebunkport, Maine to Southern California; from Quebec, Canada to Key West, Florida; from Martha's Vineyard, Massachusetts to Seaview, Washington. We have inns in the Blue Ridge Mountains, on ranches in the western desert, near state parks and forests and nature preserves, in restored villages in historic districts, on lakes and by the sea. Choose your pleasure.

An Independent Innkeepers' Association gift certificate is good for two years and may be purchased through the Independent Innkeepers' Association office by personal check or Mastercard or Visa. With each gift certificate we send along a brand new copy of the *Innkeepers' Register*. For further information call **800-344-5244**.

A five dollar ($5) postage and handling fee will be added to all gift certificate purchases.

How to Use This Book

Maps - The numbers on the maps indicate where Independent Innkeepers' Association inns are located. Information about those inns is presented, following the state map, in the same numerical order as indicated by the numbering on the map. This will permit the traveler to locate a section of a state in which he wants to travel, spot the numbers indicating inns in that area, and then locate details about the inns on the following pages.

Details about each inn: Included with a picture for each inn, you will find pertinent information about that inn. A key for the symbols used beside the picture is located on page 13 for quick reference. Easy to follow directions for driving to the inn are included with each entry as well as other necessary details and the innkeeper's own description of his/her property. In italics, beneath the write-up about the inn, are *Style, Location,* and *Type* descriptors and the date the inn became a member of the Association. The descriptors are defined on page 14 thus permitting the traveler and the writer to have a common understanding of the meanings of the terms.

Definitions of Rates: On pages 6, 62, and 189, the reader will find further information explaining terms such as AP, MAP, EP, and B&B. Rates are quoted for 2 people for 1 night unless otherwise indicated, and rates are quoted in US funds unless otherwise indicated.

Inns that honor travel agent fees: Inns which pay travel agent fees are indicated by a "dot" in front of the name of the inn in the Index.

Comment cards: The last page of the book contains two perforated, self-addressed comment cards on which we invite comments from guests. All comment cards are given full attention and eventually are returned to the innkeeper about whose inn the comments are directed.

KEY TO SYMBOLS

	ENGLISH	FRENCH	GERMAN	JAPANESE	SPANISH
	number of rooms; rates and rate plan for 2 people number of suites; rates and rate plan for 2 people credit cards accepted	nombre de chambres, les prix pour deux personnes, plan de repas; nombre d'appartements, les prix pour deux personnes, plan de repas les cartes de crédit acceptées	Anzahl der Zimmer; Tarif-und Tarifplan Anzahl der Zimmerflüchte; Tarif-und Tarifplan Kreditkarten angenommen	部屋数：宿泊料金と料金別プラン スイート数：宿泊料金と料金別プラン クレジットカード通用	número de habitaciones; tarifas y tablas de tarifas para dos personas número de apartamentos; tarifas y tablas de tarifas para dos personas tarjetas de crédito que aceptamos
	baths—private/shared	salle de bains et WC privés ou communs	Bäder privat/geteilt	バス付 / 共同バス	habitaciones con baño / sin baño
	open/close	période de fermeture ou ouverture	offen: geschlossen	営業中 / 休業ーーシーズン	temporado—fecha en que se abre / fecha en que se cierrar
	children and pets acceptability, inquire for rates	les enfants admis? chiens admis? renseignez-vous sur les tarifs	Kinder und Haustiere erlaubt; nach Tarifen erkundigen	子供とペット可、別料金	reglamentos para niños y animales domésticos (pídase tarifas)
	recreation and attractions on premises or in area	les sports et les divertissements à l'hôtel ou l'environs	Erholung und Sehenswürdigkeiten; an Ort und Stelle oder in der Gegend	当地のレクレーション・催し物	atracciones y diversiones / en los terrenos o cercanos
	meals available; wine & liquor available	repas offerts et bar sur place	Mahlzeiten und Spirituosen erhältlich	食事と飲食可	comida y licores en venta / no se venden
	smoking acceptability	zone fumeur ou non fumeur	Rauchen erlaubt/ begrenzt/verboten	喫煙可	se puede fumar / no se puede fumar
	wheelchair access	accés pour fauteuil roulant	Fuer Koerperbehinderte Geeignet	車イス出入口	a notar: acceso para sillas de ruedas
	conference facilities	capacité pour séminaires	Konferenzräume	特別施設　会議室	facilidades para conferencias
MAP	Modified American Plan	Breakfast & dinner included in rate demi-pension Frühstück und Abendessen im Preis einbegriffen 特別アメリカフラン―朝・夕食付 la tarifa incluye cena y desayuno			
AP	American Plan	3 meals included in rate pension complète (3) drei Mahlzeiten im Preis einbegriffen アメリカプラン―3食付 la tarifa comprende desayuno, almuerzo y cena			
EP	European Plan	no meals included in rate les repas ne sont pas compris Keine Mahlzeiten im Preis einbegriffen ヨーロッパプラン―食事なし la tarifa no incluye comida alguna			
B&B	Bed & Breakfast	Breakfast included in rate le petit déjeuner est compris Frühstück einbegriffen 朝食付 la tarifa incluye el desayuno			

RESERVATION AND RATE INFORMATION

Rates listed herein represent a general range of rates for two people for one night at each inn, and should not be considered firm quotations. The rates cover both high and low seasons; tax and gratuities are usually not included. It is well to inquire as to the availabilty of various special plans and packages. Please be aware that reservation and cancellation policies vary from inn to inn. Listed recreation and attractions are either on the premises or nearby. For more detailed information, ask for inn brochure.

STYLE, LOCATION, AND TYPE DESCRIPTORS

At the end of each Inn's "write-up" beneath its picture, you will find (in parentheses) three words chosen from the categories below. The innkeepers at these inns have selected their "descriptors" from these lists in order to uniformly and concisely convey information to the traveler concerning the Location, Style and Type accommodation found at that particular Inn. We hope these *descriptors* will help you select just the right place for you.

STYLE

Decor and Ambiance

Elegant - Emphasis on high style (and cost) furniture, fixtures, furnishings and service.

Traditional - Eclectic but comfortable and well appointed guest rooms and common areas. Furniture and furnishing often from several periods. Attentive but relatively informal service.

Rustic - Emphasis on naturalness, solidity, and straightforward presentation in buildings, furniture and furnishings, and service, and an ambiance of informal comfort. (Rustic at our inns does not mean spare or primitive.)

Contemporary - Modern-to-striking furniture, furnishings and decor. Service tone may range from stylish to relatively informal.

Architecture

Georgian or Colonial, Federal, Greek Revival, Victorian, Western or Southwestern, Contemporary

LOCATION

In Town - Larger town or city, with the range of cultural and other facilities expected in such locations. Properties in smaller towns may offer access to natural attractions as well.

Village - Smaller community of a few hundred to a few thousand people. The smallest may be relatively isolated. Many offer historic, natural, or specialized cultural attractions.

Country - Rural setting, with the conveniences of population centers several-to-many miles away. May offer access to recreation opportunities such as fishing, skiing, bird watching.

Mountain - Country, with "topographical irregularities".

Waterside - River-, lake-, or ocean-side, with related recreational opportunities. May or may not be near population centers.

TYPE

Hotel - Generally fifty rooms or more, with the range of amenities and services traditionally associated with hotels.

Inn - Generally ten to thirty or forty rooms, with an emphasis on personal but professional hospitality from owner and staff. Inns will offer breakfast daily and dinner (to guests only, or to guests and public) four or more nights a week, and furnishings will vary substantially in type among rooms.

Breakfast Inn - Typically five to ten or fifteen rooms offering full morning meals. Decorations, furnishings and hospitality comparable to Inns.

Ranch - An inn, often multiple buildings, located in a ranch setting, with the recreational opportunities associated with that kind of operation. Ranches most often will be in a country location but may be mountain or seaside.

Retreat/Lodge - A property at which the guests' personal and physical privacy is emphasized. The setting most often is one of solitude. Recreational opportunities may include hiking, nature exploration, hunting or fishing, and the like.

Resort - A hotel or inn offering on its own or adjacent grounds, a variety of organized recreational activities such as golf, tennis, racquetball, riding, health and fitness facilities, etc.

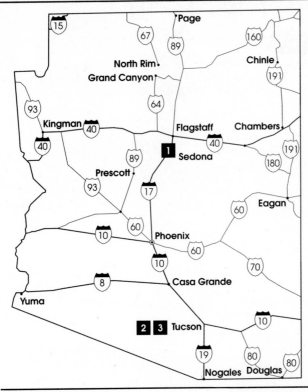

1. Canyon Villa B&B Inn, Sedona
2. Lodge on the Desert, Tucson
3. Tanque Verde, Tucson

CANYON VILLA INN

11 Rooms, $135/$215 B&B

Visa, MC

All Private Baths

Open Year-round
Appropriate for children over 10; No Pets

Heated Swimming Pool on premises, Nearby Golf, Tennis, Hiking, Jeep Tours, Balooning, Horseback Riding, Galleries, 2 1/2 hr to Grand Canyon Scenic Train Rides

Full Gourmet Breakfast, Evening Hors d'ouevres, BYOB

No Smoking

Wheelchair Access (1 rm. dining rm.)

From I-17 turn (W) on SR179 8 mi, turn L (W) on Bell Rock Blvd. 1 blk, turn R (N) on Canyon Circle Dr., Inn on R. From U.S. 89-A, turn (S) on SR179 6 mi, turn R (W) on Bell Rock Blvd. 1 blk, turn R (N) on Canyon Circle Dr., Inn on R.

TEL. 520-284-1226
800-453-1166
FAX 520-284-2114
125 Canyon Circle Dr.,
Sedona, AZ 86351
Chuck & Marion Yadon, Innkeepers

1 Just 2 1/2 hours south of the Grand Canyon this mission style inn provides spectacular views of the Red Rock Formations for which Sedona is famous. Elegantly furnished guest rooms have whirlpool tubs, showers, cable tv and phones. Guests enjoy full gourmet breakfast, afternoon Hors d'oeuvres, nightly turn-down and "sweet dreams." AAA ♦♦♦♦, MOBIL ★★★★
(*Southwestern Traditional, Village, Breakfast Inn. Member since 1995*)

THE LODGE ON THE DESERT

🛏️	33 Rooms, $58/$180 B&B 7 Suites $74/$180 B&B
💳	Visa, MC, Amex, Diners, CB, Discov.
🛁	All Private Baths
🛋️	Open year-round Children Welcome
🐕	Pets by prior arrangement
☀️R	Golf, Tennis, & Racquet ball are located at Randolph Park—less than 1 mile south. (Golf has 2 eighteen (18) hole courses)
🍽️	Continental Breakfast, Lunch, Dinner; AP & MAP available 11/1-6/1
🚬	Wine & Liquor available Smoking accepted
🏨	Conference Facilities (40)
♿	Wheelchair Access (7 Rooms)

2 The feeling of old Mexico and of the Southwest is everywhere in the adobe-colored casas grouped around intimate patios at this Mexican hacienda-style resort-inn. Magnificent mountain and desert views, spacious lawns, and colorful gardens belie the proximity of fine residences and nearby downtown Tucson, with all its cultural and recreational attractions.

(*Traditional, In-town, Inn. Member since 1976*)

From I-10 take Speedway exit, 5 mi. (E) to R. turn (S) at Alvernon Way. .8 mi. to Lodge on L. bet. 5th & Broadway.
TEL 520-325-3366 or 800-456-5634; FAX 520-327-5834
306 N. Alvernon Way,
P.O. Box 42500
Tucson, AZ 85733
Schuyler & Helen Lininger, Innkeepers

TANQUE VERDE RANCH

🛏️	50 Rooms,$140/$190 APPP (InSeason);$115/140 APPP (Off Season)
💳	15 Suites, $200 AP PP (In Season); $140 AP PP (Off Season)
🐑	Visa, MC, Amex
🛋️	All Private Baths
🐕	Open Year-round
	No Pets
☀️R	Horseback Riding, Tennis, Hiking, Swimming, Fishing, Nature Programs
🍽️	All Meals AP (including activities)
🚬	Wine & Liquor Available Smoking Restrictions
🏨	Conference Facilities (130)
♿	Wheelchair Access (50 rms., dining rm., & conf. fac.)

3 In a spectacular setting of desert and mountains, this 125-year-old ranch evokes the spirit of the Old West. Horseback riding, guided nature hikes, bird study programs, as well as a modern health spa, tennis, indoor and outdoor pools, selective menus, and a casual, relaxed atmosphere mean good times for lucky guests. It has a 4-star rating by Mobil. (*Western, Country, Ranch. Member since 1970*)

In Tucson proceed (E) on Speedway Blvd. (E) to dead end.
TEL. 520-296-6275
FAX 520-721-9426
14301 E. Speedway Blvd.,
Tucson, AZ 85748

Robert Cote, Innkeeper

1. Carter House, Eureka
2. The Gingerbread Mansion, Ferndale
3. Grey Whale Inn, Fort Bragg
4. Joshua Grindle Inn, Mendocino
5. The Stanford Inn by the Sea, Mendocino
6. Harbor House Inn by the Sea, Elk
7. Madrona Manor, Healdsburg
8. Wine Country Inn, St. Helena
9. The Inn at Occidental, Occidental
10. Groveland Hotel, Groveland
11. The Babbling Brook, Santa Cruz
12. The Inn at Depot Hill, Capitola-by-the-Sea

13. The Martine Inn, Pacific Grove
14. Old Monterey Inn, Monterey
15. Sandpiper Inn at-the-Beach, Carmel-by-the-Sea
16. Vagabond's House, Carmel
17. Ballard Inn, Ballard
18. Simpson House, Santa Barbara
19. Inn on Summer Hill, Summerland
20. Seal Beach Inn and Gardens, Seal Beach

CARTER HOUSE/HOTEL CARTER

	19 Rooms, $95/$155 B&B 11 Suites $145/$295 B&B Full MAP, Add'l $50 PP
	Visa, MC, Amex, Discover DC, CB
	All Private Baths
	Open Year-round Children Welcome; No Pets
	Golf, Beaches, Tennis, Horseback Riding, Swimming, Redwood Forests, Camping, Hiking, Birdwatching, Kayaking
	Breakfast; Dinner; Wine & Cordials available
	No Smoking
	Conference Facilities (30)
	Wheelchair Access (21 rms., dining rm. & conf. fac.)

1 A remarkably detailed re-creation of an 1884 San Francisco mansion, the inn sits at the gateway to Eureka's historic district. It offers guests exquisite decor, unrivaled hospitality, and what has been called "the best breakfast in California." Hotel Carter next door, another marvelous replica, offers more rooms, a fine restaurant, and conference facilities. The recently restored "Belle House" next to the Inn has three suites with jacuzzi and fireplaces, cable TV, VCRs, and a large common kitchen perfect for groups. (*Contemporary, In-Town, Inn. Member since 1988*)

From Hwy. 101 (N) (5th St.) turn L. on "L" St. From Hwy. 101 (S) (4th St.) turn R. on "L" St. Inn is at 3rd & "L" Sts.

TEL. 800-404-1390
707-444-8062
FAX. 707-444-8067
301 L. Street
Eureka, CA 95501
Mark & Christi Carter, Innkeepers

THE GINGERBREAD MANSION

	6 Rooms, $140/$180 B&B 5 Suites, $170/$350 B&B
	Visa, MC, Amex
	All Private Baths
	Open Year-round
	Appropriate for Children over 10; No Pets
	Games, Library, English Garden, Redwood Parks, Beach, Fishing, Galleries, Unique Shops
	Breakfast, Afternoon Tea with homemade cookies, cakes, candies, and bars
	No Smoking
	N/A

2 Exquisitely turreted and gabled, the Gingerbread Mansion Inn is truly a visual masterpiece. Located in the Victorian village of Ferndale, the inn is surrounded by lush English gardens. Featuring a grand suite, "the Empire Suite," the eleven romantic guest rooms all offer private baths; some have old-fashioned tubs and fireplaces, for fireside bubble baths. Amenities include a morning tray service, full breakfast, afternoon tea, turn-down service with bedside chocolates, bathrobes. AAA ♦♦♦♦ (*Elegant, Victorian, Village, Breakfast Inn. Member since 1988*)

Hwy. 101, 15 mi. (S) of Eureka, take Ferndale exit. From (N) turn R (from (S) turn L) at stop sign, continue over bridge 5 mi. to Main St. Turn L. at Bank of America bldg. Go l block.
TEL. 707-786-4000
800-952-4136
FAX: 707-786-4381
E-mail: kenn@humboldt1.com
400 Berding St.,
P.O. Box 40
Ferndale, CA 95536-0040
Ken Torbert, Innkeeper

GREY WHALE INN

	14 Rooms $90/$180 B&B
	Visa, MC, Discov, Enroute, Amex, JCB
	All Private Baths; 1 Jacuzzi
	Open Year-round
	Appropriate for Children over 12; No Pets
	TV theater with VCR, rec. room with pool table, fishing, hiking, whale-watching. Phones in rms.
	Buffet Breakfast Complimentary sparkling beverages for special occasions
	Non-smoking inn
	Conference Facilities (34)
	Wheelchair Access (1 rm. conference fac.)

Hwy. 101 to Cloverdale, then Hwy. 128 W. to Hwy. 1. Continue (N) to Fort Bragg (3 1/2 hrs. from S.F.). Or Hwy. 1 along the coast (5 hrs. from S.F.)
TEL. 707-964-0640
FAX 707-964-4408
Res. 800-382-7244
E-mail: gwhale@mcn.org
615 No. Main Street
Fort Bragg, CA 95437
John & Colette Bailey, Innkps.

 Mendocino Coast landmark since 1915, and Fort Bragg's premier Bed & Breakfast Inn. Classic revival architecture. Spacious comfort and the utmost in privacy. Ocean, garden or hill views; fireplaces, decks, Jacuzzi. Decor varies: French floral countryside, Traditional elegance, American country comfort, Romantic hideaway. Lavish breakfast buffet includes hot entree, prize-winning coffee cake, fresh fruit. Stroll to ocean, restaurants, shops, galleries, theatre, and Skunk Train. AAA and Mobil approved accommodations.
(*Traditional, In-Town, Breakfast Inn. Member since 1980*)

JOSHUA GRINDLE INN

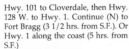	10 Rooms, $90/$185 B&B Visa, MC
	All Private Baths; 1 with Whirlpool tub
	Open Year-round Appropriate for Children over 12; No Pets; We provide 2 cats
	Hiking, Mountain Bikes, Canoes & Kayaks, Golf, Whale-Watching, Horseback Riding, Wine Tasting, Art Galleries, Art Center, Little Theatre
	Breakfast, Evening Sherry, Tea & Fresh Baked Goodies served in parlor
	No Smoking
	N/A

From San Francisco, Hwy 101 to Cloverdale, then 128 W. to Hwy 1. Continue N. to Mendocino, then take 2nd L. at Little Lake Rd. 1st driveway on R.
TEL. 707-937-4143
800-GRINDLE
E-mail: joshgrin@mcn.org
www.joshgrin.com
P.O. Box 647
Mendocino, CA 95460
Arlene & Jim Moorehead, Innkeepers

 A prominent, architecturally significant home in the National Register Historic District of Mendocino. Fireplaces. Ocean views. Situated on two beautifully landscaped acres overlooking the village and the rugged Pacific Ocean headlands. Park and forget your car; explore on foot the Headlands and beach, shops, art galleries and restaurants. Chat with fellow guests over evening sherry, tea and snacks. Walk to superb dining created by some of California's best chefs. Savor gourmet breakfasts. Relax. Refresh. Rejuvenate! AAA ♦♦♦.
(*Traditional, Victorian, Waterside, Breakfast Inn. Member since 1996*)

THE STANFORD INN BY THE SEA

	23 Rooms, $175/$225 B&B 10 Suites, $200/$350 B&B
	Visa, MC, Amex, Discov, DC, CB, JCB
	All Private Baths
	Open Year-round Children & Pets Accepted
	Canoeing & Kayaking on Big River Estuary, Bicycling on complimentary Mountain Bikes, Solarium enclosed Swimming pool, Spa & Sauna, Exercise Room with Universal Equipment, Organic Gardens & Gardening Seminars
	Breakfast, Wine, hors d'oeuvres & tea & cakes No Smoking
	Conf. Facilities (max. 30)
	Wheelchair Access (2 rms., dining rm. & conf. fac.)

5 Elegantly rustic inn with beautifully landscaped grounds including an organic nursery, pond, llamas, and horses. The lodge sits atop a meadow overlooking the ocean and Mendocino. Accommodations are furnished with antiques and sofas for evenings in front of woodburning fireplaces. Combining the best of hotels and pensions, all have private baths, telephones, television and VCR's. The Stanford's provide a large solaruim enclosing a pool, sauna, and spa. Canoes, kayaks and mountain bikes are available. AAA ♦♦♦♦

(Elegant, Rustic, Waterside, Retreat/Lodge. Member since 1995)

1/4 mi. (S) of Mendocino at Hwy. 1 & Comptche-Ukiah Rd.
TEL. 707-937-5615
800-331-8884
FAX 707-937-0305
E-mail: stanford@stanfordinn.com
P.O. Box 487
Mendocino, CA 95460
Joan & Jeff Stanford, Innkeepers

HARBOR HOUSE INN BY THE SEA

	10 Rooms, 4 of which are cottages, $145/$270 MAP
	No Credit Cards
	All Private Baths
	Open Year-round
	Children over 12 No Pets
	Private beach, Kayaking, Wineries, Galleries, Golf, Riding, Tennis, Hiking
	Breakfast & Dinner Wine & Beer available
	Smoking in garden and decks only
	N/A

6 Harbor House, on the outskirts of the quiet, rural village of Elk on the spectacular Mendocino Coast, is a unique sanctuary— a memorable lodging and dining experience. Dramatic ocean views, where massive rocks jut from the sea, benches along a winding wildflower-edged path down to a private beach, quiet moments for solitude and reflection—all of this and more at this gracious inn, built entirely of virgin redwood.

(Traditional, Waterside, Inn. Member since 1975)

From S.F., 3 hrs. (N) on Hwy. 101. In Cloverdale take Hwy. 128 (W) to Hwy. 1 (S) 5 mi. to Elk.
TEL. 707-877-3203
Box 369
5600 S. Highway One
Elk, CA 95432

Dean & Helen Turner, Innkeepers

MADRONA MANOR

	18 Rooms, $140/$195 B&B 3 Suites, $190/$240 B&B
	Visa, MC, Amex, Discov
	All Private Baths
	Open Year-round
	Children accepted Leashed Dogs, outer bldgs.
	Swimming pool on site, Tennis, Golf, Wine tasting, Canoeing, Balloon Rides nearby
	Full Breakfast; Dinner Wine & Beer available
	Smoking in restricted areas
	Conference Facilities (40)
	Wheelchair Access (1 rm., dining rm. & conf. fac.)

Rte. 101 (N) to Central Healdsburg exit. At 3-way light, sharp L. on Mill St., 3/4 mi. to arch.
TEL. 707-433-4231
FAX 707-433-0703
800-258-4003
101 Westside Rd.
Healdsburg, CA 95448
John & Carol Muir
Innkeepers

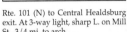 This majestic Victorian manor, on the National Register of Historic Places, conveys a sense of homey elegance and gracious hospitality. Guests enjoy thick terry robes, unique and tantalizing cuisine, beautiful mountain views and surrounding Sonoma wine country. Beautiful grounds, eight acres. A new suite, with fireplace & sitting room, boasts a king bed, deck, marble bath and jacuzzi. Internationally acclaimed restaurant serves superb dinners by candlelight. Gold medal wine list. We keep getting better! (*Elegant, Victorian, Country, Inn. Member since 1987*)

THE WINE COUNTRY INN

	21 Rooms, $80/$260 B&B 3 Suites, $195/260 B&B
	Visa, MC
	All Private Baths
	All Year
	No Children under 13, No Pets
	Pool & Jacuzzi, Wineries, Tennis, Golf, Hiking
	Breakfast
	No Smoking
	Conference Facilities (20)
	Wheelchair Access (dining room)

From S.F. take I-80 (N) to Napa exit. Follow Hwy. 29 (N) 18 mi. to St. Helena & 2 mi. beyond to Lodi Lane. Turn R. for 1/3 mi. to inn.
TEL. 707-963-7077
FAX 707-963-9018
E-mail: countryin@aol.com
1152 Lodi Lane,
St. Helena, CA 94574
Jim Smith, Innkeeper

 Perched on a small hill, overlooking the manicured vineyards and nearby hills of the Napa Valley, this inn is known for its casual and quiet atmosphere. The intimate rooms boast family-made quilts, private balconies, fireplaces and pine antiques. Famous restaurants and wineries tours round out the Napa Valley experience. (*Traditional, Country, Inn. Member since 1978*)

CALIFORNIA
THE INN AT OCCIDENTAL

🛏	4 Rooms, $95/$145 B&B 4 Suites, $145/$195 B&B
💳	Visa, MC, AMEX, Discov
🛁	All Private Baths
🌳	Year-round Children over 10; No Pets
🐩	Tennis, Golf, Horseback Riding, Fishing, Boating, Bicycle Riding nearby,
R	Osmosis Enzyme Bath and Massage Therapy, Gardens, Hiking, Canoeing
🍽	Breakfast, Dinner on occasions private or promotional
🚭	Smoking Restrictions— Porches & Courtyard
🏠	Conference Facilities (40)
♿	Wheelchair Access (1 rm., dining rm. and conf. fac.)

9 World Class Elegance In A Country Setting

Tucked in among towering redwoods, just minutes from the Sonoma Coast and the Wine Country, there's a place where time stands still: A Victorian bed and breakfast with the perfect mix of comfort, charm and elegance. Completely restored by innkeeper, Jack Bullard and furnished with antiques, family heirlooms and original artwork. The Inn offers guests a choice of eight bedrooms with private baths, fireplaces, Jacuzzi spa tub and outdoor private hot tub. A full gourmet breakfast, afternoon refreshments and Sonoma County wine make for a very special stay.

(*Elegant, Victorian, Village Country, Breakfast Inn. Member since 1995*)

From San Francisco (N) 101 to Sebast-opol/Rohnert Park. Exit 116 (W) for 7.4 mi. L Bodega Hwy. (Rte. 12) for 6.4 mi. R Freestone on Bohemian Hwy. for 3.7 mi. to Occidental. R Stop sign to Inn.
TEL. 707-874-1047
800-522-6324
FAX 707-874-1078
E-mail: innkeeper@innatoccidental.com
Page: http://www.innatoccidental.com
P.O. Box 857
3657 Church St.
Occidental, CA 95465
Jack Bullard, Innkeeper

GROVELAND HOTEL

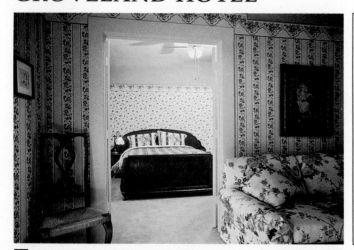

🛏	14 Rooms, $95/$115 B&B 3 Suites, $175 B&B
💳	Visa, MC, Amex, CB, DC, DISC
🛁	All Private Baths Year-round
🌳	Kids find us boring; Pets by prior Arrangement
🐩	Yosemite National Park (23 m.), Golf, Tennis, Hiking, Fishing, Swimming, (Lake
R	w/ 3 beaches), Pool, World-class White Water Rafting
🍽	Continental Breakfast, Afternoon Tea, Wine, Gourmet Restaurant
🚭	Smoking outside only; $200 cleaning charge for smoking inside
🏠	Conference Facilities (25)
♿	Wheelchair Access (6 rms and dining rm)

10 The 1849 Adobe and 1914 Queen Anne buildings offer 14 rooms and 3 suites with European antiques, terry robes, down comforters, upscale linens and private baths. Some have private entrances to the verandas where white wicker abounds. Suites have separate sitting rooms, fireplaces, and spa tubs. The parlour has books, games, a fireplace, and television. Listed on National Register of Historic Places. Fall/Winter Calendar of Events.

(*Traditional, Victorian, Country, Inn. Member since 1993*)

From Bay Area 3 hours, 80/680 to 580 to 120 at Tracy. From Sacramento & Central Valley, Hwy 5 or 99 to 120 at Manteca. Hotel is located on 120 (18767 Main St.).
TEL 209-962-4000;
800-273-3314—Reservations
FAX 209-962-6674
Internet: www.groveland.com
E-mail: peggy@groveland.com
18767 Main Street
PO Box 481
Groveland, California 95321
Peggy A. & Grover C. Mosley, Innkeepers

THE BABBLING BROOK

 12 Rooms, $85/$165 B&B
Visa, MC, Amex, Carte
Bl, Discov

 All Private Baths

 Open Year-round

 Children with restrictions; No Pets in rooms

 Near Tennis, Golf, Fishing, Boating, Beaches, Parks, Redwoods, Narrow-gauge Railroad, Wineries, Shopping, Local Artists, Climate year around 50°–80°

Breakfast, Afternoon Tea, Mrs King's Cookies, Wine & Cheese Evenings

No Smoking

Conf. Facilities (12-15)

Wheelchair Access (2 rm., dining rm. & conf. fac.)

From Hwy. 17 take Half Moon Bay exit to Hwy. 1 (N). Continue on Mission St. to L. on Laurel at signal, 1 1/2 blks. down hill on R. From (S) on Hwy. 1, turn L. on Laurel, 1 1/2 blks. on R. From (N) on Hwy. 1 turn R. on Laurel St.

TEL. 408-427-2437; 800-866-1131; FAX 408-427-2457

1025 Laurel St.
Santa Cruz, CA 95060
Helen King, Innkeeper

11 Historic waterwheel, falls and brook in an acre of redwoods and pines surround this secluded inn. Built in 1909 on the foundation of a 1790 gristmill and 2000-year-old Indian fishing village, it's on the National Register of Historic Places. Rooms in French decor with four jet bathtubs, private entrances, decks overlooking the gardens, most have fireplaces. Gazebo is popular for weddings. Top Inn Award, *Country-Inn Magazine*, 1994.
(Traditional, Waterside, Breakfast Inn. Member since 1990)

THE INN AT DEPOT HILL

 6 Rooms, $165/$195 B&B
6 Suites, $210/$250 B&B

Visa, MC, Amex

All Private Baths, 5 Hot Tubs

Open Year-round

No Pets; Prefer no children

 Golf, Fishing, Water Sports

 Breakfast, Complimentary wine, hors d'oeuvres, dessert

 No Smoking

 Conference Facilities (16)

 Wheelchair Access (1 rm., dining rm. & conf. fac.)

From 1 take Park Ave. exit turning towards the ocean for 1 mile. Left on Monterey Ave. and immediately left into our driveway. Look for white columns and international flags.

TEL. (408) 462-3376
800-572-2632
FAX (408) 462-3697
Website: http:||www.innatdepothill.com
E-mail: lodging@innatdepothill.com
250 Monterey Ave.
Capitola-by-the-Sea, CA 95010
Suzie Lankes, Innkeeper

12 Near a sandy beach in a quaint, Mediterranean-style resort, this award-winning inn was named 1 of top 10 inns in the country. A decorator's delight, upscale rooms resemble different parts of the world. All rooms have fireplaces, TV/VCR, stereo systems, phones, modems, robes, featherbeds, and flowers. Most have private hot tubs in private garden patios. Mobil 4 Stars!
(Elegant, Waterside, Breakfast Inn. Member since 1992)

THE MARTINE INN

🛏	17 Rooms, $135/$245 B&B 3 Suites, $260/$295 B&B
💳	Visa, MC, Amex, Discv
🛁	All Private Baths
🕯	Open Year-round Children OK; No Pets
🐎	Spa, Pool Table, Vintage Auto Collection, Fishing, Hiking, Bike Riding, Bird & Otter Watching, Roller
☀R	Blading, Shopping, Sightseeing, Monterey Bay Aquarium
🍷	Breakfast, Wine & Beer available, Lunch & Din- ner for groups only
🚭	Smoking Restrictions (in guest rooms with fire- places only)
⊢♦♦♦⊣	Conference Facilities (20)
♿	Wheelchair Access (6 rm., dining rm. & conf. rm.)

13 Come relax & enjoy breathtaking views of the Monterey Bay where seals, otters, and whales can be seen while staying at this romantic cliffside mansion. Your room may have a view of the crashing surf or a woodburning fireplace to snuggle up to that special person. Awake to a sumptuous breakfast awaiting you in the parlor. Relish the fine collection of museum quality American antiques in every room.

(Elegant, Victorian, Waterside, Breakfast Inn. Member since 1992)

Hwy. 1 to Pebble-Beach-Pacific Grove Turnoff to Hwy. 68 to Pacific Grove. R on Ocean View Blvd. R at 255.
TEL. 408-373-3388
or 800-852-5588
FAX: 408-373-3896
255 Oceanview Blvd.
Pacific Grove, CA 93950
Marion & Don Martine &
Tracy Harris, Innkeepers

OLD MONTEREY INN

🛏	8 Rooms, $170/$240 B&B 2 Suites, $170/$240 B&B
💳	Visa, MC
🛁	All Private Baths
🕯	Closed Dec. 24-25
🐎	No Pets; not suitable for small children
☀R	Golf, Tennis, Horseback Riding, Beach Activities, Bicycling, Monterey Bay Aquarium, Carmel, Big Sur coast near by
🍷	Breakfast, Evening hors d'oeuvres & Spirits
🚭	No Smoking
⊢♦♦♦⊣	
♿	N/A

14 Discriminating guests will enjoy this unique country inn experience. A *Mobil 4-star* recipient since 1983, the Inn provides warm hospitality and gracious surroundings. The 1929 Tudor mansion, surrounded by over an acre of lush gardens, has all the modern comforts, as well as wood burning fireplaces, jacuzzi, gourmet breakfasts, and evening hors d'oeuvres. The Inn, located in the heart of Monterey, is within walking distance to Monterey's Historic downtown, the Monterey Bay Aquarium, Fisherman's Wharf, and Cannery Row.

(Traditional, In-Town, Breakfast Inn. Member since 1993)

S. on Hwy. 1, take Soledad-Munras Ave. exit. Cross Munras. R. on Pa-cific, then 1/2 mile to Martin, on left; N. on Hwy 1, take Munras exit. Im-mediate L. on Soledad. R. on Pacific, then 1/2 mile to Martin, on left.
408-375-8284
1-800-350-2344
FAX 408-375-6730
Webpage: www.oldmontereyinn.com
E-mail: omi@oldmontereyinn.com
500 Martin St.
Monterey, CA 93940
Ann & Gene Swett, Innkeepers

SANDPIPER INN AT-THE-BEACH

	13 Rooms, $95/$190 B&B 3 Cottage rooms, $95/$150 B&B
	Visa, MC, Amex
	All Private Bathrooms
	Open Year-around
	Appropriate for Children Over 12; No Pets
	Pebble Beach, 17-Mile Drive, Famous Golf Courses, Big Sur Coast & Point Lobos Reserve, Carmel Mission Basilica (1771).
	Continental Buffet Breakfast, Five O'clock Sherry Smoking in restricted areas
	Conference Facilities (15)
	N/A

Hwy. 1, R. at Ocean Ave. (W) thru Carmel 1 mi. L. at Scenic Rd. (S) .8 mi. to end of beach at Martin Way (S).

TEL. 408-624-6433;
800-633-6433
FAX 408-624-5964
2408 Bay View Ave.
Carmel by-the-sea, CA 93923

Graeme & Irene Mackenzie
Innkeepers

15 Just 100 yds. from Carmel's white beaches, with unique ocean views across the bay to Pebble Beach. Early California architecture is complemented by country antiques, gardens & patios. Comfortable lounge has a cathedral ceiling & fireplace. Rooms are individually decorated, and some have fireplaces. A romantic getaway in a beautiful, quiet residential area with warm, restful ambiance.
(*Traditional, Ocean-Side, Breakfast Inn. Member since 1981*)

VAGABOND'S HOUSE INN

	11 Rooms, $85/$165 B&B Suites, $220 B&B
	Visa, MC, Amex
	All Private Baths
	Open Year-round
	Appropriate for Children over 11; Pets accepted
	Carmel Beach, 17-Mile Drive, Golf, Tennis, Big Sur, Monterey Bay Aquarium
	Breakfast; Cream Sherry
	Smoking Restrictions
	N/A

Turn off Hwy. 1 to Ocean Ave., (W) to town center. R. onto Dolores for 2.5 blocks to inn.

TEL. 408-624-7738 or
800-262-1262
FAX 408-626-1243
P.O. Box 2747
Dolores & 4th
Carmel, CA 93921

Dennis LeVett
Owner/Innkeeper

16 The stone courtyard here is an almost magical experience, with the great oak and cascading waterfalls, surrounded by vines, ferns, and gorgeous flowers. Tuffy, the watch cat, suns on a doorstep. Around the courtyard are unique rooms with fireplaces. All the natural beauty and fascinating shops of Carmel are just around the corner.
(*Traditional, Village, Breakfast Inn. Member since 1976*)

CALIFORNIA
BALLARD INN

🛏	15 Rooms, $150/$220 B&B
💳	Visa, MC, Amex
🛁	All private baths
🛋	All Year except Christmas Eve and Christmas
🐕	No Pets, Well-behaved Parents with Children
☀	Wineries, Golf, Art Galleries, Biking, Hiking, Shopping, Antiques, Glider Rides, Horseback Riding, Horse Ranches
🍷	Dinner served, Wed.—Sun. at Cafe Chardonnay Beer & Wine Available
🚬	Smoking permitted on the veranda outside
🏨	Conference Facilities (30)
♿	Wheelchair Access (1 rm., dining rm. & conf. fac.)

17 Comfortably elegant accommodations in the heart of the Santa Barbara wine country. Just 40 minutes from Santa Barbara, yet nestled in a country neighborhood of orchards and vineyards, the Ballard Inn offers an intimate retreat. Each of the 15 guest rooms possesses its own special charm and character reflecting local history. Visit Fess Parker at his winery, or drop by any of the award-winning wineries close by! AAA♦♦♦♦.
(*Traditional, Country, Inn. Member since 1993*)

From Highway 101, take Solvang Exit. Follow Route 246 E. through Solvang to Alamo Pintado Road; turn left. Drive 3 miles to Baseline Ave., turn right and Inn is 50 yards on the right.
TEL. 805-688-7770,
1-800-638-2466
FAX 805-688-9560
2436 Baseline Ave
Ballard, CA 93463
Kelly Robinson, Innkeeper

SIMPSON HOUSE

🛏	7 Rooms, $140/$325 B&B 4 Suites, 3 Cottages, $270/$325 B&B
💳	Visa, MC, Disc
🛁	All Private Baths
🛋	Open Year-round
🐕	No pets and no facilities for children
☀	Lawn Croquet, Bicycles, Picnic Baskets, Beach Equipment
🍷	Breakfast, Full Gourmet, Wine, & Hor d'oeuvres
🚬	Smoking Restrictions
🏨	Conference Facilities (20–25)
♿	Wheelchair Access (1 rm., dining rm. and conf. fac.)

18 Awarded Grand Hotels Award by travel writers and editors—best bed and breakfast in Southern California. The 1874 Victorian, historic landmark estate, secluded in an acre of beautiful English gardens, is elegantly decorated with European antiques, oriental carpets, and fine art. Guest rooms with handprinted Victorian reproduction papers, luxurious suites, and private cottages. Seclusion and luxury within walking distance to downtown. (*Elegant, Victorian, Breakfast Inn. Member since 1993*)

From north on 101, exit on Mission St, go left, at Anacapa St right and at Arrellaga St left. From south on 101, exit Laguna-Garden St. Right on Garden St., at Gutierrez St. left, then right on S. Barbara St. At Arrellaga St. left.
TEL 805-963-7067; 1-800-676-1280; FAX 805-564-4811
E-mail: bebt84a@prodigy.com
121 East Arrellaga St.
Santa Barbara, CA 93101
Linda Davies & Glyn Davies, Innkeepers

INN ON SUMMER HILL

15 Rooms, $165/$195
B&B

1 Suite, $295/$325 B&B
($25 per each add'l person)

Visa, MC, Amex, Discov
All Private Baths

Open Year-round

Prefer Children over 10;
No pets

Nearby Beaches, Wineries, Museums, Zoo, Botanical Gardens, Antique Shops, Historic Mission
—all within 5 miles

Breakfast

No Smoking

Wheelchair Access,
(1 rms, dining rm.)

Southbound 101 Freeway; exit Summerland; L. to Lillie Ave.; R. on Lillie; 1/4 mi. to Inn. North bound 101; Exit Summerland; follow Summerland signs; R then L; 1/4 mi. to Inn.
TEL. 805-969-9998
RES. 800-845-5566
FAX 805-565-9946

2520 Lillie Ave.
Summerland, CA 93067
Verlinda Richardson,
Innkeeper

19 AWARD WINNING California Craftsman styled Inn in the seaside village of Summerland, known as the areas antique haven and breathtaking beach. Built in 1989, the Inn's mini-suites offer OCEAN/ISLAND VIEWS, FIREPLACES, WHIRLPOOL TUBS, CANOPY BEDS and first class amenities with European styled English country decor. Sumptious breakfasts, hor D'oeuvres, wines, fresh baked cookies and evening dessert are served in the candlelit dining room featuring a "Teapot Collection," pine farm table with barnyard animal chairs, and a glowing fireplace.
(Elegant, Waterside, Breakfast Inn. Member since 1996)

THE SEAL BEACH INN AND GARDENS

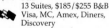
10 Rooms, $118/$195
B&B
13 Suites, $185/$255 B&B
Visa, MC, Amex, Diners,
Discovery
All Private Baths, some
Jacuzzis/Fireplaces
Open Year-round

No Pets, children
discouraged
Beach, Pool, golf nearby,
Walk to tennis, Skating,
Water Sports, Close to
Disneyland, Universal
Studios, All LA/Orange
County Site

Breakfast, Lunch &
Dinner by request, 18
restaurants within
walking distance, others
nearby

No Smoking Inside
Conference Facilities (24)

Wheelchair Access (1 rm.,
living rm and conf. fac.)

Hwy. 405 Fwy., Seal Beach Blvd. exit, turn L. for 2.7 mi. R. on Pacific Coast Hwy. for .7 mi. L. on 5th St.
TEL. 310-493-2416; (Reservations only) **1-800-HIDE AWAY**
FAX 310-799-0483
Area Code 562 as of 2/97

212 5th Street
Seal Beach, CA 90740
Marjorie Bettenhausen Schmaehl
& Harty Schmaehl, Innkeepers

20 The Seal Beach Inn and Gardens is an elegant, historic inn one block from the Pacific Ocean. The Inn sits in lavish colorful flowering gardens in a charming urban seaside village setting. Exquisitely detailed rooms and suites, library, tea room, pool, and accommodations artfully provide a soothing welcome and capture this area's culture and history. Our caring staff look forward to serving you in the Old World tradition of warmth and hospitality. *(Elegant, Village, Inn. Member since 1981)*

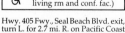

The Beacon of Hospitality Now Lights a Path Beyond Our Door!

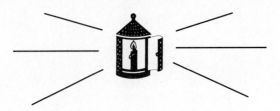

The **Independent Innkeepers' Association** has resolved to pledge our organization to **charitable work** and to help those less fortunate than ourselves.

Our Innkeepers have initiated, on a voluntary basis, the **Quarters for Quarters** campaign to **help build houses** for those in need.

In the spirit of the Independent Innkeepers' Association member inns' welcoming of all people, regardless of Faith, Race, Sex and Culture, we join together to assist and empower people to develop self-sufficiency and life with dignity.

To this end the **Quarters for Quarters** campaign will this year be dedicated to support the work of **Habitat For Humanity International.**

The Independent Innkeepers' Association supports Habitat for Humanity because Habitat challenges people of compassion to provide support—through tax-deductible donations, no-interest loans and volunteer labor—to build or renovate simple, decent houses for the inadequately sheltered. Construction is a partnership venture between volunteers for future homeowners. Houses are sold at no profit and with a no-interest mortgage repaid over a 15 to 25 year period. House payments are recycled into a Fund for Humanity used to build more houses.

Please ask participating Innkeepers for information about Habitat for Humanity and how
Quarters For Quarters Can Help Build Houses

Habitat for Humanity International
121 Habitat St, Americus, GA 31709-3498

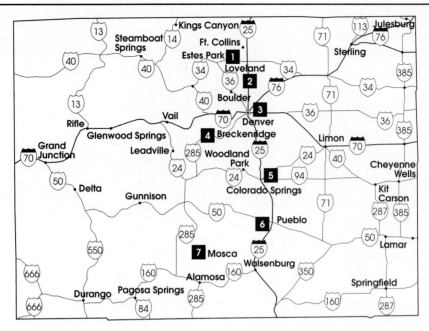

1. Romantic RiverSong, Estes Park
2. The Lovelander Bed & Breakfast Inn, Loveland
3. Castle Marne, Denver
4. Allaire Timbers Inn, Breckenridge
5. Hearthstone Inn, Colorado Springs
6. Abriendo Inn, Pueblo
7. Inn at Zapata Ranch, Mosca

ROMANTIC RIVERSONG

4 Rooms, $135/$170 B&B
5 Suites, $190/$250 B&B
Visa, MC
All Private Baths
Open Year-round
No Pets; only 1 rm. with accommodations for a 3rd person
Snowshoeing, Cross Country Skiing, Trout Fishing (on property), Hiking, Horseback Riding, Mountain Climbing, Outstanding Wildlife Viewing, Bird Watching, Wonderful Day Trips to Other Mountain Areas.
Shopping, Galleries, Antiquing, Golfing
Breakfast; Dinner

Smoking outside only

Conference Facilities (16)

Wheelchair Access, (3 rm. & dining rm.)

Hwy. 36 to Estes Park in Midtown of Estes, Hwy. 36 to Mary's Lake Rd; L. at Mary's Lake Rd; go 1 blk. Cross bridge. Turn R. immediately. Take Country Road following River to the Road End. Road ends at RiverSong.

TEL. 970-586-4666
FAX 970-577-1961
E-mail: riversng@frii.com
P.O. Box 1910
Estes Park, CO 80517
Sue & Gary Mansfield, Innkeepers

1 Imagine lying in a magnificent antique bed with the glaciers of the Rocky Mountain National Park looming just over the tops of your toes, or seeing the stars through the skylights above your brass bed, or thrill to feeding a gentle fawn outside your door, or being lulled to sleep by a melodious mountain stream. After snow shoeing in the Park, come home to your own romantic fireside jacuzzi. Ahhhh, at RiverSong, Time seems to stand still.

(*Traditional, Mountain, Retreat/Lodge. Member since 1987*)

COLORADO
THE LOVELANDER B&B INN

	11 Rooms, $90/$135 B&B
	Visa, MC, Amex, Discov
	All Private Baths
	Open Year-round
	Children over 10 welcome; No Pets
R	Rocky Mountain Natl. Park, Big Thompson Canyon, Benson Sculpture Park, Galleries
	Breakfast; Beverages & Snacks Available; Dinner by reservation
	Wine & Liquor available No Smoking
	Conference Fac. (15-30)
	Limited Wheelchair Access

2 Combining the essence of Victorian style with contemporary convenience, the Lovelander lies nestled in the Rocky Mountain foothills, a short drive from breathtaking Rocky Mountain National Park. Beautifully appointed rooms, peaceful surroundings, gourmet breakfasts, and old-fashioned hospitality from the heart create a haven for recreational and business travelers alike.
(*Elegant, Victorian, In-Town, Breakfast Inn. Member since 1990*)

I-25, Exit 257B, to U.S. Hwy. 34 (W) for 5 mi. to Garfield Ave. Turn L. 10 blks. to 4th St., then R. to 2nd house on R.
TEL. 970-669-0798
800-459-6694
E-mail: love@ezlink.com
217 W. 4th St.
Loveland, CO 80537
Marilyn & Bob Wiltgen, Innkeepers

CASTLE MARNE—A LUXURY URBAN INN

	7 Rooms, $85/$165 B&B 2 Suites, $165/$200 B&B
	Visa, MC, Amex, Discov, DC, CB
	All Private Baths
	Open Year-round
	Well-behaved children Over 10; No Pets
R	Game Room, City Park w/ Tennis, Running Paths, Golf, Zoo, Museum, Botanic Gardens, Shopping, Historic Sites
	Full Breakfast; Lunch & Dinner by reservation Afternoon Tea
	Smoke-Free Inn
	Conference Facility (12)
	Wheelchair Access (1 rm., dining rm. & conf. fac.)

3 Denver's grandest historic mansion B&B (National and Local Register). Close to Museum of Natural History, Zoo, Botanic Gardens, Cherry Creek Business and Shopping district. Near downtown's 16th Street Mall, Larimer Square, Art Museum, US Mint and Molly Brown's House. Hand rubbed woods, stained glass "Peacock Window," ornate fireplaces blend with period antiques and family heirlooms to create a charming Victorian atmosphere. Game Room and English Garden. Full gourmet breakfast and Afternoon Tea.
(*Elegant, Victorian, Urban, Breakfast Inn. Member since 1991*)

From Denver International Airport, take Peña Blvd. to I-70 (W) to Quebec (S) to 17th Ave., right (W) to Esplanade, left (S) one block to 16th Ave., right (W) 4 blocks to Race St.
TEL. 303-331-0621;
800-92-MARNE;
FAX 303-331-0621
E-mail: themarne@ix.netcom.com
1572 Race St.,
Denver, CO 80206
The Peiker Family, Innkeepers

ALLAIRE TIMBERS INN

 8 Rooms, $125/$195 B&B
2 Suites, $185/$275 B&B

 Visa, MC, Discov, Amex

 All Private Baths

 Open Year-round

 Children over 12 welcome; No Pets

 Alpine & X-Country Skiing, Historic Tours, Snow Mobiling, Fishing, Golf, Bicycling, Hiking, Music Festivals

 Breakfast

No Smoking

Conference Fac. (20) (when renting whole Inn)
Wheelchair Access (1 rm., dining rm., & conf. fac.)

From Denver, I. 70 (W) to Frisco, Exit 203. Hwy 9 (S) to Breckenridge. Stay on Main St. thru town, pass Boreas Pass Rd. on L, gas station on R. Take next R after gas station bear R into Allaire Timbers parking lot.
TEL. 970-453-7530
800-624-4904
FAX 970-453-8699
P. O. Box 4653
9511 Hwy #9
Breckenridge, CO 80424
Jack & Kathy Gumph, Innkeepers

4 An award winning mountain Inn combining contemorary southwest and rustic log furnishings in a newly constructed log setting. Guest rooms are individually decorated and named after Colorado mountain passes. Suites offer private fireplace and hot tub. The greatroom with fireplace, sunroom, loft and outdoor spa all have spectacular views of the Colorado Rockies. A hearty breakfast and afternoon refreshments are included daily. Located just steps from historic Main Street Breckenridge, Colorado's oldest victorian mountain town.
(*Western-Rustic, Mountain, Breakfast Inn. Member since 1995*)

HEARTHSTONE INN

20 Rooms, $85/$135 B&B
3 Suites, $145/$155 B&B

Visa, MC, Amex

All Private Baths

Open Year-round
Children Accepted; No Pets
On property—Croquet, Puzzles, Games. Nearby—Walking, Jogging Trail, Golf, Tennis, Pikes Peak, Museums, Rafting, Air Force Academy, Olympic Training Center, Colorado College
Breakfast; Lunch, groups 20+; Dinner, groups 20+

No Smoking
Conference Facilities (up to 40 People)

Wheelchair Access (1 rm., dining rm. & conf. fac.)

From I-25, Exit 143 (Uintah St.) (E) away from mountains 3 blocks to Cascade. Turn R. (S) 7 blocks to corner of Cascade & St. Vrain.
TEL. 719-473-4413, 800-521-1885; FAX 719-473-1322

506 No. Cascade Ave.
Colorado Sprgs, CO 80903
Dot Williams, Ruth Williams, Innkeepers

5 Bright Victorian colors of plum, bittersweet, and lilac accent this stunning inn. Antiques throughout, color-coordinated linens, gourmet breakfasts, and friendly, helpful people make this in-town inn a comfortable change of pace. Rooms with working fireplaces are especially popular in the winter while those with open air porches are sought after in the spring and summer. With all the activities of the Pikes Peak Region, you'll find exciting things to see and do for several days!
(*Traditional, In-Town, Breakfast Inn. Member since 1979*)

COLORADO
ABRIENDO INN

10 Rooms, $58/$115 B&B
1 Suite, $83 B&B

Visa, MC, Amex, Diners

All Private Baths,
3 Whirlpool Tubs

Open Year-round

Children over 7
Welcome; No Pets

Museums, Nature, Bike
Trails, Historic Walking
Tour, Rafting, Fishing,
Boutiques, Galleries,
Shops

Breakfast, 24 hr. Snack/
Refreshment Center;
BYOB

Smoking permitted on
veranda and grounds

N/A

6 Make this classic mansion your home while visiting Pueblo. Experience the comfortable elegance of the beautiful Foursquare architecture. Feel like you belong here at the Abriendo Inn as you stroll the park-like grounds, view the surrounding neighborhood, and walk through nearby Historic Union Ave. district. From the spiral staircase to the curved stained glass windows and parquet floors, the Inn provides an enchanting ambiance. For your convenience all rooms have the privacy of in-room phones and TV. (*Traditional, Victorian, In-Town, Breakfast Inn. Member since 1992*)

I-25 to Exit 97-B Abriendo Ave. 1 Mile from exit on left side of street
TEL. (719) 544-2703
FAX (719) 542-6544
300 West Abriendo Avenue
Pueblo, CO 81004

Kerrelyn M. Trent,
Innkeeper

INN AT ZAPATA RANCH

14 Rooms, $90/$180 B&B
1 Suite, $150/$250 B&B;
Golf pkgs. Available
Visa, MC, Amex, Discov

All Private Baths

Open May 1st, 1997-Oct.
31st, 1997

Children & pets accepted
for an additional fee

18 hole Championship
Golf Course, Outdoor
Heated Pool, Hot Tub,
Fitness Facilities,
Mountain Biking, Hiking,
Horseback Riding

Breakfast, Lunch, Dinner;
Wine & Liquor available

No Smoking

Conference Facilities (35)

Wheelchair Access (1 rm.
dining rm. & conf. rm.)

7 "The architecture and setting may evoke the wild west but cowboys never lived this comfortably." Nestled next to the majestic Sangre de Cristo Mountains and the Great Sand Dunes National Monument, this rustic yet luxurious historic inn offers a unique setting where over 2,500 bison roam on the Zapata Ranch. Experience this secluded 15 room property where the amenities include a championship 18 hole golf course, a dining room and a variety of seasonal workshops. Formerly Great Sand Dunes Country Club and Inn. (*Rustic, Country, Retreat. Member since 1994*)

From E & W take US Hwy 160 to State Hwy 150 N 12 mi. Located 4 mi. S of the Great Sand Dunes Nat'l Monument.
TEL. 719-378-2356
or 800-284-9213
FAX: 719-378-2428
5303 Highway 150
Mosca, CO 81146
Hisa & Kris Ota, Owner

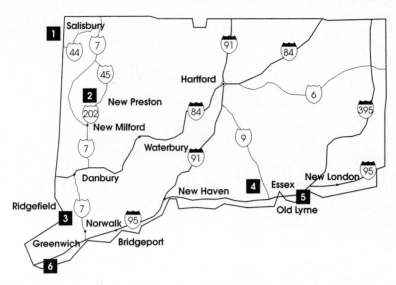

1. Under Mountain Inn, Salisbury
2. Boulders Inn, New Preston
3. West Lane Inn, Ridgefield
4. Griswold Inn, Essex
5. Bee and Thistle Inn, Old Lyme
6. Homestead Inn, Greenwich

UNDER MOUNTAIN INN

7 Rooms, $170-$210 Per Rm. double occ. MAP

Visa, MC

All Private Baths

Open Year-round

Appropriate for Children over 6; No Pets

Boating, Hiking, Alpine/Nordic Skiing, Rafting, Antiquing, Music & Theater, Golf, Tennis, Fishing, Horsebk. Riding

Breakfast, Dinner, Afternoon Tea; Liquor & Wine available

Limited Smoking; No Pipes or Cigars

Conference Facilities (15)

Wheelchair Access (dining rm.)

From Boston: Mass. Turnpike, Exit 2, (W) on 102, (S) on 7, (W) on 23 in Gt. Barrington, MA, S on 41. Inn is .7 mi. (S) of CT border. From NYC: (N) on Taconic Pkwy., (E) on 44, (N) on 41 for 4 mi. to inn.
TEL. 860-435-0242
FAX 860-435-2379
482 Undermountain Road
Salisbury, CT 06068
Peter & Marged Higginson, Innkeepers

Enjoy British-flavored hospitality in an 18th century farmhouse, with a proper cup of tea, *The Manchester Guardian*, and a full English breakfast. Dinners could be bangers & mash, steak & kidney pie, or other English specialties cooked up by Manchester-born owner-chef Peter Higginson. A well-stocked library and cozy fireplaces vie with the lure of outdoors and many cultural attractions. *Travel and Leisure* raved, "This is the country getaway we all wish we had."

(Traditional, Colonial, Mountain, Inn. Member since 1991)

THE BOULDERS INN

🛏	17 Rooms, Suites, Guesthouses, $150/$250 B&B; $200/$350 MAP Weekend premium June–October
🛁	Visa, MC, Amex
🛁🌂	All Private Baths, 5 Whirl-pool Baths (Jacuzzis)
🐕	Open Year-round Children Under 12 by special arrangement; No Pets
☀R	Tennis, Beach, Boating, Hiking, Bicycles, Down-hill & XC Skiing, Antiqu-ing, Golf, Music Festival
☕️	Breakfast, Dinner, Wine & Liquor Available
🔥	Non-smoking Dining Room & Inn rooms
🏩	Conference Facilities (20)
♿	Wheelchair Access (guest-house only)

2 This striking 1895 Victorian mansion is set in a spectacular location at the foot of Pinnacle Mountain and on the shore of a lake. Breathtaking sunsets over Lake Waramaug are enjoyed from the elegantly appointed living room or glass enclosed dining room, as well as from most rooms and guesthouses, 11 of which have fireplaces. The widely renowned cuisine may be enjoyed on the outside terraces in summer. Award winning wine list.
(*Victorian, Waterside, Inn. Member since 1990*)

Rte. 84(E) Exit 7 to Rte. 7(N) to New Milford. Take Rte. 202 to New Preston. L. on E. Shore Rd. (Rte. 45) to Lake Waramaug.
TEL. 860-868-0541
800-55-BOULDERS
East Shore Rd. (Rte. 45)
New Preston, Ct 06777

Ulla & Kees Adema, Innkeepers

WEST LANE INN

🛏	15 rooms, $110/$165 B&B With Fireplaces st. at $145
🛁	Visa, MC, Amex, Diners, CB
🛁	All Private Baths
🌂	Open Year-round
🐕	Children Accepted No Pets
☀R	Golf, Tennis, Swimming, Antiques, Boutiques, Shopping, Award Winning Restaurants, Museums, Cross-Country Skiing, Horseback Riding
☕️	Breakfast
🔥	Smoking Permitted
🏩	Conference Facilities (20)
♿	N/A

3 Zagat's considers it a "Great Getaway"—Judged by USA Today as one of America's finest inns—Rated "Excellent" by American Bed & Breakfast. Built in 1849 and registered in America's Historic Inns, this grand manor estate uniquely combines the graceful charm of an intimate country inn with every convenience of a luxury hotel. Amenities abound . . . spacious, individually appointed climate controlled rooms, all oversize with sitting areas and 1 or 2 queensized four-poster beds. Located in one of New England's loveliest towns, only 50 miles from New York City but far from the maddening crowd.
(*Elegant, Colonial, Village Inn. Member since 1979*)

From NYC & Westside Hwy. (N) to Sawmill River Pkwy. & Exit 43 (Katonah). Turn R. on Rte. 35 (E) 10 mi. to Ridgefield. Inn is on L. From Rte 90 & I-84, Exit 3 to Rte. 7 (S) to Rte. 35 and Ridgefield.
TEL. 203-438-7323
FAX 203-438-7325
22 West Lane
Ridgefield, CT 06877
Maureen Mayer, Innkeeper

THE GRISWOLD INN

 14 Rooms, $90/$185 B&B
14 Suites, $105/$185 B&B

 Visa, MC, Amex

 All Private Baths

 Dining Room Closed
Christmas Eve/Day

 Children Welcome
Pets Accepted

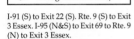 Tennis, Golf, Swimming, Goodspeed Opera, Valley Railroad Steamtrain; Mystic Seaport

 Free Continental Breakfast, Lunch, Dinner; Sunday Brunch, Hunt Breakfast; Wine & Liquor Available

 Non-smoking areas of restaurant

Conference facilities (75)

Wheelchair Access (1 rm., dining rm. & conf. fac.)

I-91 (S) to Exit 22 (S). Rte. 9 (S) to Exit 3 Essex. I-95 (N&S) to Exit 69 to Rte. 9 (N) to Exit 3 Essex.

TEL. 860-767-1776
FAX 860-767-0481
36 Main St.
Essex, CT 06426
Douglas Paul, Innkeeper

4 A kaleidoscope of nostalgic images delights the eye here: myriad Currier & Ives steamboat prints and Antonio Jacobsen marine art, ship models, firearms, potbellied stove, to name a few. The superb New England cuisine features seafood, prime rib, meat pies, and the Inn's own 1776© sausages. Lucius Beebe considered the Taproom the most handsome bar in America. (*Traditional, Village, Inn. Member since 1974*)

BEE AND THISTLE INN

 11 Rooms, $74/$155 EP
1 Cottage, $215/$215 EP

 Visa, MC, Amex, Diners

 12 Private Baths

 Closed 3 wks in Jan.

 Appropriate for Children Over 12; No Pets

 Gardens, River, Golf, Museums, Art, Beach, Mystic

 Breakfast, Lunch, Dinner; Sun. Brunch, English tea Wine & Liquor available

 Smoking in Restricted Areas

 Conference Facilities (10-12)

N/A

I-95 (S) Exit 70, turn R. off ramp to inn, 3rd bldg. on L. I-95 (N) Exit 70, turn L. off ramp to 2nd light, R. to T in road, then L. to inn. 3rd bldg. on L.

TEL. 860-434-1667; 800-622-4946; FAX 860-434-3402
100 Lyme Street
Old Lyme, CT 06371
Bob, Penny, Lori & Jeff Nelson, Innkeepers

5 In an unspoiled historic village on the Lieutenant River, sits this lovely 1756 inn. Its English gardens, sunlit porches, fireplaces, beautiful, carved staircase, canopied and 4-poster beds, antique quilts and furnishings reflect a gracious lifestyle. Widely commended for its cuisine, it has been voted the best restaurant and most romantic place to dine in Connecticut. (*Traditional, Village, Inn. Member since 1984*)

THE HOMESTEAD INN

🛏	17 Rooms, $92/$160 6 Suites, $160/$185
💳	All Major Credit Cards
🛁	All Private Baths
🏺	Open Year-round
🐕	Children Accepted No Pets
☀	Walking, Running Trails, Parks, Beaches, Shopping, Movies, Theater—all nearby
☕	Breakfast, Lunch, Dinner, Sun. Brunch Wine & Liquor Available
🚬	Smoking Permitted Conference Facilities (24)
♿	Wheelchair Access (1 rm., dining rm. & conf. fac. limited)

6 Gracious, historic elegance with a convivial atmosphere. Exquisitely decorated. Three-star French restaurant under the talented guidance of Parisian chef, Jacques Thiebeult. Described by Fodor's as, ". . . one of the finest lodgings in America." Only 45 minutes from New York City. Unique serene meeting facilities.
(*Elegant, In-Town, Inn. Member since 1969*)

From NYC: I-95 to Greenwich, Exit 3. Turn L. off ramp; from New Haven: turn R. off ramp, then L. at light onto Horseneck Ln. (just before RR overpass), to L. at Field Point Rd. Continue 1/4 mi. to inn on R.
TEL. & FAX 203-869-7500
420 Field Point Rd.
Greenwich, CT 06830
Lessie Davison & Nancy Smith, Innkeepers

WE ASSURE QUALITY

When the innkeeper gave you this Association guidebook, *The Innkeepers' Register*, the intention of his generosity was, *Here is a guidebook of my fellow innkeepers' Inns. If you liked our Inn, you will probably like the others found in this book. We're all very different, but we hold the same very high standards of excellence.*

The reason this very bold statement can be made is the Quality Assurance Program adopted by the Independent Innkeepers' Association several years ago. The innkeepers' so strongly believed that they wanted to continue their quality protecting role in this industry, that a schedule was established under which every Inn in the Association will be inspected regularly to insure that they do not slip-up in their commitment to being ". . . the best at what we do."

You see, we realize that Inn-traveling has become very popular in recent years. As a matter of fact, so has it become popular "With this rapid growth in our industry, a plethora of guidebooks have become available from which the traveler must select from a plethora of Inns.

In protecting our own quality and the integrity of *The Register* in this growing market, we hopefully will be protecting the true tradition and spirit of American innkeeping. In 1966 Norman T. Simpson started us down the road toward "professional excellence and a genuine feeling of friendly welcome" for our guests. We are constantly aware of our need to protect our leadership position in the Country Inn industry as well as the integrity of *The Innkeepers' Register*. If you liked one of the Inns in this guidebook, we want to assure that you will like them all.

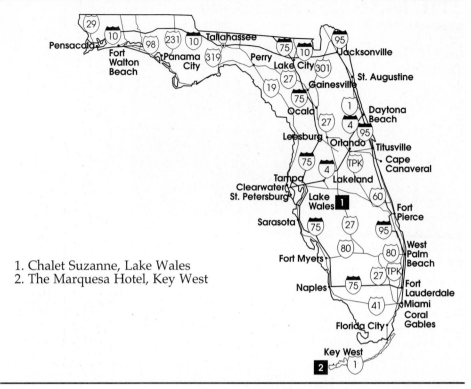

1. Chalet Suzanne, Lake Wales
2. The Marquesa Hotel, Key West

CHALET SUZANNE

30 Rooms, $135/$165 B&B
4 Suites, $195/$195 B&B
$279 MAP per couple

Visa, MC, Amex, Discov, DC

All Private Baths

Open Year-round

Children Welcome
$20 per Pet per night

Swimming, Croquet, Volleyball, Jogging

Breakfast, Lunch, Dinner; Special Packages Intimate Lounge, Extensive Wine Collection

Smoking restrictions

Conference Facilities (50)

Wheelchair Access (2 rms & dining rm.)

From I-4 take US Hwy 27 (S) (exit 23) 18.5 mi to Chalet Suzanne Rd. Turn L, go 1 1/2 mi to entrance (Chalet Suzanne Lane) on R.
TEL. 941-676-6011 or 800-433-6011
FAX 941-676-1814
E-mail: chalet@world.att.net
U.S. Hwy 27 & Co. Rd. 17A
3800 Chalet Suzanne Dr.
Lake Wales, FL 33853-7060
Carl & Vita Hinshaw,
Innkeepers

1 "Fairy tales can come true . . ." A storybook inn with an around-the-world look to its cottages grouped at odd angles, its fountain courtyards, balconies and fascinating furnishings. Winner Uncle Ben's — Ten Best Country Inns of 1991–'92. The Mobil 3-star restaurant is famous for superb fare and caring attention. Chalet Suzanne is AAA 3 diamond Inn and listed on Nat'l Register of Historic Places.
(*Traditional, Country, Inn. Member since 1973*)

FLORIDA
THE MARQUESA HOTEL

14 Rooms, $120/$240 EP
13 Suites, $180/$295 EP
Room only—Breakfast a
charge of $7 PP
Visa, MC, Amex, Diners
All Private Baths

Open Year-round

Not appropriate for
Children under 12
Pets not Accepted

Heated Pools, nearby
Snorkeling, Fishing, Sailing, Historic attractions
and homes

Restaurant or Room ser-
vice for Breakfast, Din-
ner; Poolside beverage
service; Wine & Liquor
available

Non-Smoking Cafe
Conference Facilities (25)

Wheelchair Access

2 In the heart of Key West's historic district, the Marquesa Hotel and Cafe is a landmark 113-year-old home, restored to 4-Diamond status in 1988. Floor-to-ceiling windows, large bouquets of flowers, two shimmering pools and lush gardens are Marquesa trademarks. Rooms and suites are luxurious, all with private marble baths. Located within walking distance to Duval Street for galleries, shops, and nightlife. The *Miami Herald* rated it as one of Florida's 10 top inns.
(*Elegant, Greek Revival, In-Town, Hotel. Member since 1991*)

U.S. 1, R. on No. Roosevelt Blvd., becomes Truman Ave. Continue to R. on Simonton for 5 blks. to Fleming. Turn R. to front of hotel.
TEL. 305-292-1919; 800-869-4631; FAX 305-294-2121
600 Fleming St.
Key West, FL 33040
Richard Manley,
Erik de Boer, Owners;
Carol Wightman, Manager

SELECTING "YOUR" INN

Perhaps the first image conjured up by the term "Country Inn" is a beautifully-appointed and cozy guest room located in an architecturally attractive (perhaps historic) structure with inviting gardens and surroundings. Standing in the door way of this attractive structure is the smiling, gregarious innkeeper extending a warm greeting. Mentally continuing into the apparition, the experienced inn-traveler will immediately begin to contemplate the special, appetizing fare which has become so much a part of country inn hospitality. Thoughts of a weekend getaway with this ambiance, innkeeper, and cuisine have become an energizing force which helps get some working people through the work-week.

Folks who become acquainted with and enjoy Country Inns very often select one that especially appeals to them. They enjoy returning often to "their" place, revisiting "their" special shops and restaurants, and regaling other, newer guests with a voice of knowing familiarity about such things. That kind of individual selection of an Inn can bring personal peace and solace to some inn-travelers. Their Inn becomes a pampering home away from home. Their selection becomes, for them, "ownership" in that Inn.

Other inn-travelers are into it for the adventure. They appreciate the differences in ambiance, innkeepers, and cuisine, and they want to try them all. One lady from New England says that, over the years, she has visited 128 of the Inns in this guidebook. Certainly this inveterate soul has probably become something of an authority on what it takes to make an Inn appeal to the guest.

Selection of an Inn is a personal choice with many variables. Perhaps that is what makes inn-traveling so appealing in the first place. Just as people and tastes vary, happily so do Country Inns and the manner in which innkeepers manifest their own versions of hospitality. Rest assured, each is unique and ready to be adopted as "your" place or enjoyed as part of "your adventure".

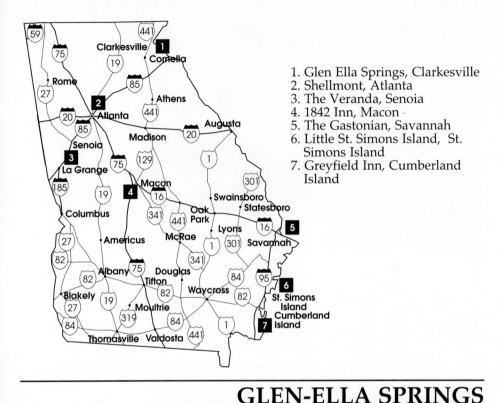

1. Glen Ella Springs, Clarkesville
2. Shellmont, Atlanta
3. The Veranda, Senoia
4. 1842 Inn, Macon
5. The Gastonian, Savannah
6. Little St. Simons Island, St. Simons Island
7. Greyfield Inn, Cumberland Island

GLEN-ELLA SPRINGS

14 Rooms $100/$160 B&B
2 Suites $160 B&B
Visa, MC, Amex
All Private Baths
Open Year-round
Children 6 yr & older in some rms. No Pets
Walking, Hiking, Bicycle Trails, nearby White-water Rafting, Boating on Calmer Waters, Trout Fishing, Horseback, Golf in the area
Breakfast (guests only), Lunch (groups only)
Dinner (by reservation, days limited in Winter), BYOB
No smoking inside the inn
Conference Facility (23)
Wheelchair Access (5 Rms., dining rm. & conf. fac.)

About 3 1/2 miles off Historic Old Hwy 441 between Clarkesville and Clayton; 90 miles north of Atlanta: I-85 to I-985, (exit 45) becomes US 441, L. on Hardeman Rd. at Turnerville, R. on Old 441 & follow signs.
TEL. 706-754-7295
FAX 706-754-1560
Bear Gap Rd., Rte 3, Bx 3304
Clarkesville GA 30523

Bobby and Barrie Aycock, Innkps.

1   The road to our inn is unpaved . . . that's how our guests like it. Located just 5 miles south of the New Tallulah State Park and just a short 90 miles north of Atlanta, this 100-year-old inn on the National Register combines charm of the past with modern comfort. All of the pine paneled guest rooms open onto porches with rocking chairs and lovely views. 17 acres of grounds contain perennial, herb, and vegetable gardens, a swimming pool, a mountain creek, and the restored mineral spring.
(Rustic, Country, Inn. Member since 1990)

SHELLMONT BED & BREAKFAST INN

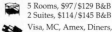	5 Rooms, $97/$129 B&B 2 Suites, $114/$145 B&B
	Visa, MC, Amex, Diners, JCB
	All Private Baths
	Open Year-round
	Children under 12 Carriage house only
	No Pets
	Botanical Gardens, Art Museums, Theatres, Historic Tours, Galleries, Symphony, Fine Dining, Shopping, GA World Congress Center, Omni, GA Dome, Underground Atlanta
	Breakfast
	Smoking on Verandas Only
	N/A

2 Impeccably restored 1891 National Register mansion located in Midtown-Atlanta's theatre, restaurant and cultural district. A virtual treasure chest of stained, leaded and beveled glass, intricately carved woodwork and hand-painted stenciling. Guest rooms are furnished with antiques, Oriental rugs and period wall treatments. Wicker-laden verandas overlook manicured lawns and gardens—including a Victorian fishpond. The experience is unforgettable. City of Atlanta landmark Building. Recipient of Mayors Award of Excellence for Historic Preservation. AAA ◆◆◆.
(Traditional, Victorian, In-Town, Breakfast Inn. Member since 1994)

I-75/85 Northbound, Exit #96; (International Blvd.), Turn L at 2nd traffic light (Ellis St.), Turn R at next traffic light (Piedmont Ave.), Go (N) 1 1/4 mile

TEL. 404-872-9290
FAX 404-872-5379
821 Piedmont Ave, N.E.
Atlanta, GA 30308
Ed & Debbie McCord, Innkeepers

THE VERANDA

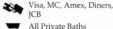	9 Rooms, $99/$135 B&B
	Visa, MC, Amex, Discov
	All Private Baths, 1 Whirlpool
	Open Year-round; Reservations necessary
	Children Accepted (inquire); No Pets
	Rare Player Piano/Organ, Extensive Library; nearby: Tennis, Golf, Fishing, Callaway Gardens, Warm Springs, NASCAR Races, Braves Baseball
	Full Breakfast; Dinner & Lunch by reservation only
	Smoking only on verandah
	Conference Facilities (20)
	Wheelchair Access (downstairs)

3 With wrap-around porch and rocking chairs, this elegant turn-of-the century inn on the National Register offers a quiet, relaxed Southern lifestyle just 37 miles south of bustling downtown Atlanta. Guests enjoy fresh flowers, kaleidoscopes, books, games, puzzles, walking canes, and historic memorabilia, plus The Veranda's acclaimed gourmet meals and lavish breakfasts. Local attractions include antiques, historic tours, Riverwood Studios (where movies such as *Fried Green Tomatoes, The War*, etc. were filmed) and The Veranda's unique gift shop. 1990 INN OF THE YEAR. *(Traditional, Village, Inn. Member since 1988)*

From Atlanta I-85 (S), Exit 12; L.(SE) on Hwy. 74 for 16.7 mi. R.(S) on Rockaway Rd. for 3.3 mi. At light turn L.(E) for 1 block to inn. Ask for brochure/map.

TEL. 770-599-3905
FAX 770-599-0806
252 Seavy St., Box 177
Senoia, GA 30276
Jan & Bobby Boal, Innkeepers

1842 INN

 21 Rooms, $95/$145 B&B

 Visa, MC, Amex

All Private Baths

 Open Year-round

Children over 12; No Pets
Walking distance to
Museum Houses &
Galleries, Health Club
Access with pool is state
of art machinery 5 blocks
from Inn

Breakfast, Evening
hors d'oeuvres desserts,
Wine & Liquor Available

Smoking permitted
Conference Facilities (20);
Adjacent property (40)

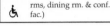 Wheelchair Access (3
rms, dining rm. & conf.
fac.)

Exit 52 on I-75 (Hardeman Ave. Exit),
Turn L from N, R from S; Go 2 Lights
to College St.; Turn L; Inn is 2 blocks
on L.

TEL. 912-741-1842
800-336-1842
FAX: 912-741-1842
353 College St.
Macon, GA 31201
Phillip Jenkins & Richard
Meils, Innkeepers

4 With an atmosphere straight from Gone With The Wind, the 1842 Inn in Macon, Georgia blends the amenities of a grand hotel with the ambience of a country inn. The 21 guest rooms and public areas are tastefully designed with English antiques, tapestries and paintings. The Inn's Courtyard Garden is a delightful setting for breakfast and evening cocktails. Amenities include in-room breakfast with morning newspaper, overnight shoe shines, fresh flowers in each guest room, evening turndown service, and access to an exclusive private dining and health club. Some rooms have four-poster beds, working fireplaces and whirlpool tubs. Listed on the National Register of Historic Places the Inn has sustained the coveted Four Diamond Award from AAA for seven years. The Inn is situated in a beautiful historic district within walking distance to restaurants and museum houses. (*Elegant, In-Town, Inn. Member since 1994*)

THE GASTONIAN

 13 Rooms, $115/$200 B&B
3 Suites, $165/$285 B&B

 Visa, MC, AMEX

All Private Baths, 9 Jacuzzis

 Open Year-round

 Appropriate for Children
over 12; No Pets

 Antiquing, Guided tours,
Beaches, Biking, Fine
Dining, Galleries, Muse-
ums, River Cruise &
nearby Golf, Sea Fishing,
Tennis

 Full Breakfast
Wine Available

 No Smoking

 Wheelchair Access (2 rm.)

From I-16 exit at W. Martin Luther
King Blvd. straight ahead with no
turns, which becomes Gaston St. Continue to inn at 220 East Gaston St.

TEL. 912-232-2869;
800-322-6603;
FAX. 912-232-0710
220 E. Gaston St.
Savannah, GA 31401
Hugh & Roberta Lineberger,
Innkeepers

5 In the largest Historical Landmark District in the U.S., this 1868 inn is furnished with English antiques, offers beautiful gardens and sundeck with hot tub. Rooms have fireplaces, heat and A/C, Jacuzzi baths, showers, cable TV, fruit and wine — plus nightly turndown with sweets and cordials. Guests feast on a full, hot, sitdown Southern breakfast. Mobil ★★★★, AAA ◆◆◆◆.
(*Elegant, In-Town, Breakfast Inn. Member since 1988*)

LITTLE ST. SIMONS ISLAND

🛏	10 Rooms, $290/$515 AP PP
	1 Suite, $390/$515 AP PP
💳	Full Island Rental, $3150/$4450
	Visa, MC
🛁	All Private Baths
💡	Open Year-Round
🐑	No Pets; Children 6 ys & up Oct.—May; all ages June–Sept.
☀R	Boating, Canoeing, Hiking, Fishing, Horseback Riding, Birding, Biking, Family Programs, Orvis Fly Fishing Schools & Guide, Nearby: Golf, Tennis, Shopping, Historic Tours
🍽	Breakfast, Lunch, Dinner; Early Light Breakfast, Snacks, Cocktails; Wine & Liquor Available
🚬	Smoking permitted outside only
⊬▦⊦	Conference Facility (24)
♿	Wheelchair Access (1 rm., dining rm. & conf. fac.)

6 One of the last remaining privately owned barrier islands along the Georgia Coast, Little St. Simons Island offers 10,000-acres of preserved natural beauty, comfortable accommodations for 24 guests, delicious regional cuisine, and gracious Southern hospitality. Seven miles of pristine Atlantic beach, acres of maritime forests, and meandering tidal creeks offer guests the opportunity to explore, hike, horseback ride, bird watch, canoe, motorboat and fish. Enjoy a natural history tour, fly fish with an Orvis endorsed guide or just relax by the pool. Rates include accommodations, meals and all activities.

(Rustic, Seaside, Retreat. Member since 1993)

Two boats daily leaving from Hampton River Club Marina on St. Simons Island.
TEL. 912-638-7472
FAX 912-634-1811
E Mail 102063,467@
Compuserve.com
PO Box 21078
St. Simons, Island, GA 31522
Kevin & Debbie McIntyre, Innkeepers

GREYFIELD INN

🛏	7 Rooms, 6 Suites, $245/$350 AP
💳	Visa, MC, Pers. Checks
🛁	5 Private, 3 Shared Baths
💡	Open Year-round except August
🐑	Children 6 years & up No Pets
☀R	Birdwatching, Hiking, Swimming, Shelling, Biking, Fishing, Photography
🍽	Breakfast, Picnic Lunches, Dinner, Wine & Liquor Available
🚬	Smoking only in Bar & Porches
⊬▦⊦	Conference Facilities (22)
♿	N/A

7 This turn-of-the-century mansion is on Cumberland Island, Georgia's largest and southernmost island. Miles of hiking trails traverse the island's unique ecosystems along with a beautiful, endless beach for shelling, swimming, sunning and birdwatching. Fine food, lovely original furnishings, and a peaceful, relaxing environment provide guests with a step back into another era. Overnight rate includes an island outing with our naturalist, bicycles for exploring the island, and roundtrip boat passage on our private ferry.

(Traditional, Colonial, Waterside, Inn. Member since 1982)

Cumberland Island is accessible only by boat; our ferry service provides transportation to island from Fernandina Beach, FL.
TEL. 904-261-6408
912-267-0180
FAX. 904-321-0666
Cumberland Island, GA
P.O. Box 900
Fernandina Beach, FL 32035-0900
Mitty & Mary Jo Ferguson, Innkps.

1. The Checkerberry Inn, Goshen

THE CHECKERBERRY INN

11 Rooms, $112/$140 B&B
3 Suites, $160/$325 B&B

Visa, MC, Amex

All Private Baths

Closed January

Children with Restrictions; No Pets

Tennis, Outdoor Pool, Croquet Green; Golf, Lakes nearby

Breakfast; Lunch, (Wed. only); Dinner, Tues.-Sat.; Beer & Wine Available

No Smoking

Conference Facilities (28)

Wheelchair Access (3 rms., dining rm. & conf. fac.)

Exit 107, Ind. toll road, (S) on State Rte. 13 to R. on State Rte. 4 to L. on County Rd. 37; 1 mi. to inn on R.
TEL. 219-642-4445
FAX 219-642-4445
62644 CR 37
Goshen, IN 46526
John & Susan Graff, Owners
Sheila Reed Executive Inn-keeper & Gen. Mgr.

1 Watch for Amish horses and buggies in this pastoral farmland. On a 100-acre wooded estate, the inn offers breathtaking views of unspoiled rolling countryside from individually decorated rooms. While away the hours enjoying fields of wildflowers, massive Beech trees, miles of country roads, and grazing horses in a nearby pasture. Imaginative meals and fine wines provide memorable dining.
(Elegant, Georgian, Country, Inn. Member since 1990)

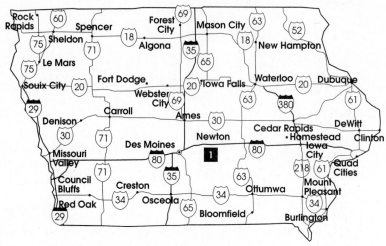

1. LaCorsette Maison Inn, Newton

LACORSETTE MAISON INN

5 Rooms, $70/$195 B&B
2 Suites, $145/$195 B&B

Visa, MC, Amex

All Private Baths

Open Year-round

Children & Pets by
Pre-arrangement

Nearby YMCA, Tennis,
Swimming, Cross
Country Skiing, Parks,
Bicycle Trails

Breakfast, Dinner by
Reservation
Wine Available

No Smoking

Conference Facility (10)

N/A

1 Erected in 1909, LaCorsette Maison Inn is a mission-style mansion. The Inn is elegant, yet comfortable, with cozy nooks and alcoves. It is on the National Historic Register. Kay Owen, the innkeeper, is also a gourmet chef and specializes in Continental food with a French flair. The Inn offers deluxe accommodations and exquisite meals to travelers. (*Traditional, In-Town, Inn. Member since 1993*)

On I-80 east of Des Moines. 7 blocks
east of the city square.
TEL. 515-792-6833
FAX 515-792-6597
629 1st Ave. East
Newton, IA 50208

Kay Owen, Innkeeper

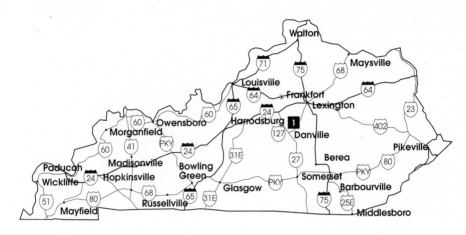

1. Beaumont Inn, Harrodsburg

BEAUMONT INN

33 Rooms $85/$125 B&B (Continental)

Visa, MC, Amex, Discov

All Private Baths

Open March–Dec.

Children Accepted; No Pets

Swimming Pool, Tennis, Shuffleboard, Golf, Fishing, Historic attractions Antique Galleries & Summer Theater

Breakfast, Dinner Daily Lunch, Tues.–Sun.

Non-smoking rms. available, non-smoking dining rm.

Conference Facilities (25)

N/A

In Harrodsburg at intersection with U.S. 68, take U.S. 127 (S) to inn, at south end of town on east side of U.S. 127.
TEL. 606-734-3381
800-352-3992
FAX 606-734-6897
638 Beaumont Inn Dr.
Harrodsburg, KY 40330
The Dedman Family, Innkeepers

Owned and operated by 4 generations of the Dedman family, this country inn, on the National Register of Historic Places, was built in 1845 as a school for young ladies. In the heart of Bluegrass country, it is redolent of Southern history, brimming with beautiful antiques, fascinating memorabilia, and the food is traditional Kentucky fare. Over 30 varieties of trees grace the grounds. The town of Harrodsburg, founded in 1774, is the first permanent English settlement west of the Allegheny Mountains. Located amid numerous historic sites and attractions. (*Traditional, Village, Inn. Member since 1979*)

1. Madewood Plantation House, Napoleonville

MADEWOOD PLANTATION HOUSE

6 Rooms, $175 MAP for 2
2 Suites, $175 MAP for 2

Visa, MC, Amex, Discover

All Private Baths

All year except Thanksgiving, Christmas, and New Year's eve and night.

No Pets; Mature Children

Swamp Tours, Historic Homes

Breakfast & Dinner

Smoking Restrictions

Conference Facility (100)

Wheelchair Access (1 rm., dining rm. & conf. fac.)

1 The "Queen of the Bayou," Madewood Plantation House offers elegant accommodations in a homelike atmosphere. This National Historic Landmark is lovingly maintained by its long-time staff, who provide the relaxed atmosphere for which Madewood is noted. Guests enjoy antique-filled rooms and cano-pied beds along with a wine and cheese hour prior to a family style candlelight dinner prepared by Madewood's cooks. One of the top 12 inns of '93 by *Country Inns* magazine.
(*Traditional, Greek Revival, Country, Inn. Member since 1993*)

75 mi. NW of New Orleans. From New Orleans, I-10 W to Exit 182 (Donaldsonville/Sorrento). Follow "Bayou Plantations" signs. Cross Sunshine Bridge to 70 to Spur 70 to L. onto 308, through Napoleonville, 2 mi. farther on 308.
TEL 504-369-7151
FAX 504-369-9848
4250 Hwy 308
Napoleonville, LA 70390
Keith & Millie Marshall, Inn-keepers; David D'Aunoy, Res. Mgr.

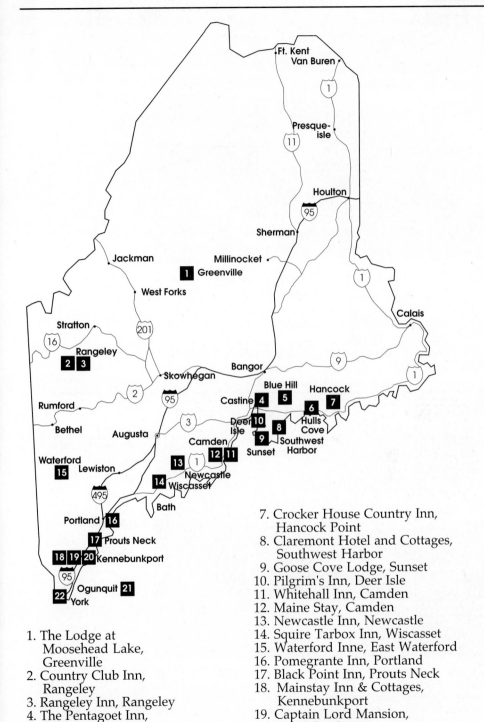

7. Crocker House Country Inn,
   Hancock Point
8. Claremont Hotel and Cottages,
   Southwest Harbor
9. Goose Cove Lodge, Sunset
10. Pilgrim's Inn, Deer Isle
11. Whitehall Inn, Camden
12. Maine Stay, Camden
13. Newcastle Inn, Newcastle
14. Squire Tarbox Inn, Wiscasset
15. Waterford Inne, East Waterford
16. Pomegrante Inn, Portland
17. Black Point Inn, Prouts Neck
18. Mainstay Inn & Cottages,
    Kennebunkport
19. Captain Lord Mansion,
    Kennebunkport
20. Old Fort Inn, Kennebunkport
21. Hartwell House, Ogunquit
22. Dockside Guest Quarters, York

1. The Lodge at
   Moosehead Lake,
   Greenville
2. Country Club Inn,
   Rangeley
3. Rangeley Inn, Rangeley
4. The Pentagoet Inn,
   Castine
5. Blue Hill Inn, Blue Hill
6. The Inn at Canoe
   Point, Hulls Cove

THE LODGE AT MOOSEHEAD LAKE

	5 Rms., \$130/\$205 B&B In season; MAP in off season
	3 Suites, \$225/\$295 B&B In season; MAP in off season
	Visa, MC, Discov
	All Private Baths
	Open Year-round
	No Children, No Pets
	Summer—Boating, Canoeing, Hiking, Bird Watching, Moose Safaris, Float Plane Tours, Fishing, Golf, Croquet, Pool table, English Darts. Winter—Alpine & Nordic Skiing, Dog Sled Rides, Snowmobiling, Snow Shoeing
	Breakfast, Dinner in off season
	No Smoking
	Conference Facilities (2)
	Wheelchair Access (5 rms. and dining rm.)

1 Overlooking the broad waters and islands of Moosehead Lake in rustic Greenville, the lodge marries the amenities of a luxury hotel with the casual intimacy of a country inn. Each room's hand carved 4 poster, jacuzzi and fireplace create a quiet retreat, yet guests often prefer the expansive pleasures of the great room, with its well-padded chairs and sofas set before a massive stone fireplace. This is the comfortable way to regard the wilds of the Great North Woods of Maine.
(*Elegant Rustic, Country, Lodge. Member since 1995*)

I-95 to Newport, 7 (N) to Dexter, 23 (N) to Guildford, 6 + 15 (N) to Greeneville; 2 1/2 mi. thru blinking light on L. From BGR Airport 6 + 15 (N) to Greenville.
TEL. 207-695-4400
FAX. 207-695-2281
upon Lily Bay Rd.
Greenville, ME 04441
Roger & Jennifer Cauchi, Innkeepers

COUNTRY CLUB INN

	19 Rooms \$149/\$165 MAP (for 2) \$112 B&B (for 2)
	25% off for off-season rates
	Visa, MC, Amex
	All Private Baths
	Open late May.–mid-Oct.; late Dec. – Mar.
	Children Welcome; No Pets
	Golfing, Swimming Pool, Lawn Games, Walking Trails on premises, Lake Swimming, Boating, Fishing, Canoeing, Antiquing, Downhill & X-Country Skiing & Snowmobiling nearby
	Breakfast & Dinner; Box lunch available; Wine, Beer & Liquor available
	No Smoking in Dining Room
	Conference facilities (50)
	N/A

2 AN INN FOR ALL SEASONS . . . " 'tis here the soul is refreshed and the mind at peace." Maine's only Country Club Inn where picture-window rooms overlook beautiful Rangeley Lake and majestic mountains. Gardens, pool and walking trails on premises, and twenty steps from our lodge entrance is the first tee of Maine's most scenic public golf course. Gourmet food and a unique bar are always the "talk" of the town. Summer or winter, skis, golf shoes, hiking boots or fishing hats are always in fashion.
(*Traditional, Country, Inn. Member since 1981*)

ME Tpke., Exit 12, then to Rte. 4 all the way to Rangeley. From VT & NH, to St. Johnsbury; (E) on Rte. 2 to Gorham & Rte. 16 (N) to Rangeley.
TEL. 207-864-3831
P.O. Box 680
Rangeley, ME 04970

Steve & Margie Jamison, Innkeepers

RANGELEY INN

50 Rooms $69/$119 on-season $60/$95 off-season $75/$98 MAP PP-optional

Visa, MC, Amex, Discov
All Private Baths;
Several Private Whirlpools
Open Memorial Day—March 31
Children Welcome; Pets Discouraged
Snowmobiling from our backdoor; Ski, Saddleback & Sugarloaf; X-country Skiing, Fishing; Boating; Canoeing; Hiking; Mountain Biking Golfing or Tennis
Breakfast & Dinner; MAP optional; Dining Open Mem. Day–Col. Day & Wint.; Wknds. and for Group Business anytime; Wine & Liquor Available
No Smoking in dining room & designated guest rooms; Smoking permitted in pub & designated guest rooms
Conference Facilities (150)
Wheelchair Access (2 rms., dining rm. & conf. fac.)

On Rte. 4 past Farmington 40 mi. to Rangeley. From west take Rte. 16. Inn is on Main St.

TEL. 207-864-3341
1-800-MOMENTS
FAX 207-864-3687

Box 160, Main St.
Rangeley, ME 04970

David & Rebecca Schinas, Innkeepers

3 The big blue clapboard building with the long veranda across the front has that grand old summer hotel look and the homelike, roomy lobby has a bit of an old-fashioned feeling. The elegant dining room is up to the minute with creative, interesting menus. Several acres of lawns and gardens border a bird sanctuary, and the area is a nature-lover's and sportsman's paradise. So return with us now to yesteryear—and visit our mountain & lake resort from our 1907 Inn. We look forward to serving you.
(*Traditional, Village, Inn. Member since 1989*)

THE PENTAGOET INN

16 Rms., $95/$130 B&B

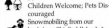

Visa, MC; Personal checks preferred

All Private Baths

Open Late May–Late October

Appropriate for Children over 12; No Pets

Boating, Hiking, Biking, Tennis, Golf

Breakfast
Wine & Liquor available

No Smoking

Conference Facility (20)

N/A

I-95 to Augusta & Rte. 3 (E) to Belfast, turn L. (N) on Rte. 1 past Bucksport 3 mi. to R. (S) on Rte. 175. Turn (S) on Rte. 166 to Castine. Inn is on Main St.

TEL. 207-326-8616
800-845-1701
FAX 207-326-9382

Main St., P.O. Box 4
Castine, ME 04421

Lindsey & Virginia Miller, Innkeepers

4 Capacious porches, overflowing window boxes and rocking chairs are the first thing to greet you at this lovely old Victorian Inn. With its feeling of a private country home, the Pentagoet enfolds you in quiet hospitality. Tiny, historic Castine provides fresh sea air and harbor activities in the most tranquil of settings.
(*Traditional, Village, Breakfast Inn. Member since 1988*)

MAINE
THE BLUE HILL INN

	9 Rooms, $140/$190 MAP (for 2) (15% service charge)
	2 Suites, $140/$190 MAP (for 2) (15% service charge)
	Visa, MC
	All Private Baths
	Open mid-May through Thanksgiving
	Children over 10
	No Pets
	Sailing, Hiking, Biking, Kayaking, Chamber Music, Art Galleries
	Breakfast, Dinner, Wine & Liquor Available
	No Smoking
	Conference Facilities (15)
	Wheelchair Access (1 rm.)

5 The Village of Blue Hill, with its mountain as backdrop, looks southeast across Blue Hill Bay to the mountains of Acadia National Park. The multichimneyed and clapboarded inn, a short walk from the head of the bay, art galleries, and chamber music, has served as the village hostelry since 1840. Down comforters, fireplaces, hors d'oeuvres hour, candlelight dining, sophisticated cuisine, extensive wine list, and attentive service create an intimate atmosphere for inn guests. (*Traditional, Village, Inn. Member since 1994*)

I-95 N. to Augusta Rte 3 E. Belfast through Bucksport to Rte 15 S. to Blue Hill to I77. Turn R heading W 1/10th mi.
TEL. 207-374-2844
800-826-7415
FAX: 207-374-2829
E-mail: bluhilin@downeast.net
Union St.
PO Box 403
Blue Hill, ME 04614
Mary & Don Hartley, Innkeepers

THE INN AT CANOE POINT

	3 Rooms, $80–$95/$135–$165 B&B; 2 Suites, $120–$150/$190–$245 B&B
	Visa, MC, Discov
	All Private Baths
	Open Year-round
	Appropriate for Children over 12; No Pets
	Acadia Natl. Pk. adjacent, Hiking, Biking, Sailing, Kayaking, Mtn. Climbing, Golf, Whale Watching, XC Skiing
	Full Breakfast, Afternoon Refreshments; BYOB
	No Smoking
	Conference Facilities (15)
	N/A

6 This secluded waterside inn among the pines is only moments away from lively Bar Harbor and next door to the unspoiled natural attractions of Acadia National Park. With views of Frenchman's Bay, mountains, trees, flowers, rocky coast and the ocean, guests will be tempted to laze by the granite fireplace in the ocean room or out on the deck, listening to the rolling surf. (*Traditional, Waterside, Bed & Breakfast Inn. Member since 1991*)

From Ellsworth, Rte. 3 (NE) approx. 15 mil. toward Bar Harbor, through Hulls Cove Village. Continue past Acadia Natl. Pk. entrance 1/4 mi. to inn on L.
TEL. 207-288-9511
FAX 207-288-2870
Box 216, Hulls Cove
(Bar Harbor), ME 04644
Tom & Nancy Cervelli, Innkeepers

CROCKER HOUSE COUNTRY INN

 11 Rooms, $90/$120 in season, B&B
$75/$95 off season, B&B

 Visa, MC, Amex, Discov

 All Private Baths

 Closed Jan.1 — Apr. 20; Open Fri. & Sat. only in Nov. & Dec.

 Well mannered Children Accepted; Pets with prior permission

 Spa, Croquet, Library, Clay Tennis courts, Antiquing, Golf, Acadia Nat'l Park region

 Breakfast & Dinner; Sunday brunch Labor Day July 1 / weekend

 Smoking & Non-smoking Dining Rooms

 Conference Facilities (36)

   N/A

From Ellsworth go 8 (eight) miles (N) on US Rt. 1, to R on Hancock Pt. Rd. Continue 5 miles to Inn on R.
TEL. 207-422-6806
FAX 207-422-3105
Hancock, ME 04640

Richard Malaby, Innkeeper

 Sequestered on Hancock Point, this restored 109-year-old inn is a three minute walk from Frenchman Bay. The carriage house, converted in 1992, adds two spacious guestrooms, an additional common room and a spa. The restaurant, open to the public, continues to draw guests from distant places for its extraordinary cuisine and live jazz piano on Friday and Saturday nights.
(*Traditional, Country, Inn. Member since 1987*)

CLAREMONT HOTEL & COTTAGES

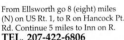 29 Rms.,off season,$90 B&B/ 172 MAP; in-season, $130 B&B / $192 MAP in season; $150 B&B / $180 MAP 12 cottages $90-$105 / $150-$180

   All Private Baths

 May 24 to October 24

 Cottages approx. Hotel & Guest House Mid June to Mid Oct.

 Children Accepted; No Pets

   Tennis, Rowboats, Bicycles, Badminton

 Breakfast and Dinner; Lunch is served daily July–Sept. only

   Wine & Liquor Available Smoking restrictions

 Conference Facilities (125)

   Wheelchair Access (5 rms.; dining rm. & conf. fac.)

ME Tpke., Exit 15 (Augusta), Rte. 3 (E) thru Ellsworth to Mt. Desert Is. Take Rte. 102 to SW Harbor, Follow signs.
TEL. 207-244-5036
RES. 1-800-244-5036
FAX 207-244-3512
Box 137,
Southwest Harbor, ME 04679
John Madeira, Jr., Manager

 The dock and the Boathouse on Somes Sound are the center of much activity at this 110-year-old summer hotel, although croquet and the annual Claremont Classic run them a close second. On the National Register of Historic Places, the Claremont, with its panoramic views of mountains and ocean, offers serene and happy sojourns to its many returning guests.
(*Traditional, Waterside, Hotel. Member since 1974*)

MAINE
GOOSE COVE LODGE

🛏	11 Rms., $145/$181 MAP 11 Cotts., $165/$350 MAP
💳	MC, Visa
	All Private Baths
🛁	Open May 15 to Oct. 15, 1995
🛋	Children Welcome; No Pets
🐕	Sea Kayaking, Sailing, Beach, Nature Trails,
☀R	Golf, Tennis, Sailing, Bicycling, Acadia Nat'l. Park
☕🍸	Breakfast & Dinner, May-Oct.; B&B Option in off-season; Wine & Liquor Available
🚭	No Smoking in Main Lodge
⊢▦⊣	Conference Facility (25)
♿	Wheelchair Access (1 rm., dining rm. & conf. fac.)

9 Secluded lodging, sand beaches, moss-covered trails, and magnificent ocean vistas. Cottages have fireplaces, sundecks, kitchenettes and ocean views. Many artists and craftspersons nearby. Pleasant daytrips on land and water. Outstanding cuisine in rustic "Down East" lodge with lobster cookouts on the beach. A Family Inn.
(*Rustic, Ocean Front, Inn/Lodge. Member since 1981*)

I-95 to Augusta, Rte. 3 to Belfast. Rte. 1 (N), 4 mi. past Bucksport. R. on Rte. 15, in town of Deer Isle R. on Sunset Rd., 3 mi. to inn sign & R. 1.5 mi. to inn.
TEL. 207-348-2508
FAX: 207-348-2624
Deer Isle,
Sunset, ME 04683
Joanne & Dom Parisi, Innkeepers

PILGRIM'S INN

🛏	13 Rms., $145/$180 MAP 1 Cottage, $195/$205 MAP
💳	Visa, MC
🛁	Private & Shared Baths
🛋	Open mid-May to mid-Oct.
🐕	Appropriate for Children over 10; No Pets
☀R	Touring, Hiking, Bicycling, Sailing, Golf, Tennis
☕🍸	Breakfast & Dinner Wine & Liquor available
🚬	Smoking in common Rooms only
⊢▦⊣	Conference Facilities (35)
♿	Wheelchair access (dining rm.)

10 Overlooking Northwest Harbor and a picturesque millpond, this 1793 Colonial home is surrounded by the unspoiled beauty of remote Deer Isle in Penobscot Bay. Glowing hearts, soft Colonial colors, pumpkin pine floors, antique furnishings, combined with warm hospitality and gourmet meals in the charming barn dining room, have pleased many happy and contented guests. On the National Register of Historic Places. Easy access to the renowned Haystack School of Crafts and the busy fishing Village of Stonington. (*Traditional, Colonial, Country Inn. Member since 1980*)

I-95 (N) to Augusta. Rte. 3 (N) to Belfast, thru Bucksport to Rte. 15 (S), thru Blue Hill. Over bridge to Deer Isle Village. Turn R., 1 block to inn on left.
TEL. 207-348-6615
FAX 207-348-7769
Deer Isle, ME 04627
Dud & Jean Hendrick, Innkeepers

WHITEHALL INN

 49 Rooms, $140/$175
MAP
Off Season $90/$120 B&B
 Visa, MC, Amex

 Private & Shared Baths

 Open May 23–Oct. 19

 Children Accepted; No Pets

 Tennis, Shuffleboard, Gardens, Library, Games, Rocking Chairs, Golf, State Park, Lakes, Sailing

Breakfast, Summer Sunday Brunch, Dinner; Wine & Liquor Available

No Smoking in Dining Room

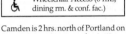 Conference Facility (85)

Wheelchair Access (6 rms, dining rm. & conf. fac.)

Camden is 2 hrs. north of Portland on Rte. 1. Inn is 1/4 mi. north of village.
TEL. 207-236-3391
1-800-789-6565
FAX: 207-236-4427
52 High St., P.O. Box 558
Camden, ME 04843
The Dewing Family, Innkeepers

 If ever an inn and a setting were made for each other, this is it— Camden, Maine and the Whitehall Inn. Tree-lined streets, comfortable old homes echo the feeling of old-fashioned friendliness and hospitality in this rambling, homey inn, originally built in 1834, and operating as an inn since 1901. The inn has been run by the Dewing family for 23 years. One of the few remaining authentic coastal summer hotels preserving not only its history, but the commitment to comfortable accomodations, fine service, and dining excellence.
(*Traditional, Village, Inn. Member since 1973*)

MAINE STAY INN

 8 Rooms, $75/$125 B&B
–20% Off Season

 Visa, MC, Amex

 Most Private Baths

 Open Year-round

 Children over 10; No Pets

 Sailing, Sea Kayaking, Hiking (Camden Hills State Park), Golf, Down Hill & X-country Skiing, Fishing

 Breakfast

 No Smoking

 Conference Facility (15)

 N/A

US Rte. 1 (High Street) 3 blocks (N) of the Village
TEL. 207-236-9636
FAX 207-236-0621
22 High St.
Camden, ME 04843

Captain Peter Smith (USN, ret.) & the twins Donny Smith & Diana Robson, Innkeepers

 Relaxed, cozy and very friendly, the Maine Stay is a grand old home located in the historic district of one of America's most beautiful seaside villages. A short walk to the harbor, shops and restaurants, the inn offers a comfortable bed and a hearty breakfast to visitors seeking the warmth of new friends and, in the words of *Vacations* magazine, "Down East hospitality at its absolute best."
(*Traditional, Village, Breakfast Inn. Member since 1995*)

MAINE
THE NEWCASTLE INN

🛏	15 Rooms, $70/$200 B&B $140/$270 MAP
💳	Visa, MC, Amex
🛁	All Private Baths
🪑	Open Year-around
🐕	Older, well behaved Children; No Pets
R	Walking trails, Beaches, Bicycling, Antiquing, Birding, Boating, Touring, XC Skiing
🍽	Breakfast – Guests only Dinner by Reservation Wine & Liquor available
🚭	No Smoking
⊢╫╫⊣	Conference Facilities (24)
♿	N/A

13 At the end of your day's travels, a warm greeting, exceptional dining with national acclaim, and a pampering atmosphere await you, overlooking the harbor and lovely flower gardens here by the broad and salty Damariscotta River. Individualized attention is reflected in the details you will find in each of our bedchambers. In one of the midcoast Maine's quintessential villages, with easy access to numerous attractions, the feeling of warmth, friendship, and seclusion make this a retreat where guests may relax and unwind. (*Traditional, Village, Inn. Member since 1990*)

Maine Tpke. to Exit 9; I-95 (N) to Brunswick Exit 22, Rte. 1(N); 6 mi.(N) of Wiscasset. Take R. on River Rd. Continue 1/2 mi. to inn on R.
TEL. 207-563-5685
800-832-8669
FAX 207-563-6877
E-mail: newcastinn@aol.com
River Road
Newcastle, ME 04553
Howard & Rebecca Levitan, Innkeepers

THE SQUIRE TARBOX INN

🛏	11 Rooms, $85/$166 B&B $139/$220 MAP
💳	Visa, MC, Amex, Discov
🛁	All Private Baths
🪑	Open Mid May to Late Oct.
🐕	Appropriate for Older Children; No Pets
R	Walking path, Rowboat and Bikes on premises, Beaches, Harbors, Antiques nearby
🍽	Breakfast for guests only; Dinner to public by reservation; Wine & Liquor available
🚬	Smoking in weather protected area
⊢╫╫⊣	
♿	N/A

14 On a road to nowhere, this comfortable colonial farmhouse on a wooded hillside by a small inlet, is a respected full-service inn offering historical significance, a natural country setting, relaxed comfort, and a diversity of Maine Coast interests. Quiet rural privacy is here for guests who seek moments of personal solitude. Known for its savory fireside dinners and goat cheese from its purebred dairy herd. Built 1763–1820, the Inn is pleasantly removed from tourist crowds, but still near to beaches, harbors, antique shops, museums, lobster shacks, and L. L. Bean. (*Colonial, Country, Inn. Member since 1974*)

I-95 to Brunswick, Exit 22, follow Rte. 1 (N) past Bath bridge 7 mi. to Rte. 144. Continue 8.5 mi. on Westport Island.
TEL. 207-882-7693
R.R.2, Box 620, Route 144
Wiscasset, ME 04578

Bill & Karen Mitman, Innkeepers

54

MAINE
THE WATERFORD INNE

 9 Rooms, $75/$100 B&B
1 Suite, $100 B&B

 Amex

 7 Private Baths; 1 Shared Bath

 Closed April only

 Children Accepted; Pets with $10 fee

 Library, Parlor Games, Down-hill & XC Skiing, Swimming, Boating, Hiking, Antiquing

 Breakfast & Dinner; BYOB

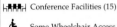 Smoking Discouraged

 Conference Facilities (15)

Some Wheelchair Access

From Maine Tpke.: Use Exit 11, follow Rte. 26 N. approx. 28 mi. into Norway. Then Rte. 118 W 8 mi. to Rte. 37. Go 1/2 mi., R. at Springer's Gen. St., up hill 1/2 mi.
From Conway, NH: Rte. 16 to Rte. 302 (E) to Fryeburg, ME. Rte. 5 out of Fryeburg to Rte. 35, then Rte. 118. Continue on Rte. 118 to Rte. 37, 1/2 mi. to Springer's Gen. St. Turn R, 1/2 mi. up hill.
TEL 207-583-4037
FAX 207-583-4037
Box 149 Chadbourne Rd.
Waterford, ME 04088
Rosalie & Barbara Vanderzanden, Innkeepers

15 A 19th-century farmhouse situated on a country lane midst 25 acres of fields and woods, Distinctively different, a *true* country inn offering uniquely decorated guest rooms, a charming blend of two centuries—the warmth of early pine furnishings combined with contemporary comforts. Outside—rolling terrain, a farm pond, an old red barn. Inside—an air of quiet simple elegance, antiques and art, barnboard and brass, pewter and primitives. Country chic cuisine to pamper your palate.
(*Traditional, Colonial, Country, Inn. Member since 1979*)

POMEGRANATE INN

 7 Rooms, $95/$165 B&B
1 Suite, $125/$165 B&B

 Visa, MC, Amex, Discov

 All Private Baths

 Open Year-round

 Not Suitable for Children; No Pets

 Bicycling, Sightseeing, Museums, Theater, Movies, Outlet Shopping, Very Good Restaurants, Whale Watching, Ferryboats to Casco Bay Islands, Charter Sailboat

 Breakfast

 No Smoking

Wheelchair Access (1 rm.)

From (S)— Maine Turnpike 95, exit 6A to 295. Take exit 4, Danforth St. Ramp. L at Vaughan St. 5 blocks to Carroll St. R for 1 block. Inn on corner of Neal & Carroll. From (N) 295(S), exit 6A, Forest Ave. (S); Bear R on Rte. 77 (State St.) Stay on State St. until top of hill. Cross Congress & turn R on Pine St. Continue on Pine—7th intersection, Neal St., turn L. Inn at end of block on L.
TEL 207-772-1006
800-356-0408
FAX 207-773-4426
49 Neal St.
Portland, ME 04102
Isabel Smiles, Innkeeper

16 Portland's beautiful Western Promenade historic residential district is the location of this special city Inn. It is a small sophisticated hotel which offers a quiet haven from the tensions of travel. The bustle of downtown is all but forgotten when you step through the Pomegranate's doors—antiques and art abound. For those who like real seclusion, the carriage house stands opposite the garden, beside the main house. The upstairs quarters hold a luxury suite and downstairs is a large guestroom with its own private terrace. Portland has so much to do and see that you may never have time to sit quietly and savor the Inn's lovely garden. Some rooms have fireplaces and all rooms are air conditioned.
(*Traditional, In-Town, Breakfast Inn. Member since 1995*)

55

MAINE
BLACK POINT INN

	74 Rms., $250/$370 MAP 6 Suites, $280/$400 MAP
	Visa, MC, Amex All Private Baths
	Open May 1–Dec. 1
	Children under 8 not permitted from July 14– Aug. 14; No Pets
	Golf, Tennis, Boating, Fishing, Indoor/Outdoor Pools, Health Club, Bikes, Massage room, Hiking Breakfast, Lunch, Dinner AP rates available
	Wine & Liquor Available
	No Smoking
	Conference Facilities (200)
	Wheelchair Access (3 rms, dining rm. & conf. fac.)

17 Quintessentially New England is this seaside resort inn, the favored retreat of generations of guests since the late 1800s. Easy, gracious hospitality and understated, genteel elegance, along with the vast ocean views, bracing salt air, hearty meals, beachcombing, sailing, and more, make this a world-class seaside resort-inn.
(*Elegant, Waterside, Resort. Member since 1969*)

From 95 N. or S. take S. take exit 6. Take L. at light (Payne Rd.). At 2nd traffic light take R. onto Rt. 114. Continue 2 mi. to Rt. 1. Cross over Rt. 1 onto BlackPoint Rd. 5 mi. on R.
TEL. 207-883-4126
FAX 207-883-9976
E-mail: bpi@nlis.net
510 Black Point Rd.
Prouts Neck, ME 04074
Normand & Agnes Dugas,
Innkeepers

MAINE STAY INN & COTTAGES

	17 Rooms (includes 4 suites & 9 cottages) Rooms $85-$115/$105- $175 B&B Suites $105- $165/$160-$220 B&B Cottages $85-$175/$125- $195 B&B
	Visa, MC, Amex All Private Baths Open Year-round Children welcome; not appropriate for children under 6 in main house No Pets
	Beaches, Bicycling, Antiquing, Shopping, Boat Cruise, Whale Watching. Golf, Tennis Breakfast & Afternoon tea
	No Smoking
	Conference Facilities (6)
	N/A

18 A beautiful 1860 Victorian inn distinguished by its suspended staircase, wrap-around porch, and cupola. The inn offers charming inn rooms, suites and delightful cottage rooms, several with fireplaces. Cottage guests may choose to have a breakfast basket delivered. The wrap-around porch is a wonderful place to enjoy breakfast and afternoon tea. The grounds offer a peaceful respite amid gigantic pines. The inn is perfectly situated in the historic district, a short walk to shops, galleries, restaurants and the harbor.
(*Traditional, Village, Breakfast Inn. Member since 1996*)

ME Tpke., Exit 3. L. on Rte. 35 for 6 mi. to Rte. 9. Turn L. on Rte. 9, go over bridge, straight through village to stop sign. Turn R. onto Maine St. go 3 blocks. Inn is on L.
TEL. 207-967-2117
Rev. 800-950-2117(U.S. Can.)
FAX 967-8757
E-mail: copeland4@cybertours.com
34 Maine St.; P.O. Box 500AI
Kennebunkport, ME 04046
Lindsay & Carol Copeland,
Innkeepers

CAPTAIN LORD MANSION

	13 Rooms, $149/$249 B&B
	3 Suites, $199/$399 Visa, MC, Discov
	All Private Baths
	Open Year-round
	Appropriate for Children over 6; No Pets
	Antiquing, Shopping, Beaches, Sailing, Whale watching, Tennis, Golf, Fishing, Bicycling
	Full Breakfast; BYOB
	No Smoking
	Conference Facilities (14)
	N/A

ME Tpke., Exit 3. L. onto Rte. 35 for 5.5 mi. to Rte. 9 (E). Turn L., go over bridge. R. onto Ocean Ave.; after 3/10 mi., turn L. onto Green St.
TEL. 207-967-3141
FAX 207-967-3172
E-mail: captain@biddeford.com
P.O. Box 800
**Kennebunkport, ME
04046-0800**
Bev Davis & Rick Litchfield, Innkeepers

19 The beautifully appointed, air conditioned, spacious rooms of this stately 1812 mansion, with its elliptical staircase and imposing cupola, feature period wallpapers, crystal chandeliers, gas burning fireplaces and many objects d'art. Superb comfort and gracious hospitality have been rewarded for many years with four diamonds by AAA. Many year-round activities are offered in this charming seacoast village. (*Elegant, Village, Breakfast Inn. Member since 1975*)

OLD FORT INN

	16 Rooms $98–$190/ $130–$275 B&B
	Visa, MC, Amex, Discov.
	All Private Baths; 4 Jacuzzis
	Open Mid-April Mid-Dec.
	Appropriate for Children over 12; No Pets
	Tennis Court, Pool, Ocean, Golf, Walking, Jogging
	Breakfast
	Non-smoking
	Conference Facilities (32)
	N/A

I-95 Exit 3, turn L. on Rte. 35 for 5 1/2 mi. L. at light at Rte. 9 for 3/10 mi. to Ocean Ave. Go 9/10 mi. to Colony Hotel, then L. & follow signs 3/10 mi. to inn.
**TEL. 207-967-5353;
800-828-3678**
FAX 207-967-4547
E-mail: oldfort@cybertours.com
Old Fort Ave., P.O. Box M
Kennebunkport, ME 04046
Sheila & David Aldrich, Innkps.

20 A short walk from the ocean along a country road, this secluded inn in an old seaport town offers rooms with antiques, canopied and 4-poster beds, color TV, A/C and phones. Guests find new friends over a buffet breakfast of fresh fruit and homemade breads; a charming antiques shop, fresh-water pool, and private tennis court provide pleasant diversion. The unique combination of yesterday's charm and today's conveniences entice many guests to return to the Inn year after year and recommend it to their friends. AAA Four Diamond Award. (*Elegant, Waterside, Resort. Member since 1976*)

HARTWELL HOUSE

🎹	11 Rooms, $90/$145 B&B 3 Suites & 2 Studio Apts., $135/$185 B&B
💳	Visa, MC, Discover
🛁	All Private Baths
	Open Year-round
🛋️	Appropriate for Children over 14; No Pets
🐕	Atlantic Ocean, Beach, Sailing, Fishing, Swimming, Boating, Golf, Tennis, Walking, XC Skiing, Biking, Horseback Riding, Shopping, Hiking
Ⓡ	
🍷	Breakfast; Lodging/ inhouse dining packages in off season Wine available
🚭	No Smoking Conference facilities (100)
♿	Wheelchair Access Available

21 Just steps away from Perkin's Cove and minutes from all that Ogunquit has to offer—a highly acclaimed three-mile stretch of beach and the Marginal Way footpath, which follows the rugged coastline to the village. View the gardens from your balcony or relax out back in the shady, quiet acre behind the main house filled with Early American and English antiques. Delicious gourmet breakfasts served in this elegant country inn are the perfect start to a day filled with touring museums, art galleries, fine shops and antiquing. Relax with Afternoon Tea and sweets and mingle with other guests before dining out in one of many fine area restaurants. Seasonal lodging and dining packages available. Ideal for weddings or functions of any kind.

(*Elegant, Village, Breakfast Inn. Member since 1981*)

I-95 (N) to Exit 4 (Ogunquit/Yorks) to Rt. 1 (N) for 4.4 mi. to R on Pine Hill Rd. L at Shore Rd. for .2 mi. to inn on L.
TEL. 207-646-7210
800-235-8883
FAX 207-646-6032
E-mail: hartwell@cybertours.com
118 Shore Rd., P.O. Box 393
Ogunquit, ME 03907
James & Trisha Hartwell,
William & Anne Mozingo,
Innkeepers

DOCKSIDE GUEST QUARTERS

🎹	15 Rooms, $106/$120 EP 6 Suites, $102/$152 EP Off season rates and packages available
💳	Visa, MC, Discov
🛁	19 Private, 2 Shared Baths
🛋️	Open Year-round Weekends only Nov-May Winter apts. available
🐕	Children welcome No Pets
Ⓡ	Beaches, Boats, Bicycles, Fishing, Shuffleboard, Badminton, Croquet, Swimming,Golf Tennis, Outlet shopping, Historic sites
🍷	Breakfast, Lunch, Dinner, Lounge; Weddings, Group Functions Wine & Liquor available
🚭	Non-smoking Rooms Conference Facilities (30)
♿	N / A

22 A small family run resort uniquely situated on a private peninsula in York Harbor. A seacoast inn and multi-unit buildings offer comfortable and attractive guest rooms, most with private decks and water views. Spacious grounds offer privacy and classic Maine scenery. The restaurant is renowned for creative presentations of fresh Maine seafood. Rated 3 diamonds by AAA.

(*Traditional, Country, Inn. Member since 1975*)

Exit 4 in York from I-95 exit to U.S. 1 South. Rte. 1-A thru Old York to Rte. 103. Cross bridge & watch for signs to inn.
TEL. 207-363-2868
1-800-270-1977
FAX 207-363-1977
Harris Island Rd.
P.O. Box 205
York, ME 03909
The David Lusty Family, Innkeepers

1. Antietam Overlook Farm, Keedysville
2. Tyler Spite House, Frederick
3. Inn at Buckeystown, Buckeystown
4. Antrim 1844, Taneytown
5. Twin Gates B&B, Lutherville
6. Robert Morris Inn, Oxford

ANTIETAM OVERLOOK FARM

6 Rooms, $120/$165 B&B

Visa, MC, Amex, Diners, Discov

All Private Baths

Open Year-around

Teenage Children Welcome: No Pets

Walking Tours, Hiking, River Recreation, Civil War Sites, Antiquing

Memorable Country Breakfast, Comp. Wine, Soda, & After-dinner drinks; Wine available, BYOB

No Smoking

N/A

Located in the Western Maryland mountains just over one hour west of Baltimore and Washington D.C.— Call for directions and availability

TEL. (800) 878-4241

P.O. Box 30
Keedysville, MD 21756
Barbara & John Dreisch,
Innkeepers

Our 95-acre mountaintop farm overlooking Antietam National Battlefield has extraordinary views of four states. The hand-hewn timber framing, rough-sawn walls and stone fireplaces juxtaposed to the softly flowered furnishings and fine crystal create a warm, comfortable atmosphere. Spacious suites include fireplaces, queen beds, sumptuous bubble baths, and private screened porches. While our seclusion and tranquillity are unparalleled, many guests also enjoy visiting the neighboring Civil War battlefields at Gettysburg, Bull Run/Manassas, and Harpers Ferry.

(*Traditional, Mountain, Retreat/Lodge. Member since 1992*)

TYLER SPITE INN

🎹	9 Rooms, $100/$300 B&B 5 Suites, $175/$300 plus 20% Tax & Service
💳	Visa, MC, Amex, Discov
🛁	10 Private Baths
🏠	Open Year-round except Thanksgiving
🐕	No Children or Pets
ℝ	Swimming Pool, Hiking, Tennis, Biking, Golf; Museum and Performing Arts Theater 3 blocks away
☕	Breakfast, High Tea at 4:00 P.M
🚭	No Smoking
⊢₳₳₳⊣	Conference Facility (12)
♿	Wheelchair Access (1 rm.)

2 A romantic 1814 Inn located in the heart of Frederick's historic district. Spacious, beautifully appointed rooms with 14 foot ceilings, marble fireplaces, oriental carpets, comfortable antique furnishings and paintings captivate our guests who are looking for the ultimate in romanticism. Walled gardens replete with color entice guests for a leisurely stroll. A stay is complete once you ascend from the carriage block located at the front door for a horse drawn carriage tour through Frederick's quaint city.
(*Elegant, In Town, Breakfast Inn. Member since 1993*)

Route 70 to Market St., left on 2nd St.,
2 blocks and left on Record St, 2 blocks
and at corner of Church St.
TEL. 301-831-4455
800-417-3264
112 W. Church St
Frederick, MD 21701

Bill & Andrea Myer,
Innkeepers

THE INN AT BUCKEYSTOWN

🎹	3 Rooms, $200 MAP 3 Suites, $225 MAP Church, $275 MAP Extra Person, $75 MAP +5% Tax & $10 per person gratuity
💳🛁	Visa, MC, Amex All Private Baths
🏠🐕	Open Year-round By Reservation Only Mature Teenagers; No Pets
ℝ	Hiking, Antiquing, Civil War & other Historic sites
☕	Breakfast (house guests) & Dinner W-Su; BYOB
🚭	No Smoking
⊢₳₳₳⊣	Conference facilities (20)
♿	N/A

3 A Nationally recognized, award winning Village Inn housed in an 1897 Victorian mansion and 1884 church. Buckeystown is a registered historic pre-revolutionary village steeped in Civil War lore, on the Monocacy River—near the Battlefield Park. Noted for: warm welcomes, excellent dining, outstanding art—antiques—collectibles. The wrap around porch, filled with wicker, overlooks elegant gardens and the village—a special place to view the changing seasons and to celebrate holidays and life as in yesteryears.
(*Victorian, Village, Inn. Member since 1987*)

From I-70 or I-270, take Rte. 85(s) to
Buckeystown. Inn is on left. (35 mi.
from Dulles Airport.)
TEL. 301-874-5755
RES. 800-272-1190
c/o General Delivery
3521 Buckeystown Pike
Buckeystown, MD 21717
Daniel R. Pelz, Chase Barnett,
Rebecca Smith,
Innkeepers

ANTRIM 1844

 9 Rooms, $150/$175 B&B
5 Suites, $200/300 B&B

 Visa, MC, Amex, Discov

 All Private Baths

 Open Year-round

 Some Restrictions

 Swimming, Tennis, Croquet, Touring Gettysburg and Countryside Wineries, and Antiquing

 Breakfast & Dinner; Wine & Liquor

 Smoking Restrictions

 Conference Facility (30)
Wheelchair Access (1 rm., dining rm. & conf. fac.)

From Wash., D.C. , 495 to I-270 W; then 15 N and 140 E to Taneytown. Through light and over tracks and then bear right on Trevanion Rd.
TEL. 800-858-1844;
410-756-6812;
FAX 410-756-2744
30 Trevanion Rd
Taneytown, MD 21787
Dort & Richard Mollett, Innkeepers

4 One of Maryland's most renowned country inn resorts. Antebellum ambience together with genuine hospitality and acclaimed cuisine has earned Antrim 1844 a place in country inn connoisseurs' hearts. Guestrooms are appointed with elegant decor, roaring fireplaces, and jacuzzis. Relax by the fire in the Pickwick Tavern, Library, Smokehouse, or Drawing Rooms. Turn-down service, tea, cocktail party, and endless amenities spoil even the most discriminating traveler. "A must see" if your are near Washington, D.C. or Baltimore.
(*Elegant, Country, Inn. Member since 1993*)

TWIN GATES B&B INN

 5 Rooms, $95/$135 B&B
1 Suite, $135/150 B&B

 Visa, MC, Amex

 All Private Baths

Open Year-round

Appropriate for Children over 12; No Pets

Antiquing, Hiking, Bicycling, Birding, Tennis, National Aquarium, Wineries, Ladew Topiary Gardens, Museums, Historic Sites

Breakfast

No Smoking

Conference facilities (10–12)

N/A

I-695 (Baltimore Beltway) Exit 25 N. R. (eastward) on Bellone Ave. 3 blocks to Morris Ave.
TEL. 410-252-3131
800-635-0370
FAX: 410-560-2641
308 Morris Ave.
Lutherville, MD 21093
Gwen & Bob Vaughan, Innkeepers

5 Surrounded by perennial gardens with a romantic wicker gazebo and magnificent trees, Twin Gates is nestled in a Victorian village on the northern edge of Baltimore City. Lutherville, a National Historic District, provides a country setting 15 minutes to the center of Baltimore and all of its attractions, including the National Aquarium. Nearby are good seafood restaurants, free winery tours in Maryland Hunt Country, and the world famous Ladew Topiary Gardens. Soft music, fresh flowers, and decadent but heart–healthy breakfasts punctuate the warm hospitality at Twin Gates B&B.
(*Traditional, Victorian, Village, Breakfast Inn. Member since 1994*)

THE ROBERT MORRIS INN

🛏	35 Rooms, $80/$230 EP
💳	Visa, MC
🛁	All Private Baths
🛋	Season–Apr.–Nov.; off season: B&B some weekends Dec.-Mar.
🐑	Appropriate for Children over 10; No Pets
⌖R⌖	Tennis, Biking, Golf, Antiquing, Sailing, Historic Car Ferry, Goose Hunting
☕	Breakfast, Lunch, Dinner; Closed for lunch Tuesday, Wine & Liquor available
🚭	All Rooms Non-Smoking
⊞	Executive Conference Facilities (10-20)
♿	Wheelchair Access, 2 rms.

6 Chesapeake Bay and the Tred Avon River play a big part in the life of this Eastern Shore country-romantic 1710 inn. Delicacies from the bay are featured in the nationally acclaimed seafood restaurant and the Tred Avon offers lovely views from many of the rooms and porches. Country furnishings add to the friendly feeling here in the historic waterside village of Oxford. James A. Michener, author of *Chesapeake*, rated the Robert Morris Inn's crab cakes the highest of any restaurant on the Eastern Shore." (*Traditional, Waterside, Inn. Member since 1970*)

Hwy. 301 to Rte. 50 (E). Turn R. on Rte. 322 for 3.4 mi. Turn R. on Rte. 333 for 9.6 mi. to inn

TEL. 410-226-5111
312 No. Morris St.
P.O. Box 70
Oxford, MD 21654

Wendy & Ken Gibson, Owners
Jay Gibson, Innkeeper

Rate Definitions

In this 1996 Innkeeper's Register, rates are quoted for 2 people for 1 night and do not necessarily include service charges and state taxes. For inns offering AP and MAP, "pp" is used to indicate rates are per person. For more detailed information, ask the inns for their brochures.

AP — American Plan (3 meals included in room rate)

MAP — Modified American Plan (breakfast & dinner included in room rate)

EP — European Plan (meals not included in room rate)

B&B — Bed & Breakfast (breakfast included in room rate)

⌖R⌖ — Represents recreational facilities and diversions either on the premises of an inn or nearby

• — A dot before the inn name in the index indicates that it can be booked through a travel agent. Travel agents should contact the inns directly for specific rates and restrictions

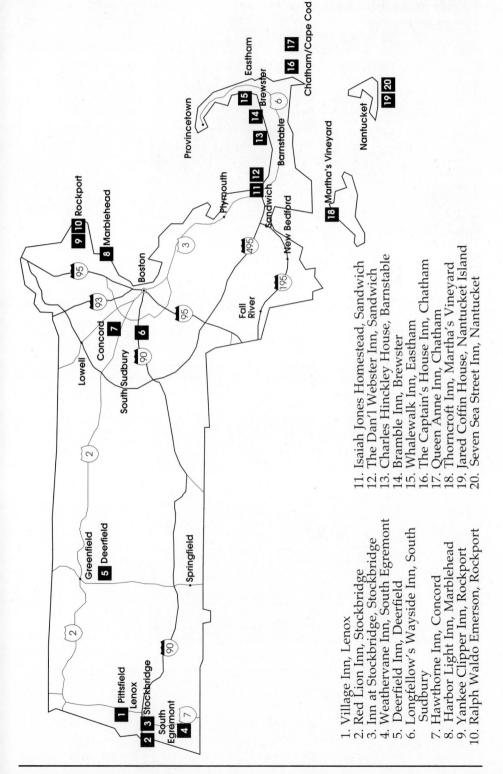

1. Village Inn, Lenox
2. Red Lion Inn, Stockbridge
3. Inn at Stockbridge, Stockbridge
4. Weathervane Inn, South Egremont
5. Deerfield Inn, Deerfield
6. Longfellow's Wayside Inn, South Sudbury
7. Hawthorne Inn, Concord
8. Harbor Light Inn, Marblehead
9. Yankee Clipper Inn, Rockport
10. Ralph Waldo Emerson, Rockport
11. Isaiah Jones Homestead, Sandwich
12. The Dan'l Webster Inn, Sandwich
13. Charles Hinckley House, Barnstable
14. Bramble Inn, Brewster
15. Whalewalk Inn, Eastham
16. The Captain's House Inn, Chatham
17. Queen Anne Inn, Chatham
18. Thorncroft Inn, Martha's Vineyard
19. Jared Coffin House, Nantucket Island
20. Seven Sea Street Inn, Nantucket

THE VILLAGE INN

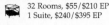 32 Rooms, $55/$210 EP
1 Suite, $240/$395 EP

 Visa, MC, Amex, Discov, CB

 All Private Baths
4 Jacuzzis

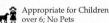 Open Year-round

Appropriate for Children over 6; No Pets

Downhill & XC Skiing, Golf, Riding, Tennis, Swimming, Fishing

Breakfast, English tea, Dinner served June–Oct. nightly except Mondays

Smoking Permitted only in downstairs tavern

Conference Facilities (50)

Wheelchair Access (6 rms.)

1 In the historic district of the Berkshire village of Lenox, this Colonial Inn, built in 1771, is near shops, galleries, library, churches, beautiful parks and wooded trails, Tanglewood and summer theatre and dance festivals, winter downhill and cross-country skiing, fall foliage and spring flower excursions, and year-round museums such as the Norman Rockwell, Clark, Grandma Moses, and Hancock Shaker Village. Every room is individually furnished with country antiques, some 4-posters and fireplaces, all with private baths and telephones, air conditioning in summer months. Special winter spring packages. (*Traditional, Colonial, Village, Inn. Member since 1977*)

Mass. Tpke. (I-90), Exit 2, Rte. 20(W) to Rte. 183(S). Turn L. for 1 mi. to R. on Church St. & inn. From Rte. 7 to Rte. 7A & Church St. in Lenox.
TEL. 413-637-0020
800-253-0917
FAX 413-637-9756
16 Church St. P.O. Box 1810
Lenox, MA 01240
Clifford Rudisill and
Ray Wilson, Innkeepers

THE RED LION INN

91 Rooms, $87/$175 EP
20 Suites, $167/$370 EP

Visa, MC, Amex, Diners, Discov

Private & Shared Baths

Open Year-round
Children & Families Welcome; No Pets

Exercise room, Pool, Golf, Tennis, Massage Therapist; Tanglewood, Jacobs Pillow, Berkshire Theatre Festival, Norman Rockwell Museum, Chesterwood

Breakfast, Lunch, Dinner; MAP available for groups
Wine & Liquor available
Non-smoking dining rms

Conference Facilities (6-90)

Wheelchair Access (1 rm., dining rm., conf. fac.)

2 This renowned, antique filled inn in the Berkshire Hills is still the lively, delightful focus of village activity it has been since 1773. As one of few American Inns continuously operated as such since the eighteenth century, the Red Lion welcomes travelers with cheerful cordiality born of longstanding tradition. Individually decorated rooms and suites. Traditional New England cuisine is served in the formal Main Dining Room, cozy Tavern or flower filled Courtyard in summer. Charming gift shop and Country Curtains store located in the Inn. (*Traditional, Village, Inn. Member since 1967*)

I-90, Exit 2 at Lee, to Rte. 102 (W) to Stockbridge.
TEL. 413-298-5545
FAX 413-298-5130
Main St.
Stockbridge, MA 01262
The Fitzpatrick Family, Owners
Brooks Bradbury, Innkeeper

THE INN AT STOCKBRIDGE

 6 Rooms, $85/$235 B&B
2 Suites, $125/$235 B&B

 Visa, MC, Amex, Discovr

 All Private Baths,
1 Whirlpool

 Open Year-round

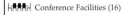 Children over 12; No Pets
Pool on premises, golf &
tennis privileges at local
club, hiking, horseback
riding, downhill &
crosscountry skiing nearby
Breakfast, Dinners for
groups can be arranged
Complimentary Wine

No Smoking

Conference Facilities (16)

 N/A

Mass. Tpke. Exit 2 & (W) on Rte. 102
to Rte. 7 (N) 1.2 mi. to inn on R. From
NYC, Taconic Pkwy. to Rte. 23 (E) &
Rte. 7 (N) past Stockbridge 1.2 mi.
TEL 413-298-3337
FAX 413-298-3406
Website: stockbridgeinn.com
E-mail: innkeeper@stockbridgeinn
Rte. 7 (North), Box 618
Stockbridge, MA 01262
Alice & Len Schiller, Innkeepers

 Consummate hospitality and outstanding breakfasts distinguish a visit at this turn-of-the-century Georgian Colonial estate on 12 secluded acres in the heart of the Berkshires. Close to the Norman Rockwell Museum, Tanglewood, Hancock Shaker Village, summer theaters, and four-season recreation. The inn has a gracious, English country house feeling, with two well-appointed living rooms, a formal dining room, and a baby grand piano. (*Elegant, Village, Breakfast Inn. Member since 1986*)

THE WEATHERVANE INN

 9 Rooms $95/$125 B&B
1 Suites, $125/$145 B&B
$175/$220 MAP
Visa, MC, Amex, Discov

 All Private Baths

 Open Year-round; closed
Christmas Day

Appropriate for Children
Over 7; No Pets

 Pool, Nature walks, Antiques, Museums, Tennis, Golf, Skiing,
Tanglewood, Summer
Theater; Downhill &
Cross Country skiing, etc.
Breakfast; Dinner weekends only (Fri. & Sat.)
Wine & Liquor available
No smoking
Conference Facilities (25)

N/A

From NYC, Taconic Pkwy. to Rte.
23(E) 13 mi. to inn on R. From Mass.
Tpke., Exit 2 & Rte. 102 to Rte. 7(S) to
Rte. 23(W) to inn on L.
TEL. 413-528-9580
800-528-9580
FAX 413-528-1713
P.O. Box 388, Rte. 23
South Egremont, MA 01258
Anne & Vincent Murphy,
Innkeepers

Renowned and caring Murphy family has been providing hospitality to their guests for the past 14 years in an elegant farm and coach house on ten acres in a quaint Berkshire village in southwestern Massachusetts. The charming fireside room with three common rooms and honor bar beckons guests seeking recreation and recuperation before experiencing the inns superb cuisine. A full breakfast is offered daily and when dinner is served a host of delectable appetizers and entrees entice you. An all seasons inn. (AAA 3 diamonds) (*Traditional, Federal, Village, Inn. Member since 1984*)

DEERFIELD INN

🛏	23 Rooms, $122/$156 B&B
💳	Visa, MC, Amex
🛁	All Private Baths
🛎	Open Year-round; Closed 12-24 to 12-26
🐕	Children Welcome No Pets
ⓡ	
🍽	Breakfast, Lunch, Dinner
🚭	No Smoking
♿	Conference Facility (2) Wheelchair Access (2 Rms, dining rm. & conf. fac.)

5 This classic country inn built in 1884 is located in the center of Deerfield along a charming mile-long way known simply as "The Street." A National Historic Landmark, this unspoiled 300-year old village is a perfect destination for those looking for the real New England. Enjoy Deerfield's tranquil life with its farms, museums, country walks, antiquing, friendly folk, and beautiful scenery. You will delight in the inn's outstanding cuisine! We very much look forward to welcoming you here....
(*Elegant, Village, Inn. Member since 1996*)

From I-91, exit 24 going N.; exit 25 going S. Deerfield Village just off Rte. 5 & 10.
TEL. 413-774-5587
800-926-3865 (out of Mass)
FAX 413-773-8712
E-mail: drfldinn@shaysnet.com
81 Old Main St.
Deerfield, MA 01342
Karl & Jane Sabo, Innkeepers

LONGFELLOW'S WAYSIDE INN

🛏	10 Rooms, $80/$130
💳	Visa, MC, Discov, DC
🛁	All Private Baths
🛎	Closed Dec. 25th & July 4th
🐕	Children Welcome; No Pets
ⓡ	Historic sites, Famous Revolutionary War landmarks
🍽	Breakfast to houseguests only/Lunch & Dinner to the public; Wine & Liquor available
🚭	No Smoking in Public Areas
🏛	Conference Facility (50)
♿	N/A

6 Immortalized in 1863 by Longfellow in his *Tales of a Wayside Inn*, the inn is located off U.S. Rt. 20 on Wayside Inn Road. Next to the inn is a working gristmill, (open April-November); the Red Stone School House of *Mary and Her Little Lamb* fame (open seasonal weather) and the Martha Mary Chapel for weddings. Reservations for lodging and for dining made well in advance.
(*Traditional, Colonial, Country Inn. Member since 1967*)

Between Boston & Worcester off Rte. 20. 11 mi. (W) of Rte. 128 & 7 mi. (E) off Rte. 495. Sign on R., for Wayside Inn Rd.
TEL. 508-443-1776
800-399-1776
FAX 508-443-2312
E-mail: innkeeper@wayside.org
Wayside Inn Rd. off Rte. 20
South Sudbury, MA 01776
Robert H. Purrington, Innkeeper

HAWTHORNE INN

 7 Rooms, $110/$185 B&B

 Visa, MC, Amex, Discov

All Private Baths

 Open Year-round

 Children Welcome; No Pets

 Swimming (Walden Pond), Museums, Wooded trails for Hiking & XC Skiing, Canoeing on Concord River

 Breakfast

No Smoking

Conference Facility (10)

N/A

Rte. 128-95, Exit 30-B (W) (Rte. 2A) for 2.8 mi. Bear R. at fork toward Concord for 1.2 mi. Inn across from Hawthorne's home.

TEL. 508-369-5610
FAX 508-287-4949
462 Lexington Rd.
Concord, MA 01742

Gregory Burch & Marilyn Mudry, Innkeepers

7 On land where Emerson, Alcott, and Hawthorne lived, and among trees planted by these illustrious men, the Hawthorne Inn follows their lead in the cultivation of art and appreciation of the spiritual in life. Friendly, caring innkeepers and nature walks, where land, sky, and water refresh the senses, imbue this winsome, intimate inn with a very special feeling.
(*Traditional, Village, Breakfast Inn. Member since 1980*)

HARBOR LIGHT INN

 19 Rooms, $95/$225 B&B
2 suites, $150/$175 B&B

 Visa, MC, Amex

All Private Baths

Open Year-round

Children under 10 by prior arrangement on premises; No Pets
Outdoor heated Pool, Sailing & Whale watch nearby

Breakfast

No Smoking

Conference Facilities (20)

N/A

From Boston/ Logan Airport-Take Rt 1A N. to 129 E. Follow into Marblehead. Take 1st right after Texaco Station onto Washington St. continue for 1/3 mile to inn. From Rt. 95 & 128 take Rt. 114 E. all the way into town turn L. on Washington St. 200 yards to inn.

TEL. 617-631-2186
FAX 617-631-2216
58 Washington St.
Marblehead, MA 01945
Peter & Suzanne Conway, Innkeepers

8 Winner of numerous national awards for excelence, including, Vacations Magazine "America's Best Romantic Inns." The Inn offers 1st class accomodations and amenities found in the finest of lodging facilities. Elegant furnishings grace these two connected federalist mansions. Formal fireplaced parlors, diningroom and bed chambers, double jacuzzis, sundecks, patio, quiet garden and outdoor heated pool combine to ensure the finest in New England hospitality. Located in historic harbor district of fine shops, art galleries and restaurants.
(*Elegant, Federal, In Town, Breakfast Inn. Member since 1996*)

YANKEE CLIPPER INN

	26 Rooms, $110/$249 B&B; Rooms w/ocean view, 5 Suites
	1 villa, $2100/$4200 per wk
	Visa, MC, Amex, Discov
	All Private Baths
	Open Mar. 1–Dec. 15
	No Pets
	Saltwater swimming pool, Tennis, Golf, Whale-watching, Deep Sea Fishing, Hiking, Biking; Boston, Southern Maine, New Hampshire all 1–3 hours driving
	Breakfast & Dinner, BYOB
	No Smoking
	Conference facilities (50)
	N/A

9 Fresh ocean breezes and sweeping panoramic views have greeted guests here for 51 years. The Inn, the Quarterdeck, the 1840 Bulfinch House and a 3-bedroom Villa all offer country inn amenities. Historic sites abound here on Cape Ann as well as in Boston, Salem, Concord and Lexington, Southern Maine and New Hampshire—all within easy reach. Life can be lazy or exciting with golf, tennis, beaches, antiquing, art colonies, whale watching, river cruises close by. A heated outdoor saltwater pool on a landscaped terrace overlooks the gardens and ocean. Our Glass Verandah restaurant features New England gourmet cuisine. Celebrating our 51th anniversary. 1994 Romantik Hoteliers of the Year, AAA, Mobil. Ask about our rental property in Ireland .
(*Traditional, Waterside, Inn. Member since 1973*)

Rte. 128 (N) to Cape Ann thru Gloucester. L. on Rte. 127 for 4 mi. to Rockport's 5 Corners & sharp L. & Pigeon Cove sign. Continue 1 mi. to inn.
TEL. 508-546-3407
800-545-3699
FAX 508-546-9730
96 Granite St., P.O. Box 2399
Rockport, MA 01966
Bob & Barbara Ellis, Innkps.

RALPH WALDO EMERSON INN

	34 Rooms, $90-$130/$100-$140 EP; 2 suites, $100-$130/$110-$140 EP
	Visa, MC, Discov.
	All Private Baths
	Open May 1–Oct. 31 April & Nov. weekends
	Children Accepted No Pets
	Heated Salt Water Pool, Sauna, Whirlpool, Game Room, Theater with Projector TV & VCR, Lawn Games, Boating, Bicycles, Whale Watching, Golf, Sight Seeing nearby
	Breakfast & Dinner (July-Labor Day)
	Smoking Permitted
	Conference Facilities (35)
	Wheelchair Access (2 rms., dining rm.)

10 One of the last of the old summer hotels on Cape Ann, the Emerson's broad porches and Greek Revival architecture give it a classic majesty. Preserving the charm of yesteryear while keeping up with the times, the inn features a heated saltwater pool, a whirlpool and sauna, and a theater for movies. Popular seafood and shore specialties are always included on the menu. The Inn is right on the ocean and many rooms have an excellent ocean view.
(*Traditional, Village, Inn. Member since 1973*)

Rte. 128 (N) to traffic light in Gloucester, left on 127 to our sign in Pigeon Cove (Phillips Ave.)
TEL. 508-546-6321
FAX 508-546-7043
E-mail:emerson@cove.com
Phillips Ave., Box 2369
Rockport, MA 01966

Gary & Diane Wemyss,
Innkeepers

ISAIAH JONES HOMESTEAD

 5 Rooms, $75-$155 B&B

 Visa, MC, Amex, Discov.

 All Private Baths

 Open Year-round

Children over 12 accepted; No Pets

Museums, Antiques, Gift Shops, Beach, Fishing, Whale Watching, Tennis, Golf, Biking, Hist. Sites

Breakfast & Afternoon Tea; Warm Cider by Fireside or Lemonade on Porch. Low Cholesterol Cooking featured

No Smoking

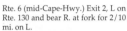

N/A

Rte. 6 (mid-Cape-Hwy.) Exit 2, L on Rte. 130 and bear R. at fork for 2/10 mi. on L.

TEL. 508-888-9115 or 800-526-1625

165 Main Street
Sandwich, MA 02563

Shirley & Bud Lamson, Innkeepers

11 This 1849 Italianate Victorian in the historic village of Sandwich, Cape Cod's oldest town, is within walking distance of most points of interest and fine restaurants. Beautifully furnished with antiques, oriental carpets, and fresh flowers, its quiet elegance harks back to a time when life was tranquil and travelers were pampered. Enjoy the elegant rooms including the master suite with over-sized whirlpool bath, the Jones Room with over-sized whirlpool (both with fireplace); and the Beale Room with fireplace. All rooms have private baths. Breakfast is served by candlelight. (*Victorian, Village, Breakfast Inn. Member since 1989*)

DAN'L WEBSTER INN

 46 Rooms, $89/$325

 Visa, MC, Amex, Discovr, CB

 All Private Baths

 Open Year-Round; Closed Christmas

 Children welcome, No Pets

 Outdoor Pool on Premise; Bicycling, Golfing, Fishing, Ocean, Tennis nearby-Health Club Membership

 Breakfast, Lunch, Dinner, & Sun. Brunch; Devil'n Dan Tavern

 Smoking restrictions

 Conference Facilities (10-200)

Wheelchair Access. (1 rm., dining rm., conf. fac.)

From Boston, MA: Rte. 3 S to Rte 6 (mid-Cape Hwy) to Exit 2. Turn L on Rte. 130. Approx. 2 mi. R at fork. Inn on L.

TEL. 508-888-3622 800-444-3566 FAX: 508-888-5156

149 Main St.
Sandwich, MA 02563

The Catania Family, Innkeepers

12 300 years ago, weary travelers found this stage coach stop a rewarding respite. Today, nestled in the quintessential New England Village of Sandwich with its tree-lined streets, old sea captains' homes, duck pond and grist mill, yet only steps from the beaches of Cape Cod Bay, this award-winning historic Inn still offers its guests the same warm and caring hospitality, with today's amenities tucked in. Relax in spacious, yet cozy, individually decorated rooms - some with canopy bed, fireplace, and whirlpool tub. Enjoy a romantic dinner by the fire in the Heritage Room, or in the beautiful glassed Conservatory. Savour the delicious New England cuisine served at the Inn, complemented by fresh salad greens, herbs, and edible flowers, all grown in the Inn's own Aquafarm, and an award-winning wine list. An informal Gathering Room complete with games, puzzles, and books bids the guest welcome to this "home away from home". (*Traditional, Colonial, Village, Inn. Member since 1994*)

CHARLES HINCKLEY HOUSE

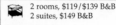	2 rooms, $119/$139 B&B 2 suites, $149 B&B
	Visa, MC, Amex
	All Private Baths
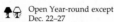	Open Year-round except Dec. 22–27
	Appropriate for Children 10 & over; No Pets
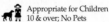	Antiquing, Beaches, Golf, Tennis, Sailing, Fishing, Museums, Historic Sites
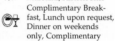	Complimentary Breakfast, Lunch upon request, Dinner on weekends only, Complimentary Sherry No Smoking
	Wheelchair Access (1 room)

13 An architectural gem listed on the National Register of Historic Places on the Olde Kings Highway is this 1809 Colonial home of an early shipwright. The young innkeepers have lovingly restored and furnished it, polishing the wide pumpkin pine floors, refurbishing the fireplaces, and putting in 4-poster beds. Where no detail is overlooked. The Charles Hinckley House defines elegant simplicity. A small intimate country inn where great expectations are quietly met. The unspoiled natural beauty of Cape Cod Bay is just a stroll away. (*Traditional, Federal, Village, Breakfast Inn. Member since 1988*)

Rte. 6 to exit 6, end of ramp stop sign go left onto Rte. 132 to stop sign, turn right onto 6A, 1 1/2 miles on left

TEL. 508-362-9924
FAX 508-362-8861
Olde Kings Hwy., (Rte. 6-A),
P.O. Box 723
Barnstable, MA 02630

Les & Miya Patrick,
Innkeepers

THE BRAMBLE INN AND RESTAURANT

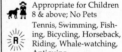	8 Rooms, $95/$125 B&B
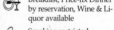	Visa, MC, Amex, Discov
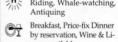	All Private Baths
	Open mid May–Dec. 31
	Appropriate for Children 8 & above; No Pets
	Tennis, Swimming, Fishing, Bicycling, Horseback, Riding, Whale-watching, Antiquing
	Breakfast, Price-fix Dinner by reservation, Wine & Liquor available
	Smoking restricted
	N/A

14 Dine superbly at one of Cape Cod's top three restaurants, where Ruth Manchester creates dishes sought after by *Bon Appetit* and *Gourmet*. Wide pine floors, antiques, and flowered wallpapers adorn the guest rooms in the two 19th century buildings of this family-owned and operated intimate inn on the historic north side. (*Traditional, Village, Inn. Member since 1977*)

Rte. 6, Exit 10 & bear L. on Rte. 124 to R. on Rte. 6A for 1/8 mi. to inn on left.

TEL. 508-896-7644
FAX 508-896-9332
2019 Main St.
Route 6A, Box 807
Brewster, MA 02631

Ruth & Cliff Manchester,
Innkeepers

THE WHALEWALK INN

 7 Rooms, $115/$175 B&B
5 Suites, $150/$190 B&B

 VISA, MC

All Private Baths

 Open April–December;
Selected Winter
Weekends

Children over 12
Welcome; No Pets

 Cape Cod National Seashore, Boating, Fishing,
Biking, Golf, Whale Watching, Antiquing, Theater

 Breakfast

No Smoking

 Conference Facility (10)

 N/A

Rte. 6 to Orleans Rotary. Rock Harbor exit off rotary. Left onto Rock Harbor Road. Right onto Bridge Road. Driving time from Boston 2 hours.
TEL 508-255-0617
FAX 508-240-0017
E-mail: whalewal@virtualcapecod.com
220 Bridge Road
Eastham, MA 02642
Carolyn and Richard Smith,
Innkeepers

15 The owners of this inn promise you an unspoiled environment on outer Cape Cod, one of the country's most beautiful areas. This 1830's home has been authentically restored and decorated with handsome antiques. The site consists of three acres, located on a back road, only minutes by car or bike to beaches, bike trials, or Orleans Village. All 12 guest rooms are beautifully decorated and are airconditioned. Five of them are suites with fireplaces. A full breakfast is served. Hors d'oeuvres provided each evening. (*Traditional, Federal, Village, Breakfast Inn. Member since 1993*)

THE CAPTAIN'S HOUSE INN OF CHATHAM

 19 Rooms, $130/$300 B&B

 Visa, MC, Amex

 All Private Baths

 Open Year-round

 Doesn't meet needs of Children; No Pets

 Beaches, Tennis, Golf, Boating, Theater, Fishing, Bicycling, Lawn Croquet

 Breakfast, Afternoon Tea

 Non-Smoking Inn

 Conference Facilities (16)

 Wheelchair Access (1 room)

Rte. 6 (Mid-Cape Hwy.) to Rte. 137, Exit 11 (S) to Rte. 28; left on Rte. 28 to Chatham Center. Continue around rotary on Rte. 28 toward Orleans 1/2 mi. to inn on left.
TEL. 508-945-0127
800-315-0728
FAX 508-945-0866
E-mail: capthous@capecod.net
369-377 Old Harbor Rd.
Chatham, Cape Cod, MA 02633
Jan & David McMaster,
Innkeepers

16 Perhaps Cape Cod's finest small inn, this historic 1839 sea captain's estate on two acres is the perfect choice for a romantic getaway or elegant retreat. Gourmet breakfasts, English afternoon teas, four-poster beds, fine antiques, fireplaces and uncompromising service are just some of the ammenities awaiting the guest. Savor the scenic beauty of Chatham and the ocean and join with the innkeepers and staff as they celebrate the Inn's 11th anniversary as a AAA 4-diamond Inn.
(*Elegant, Waterside, Inn. Member since 1989*)

MASSACHUSETTS
THE QUEEN ANNE INN

🛏	29 Rooms, $125/$257 B&B; 2 Suites, $185/$325 B&B
💳	Visa, MC, Amex, Eurocard
🛁	All Private Baths; 2 Jacuzzis, 2 Hot Tubs
🌳🍸	Open year-around Children Accepted Kennel nearby for Pets
🐕	Outdoor Swimming Pool; Indoor Spa, 3 Tennis Cts,
⚡R	Bikes, Boating, Scuba Diving, Fishing, Golf
	Breakfast, Dinner: May 1st–Oct. 31st
☕	Wine & Liquor Available
🚭	No Smoking in Guest rooms & restaurant except Lounge & porch
🏨	Conference Facilities (15)
♿	Wheelchair Access (1 rm.), Dining Room, Conference Facilities

17 Spacious guest rooms with tv, antiques, garden views, private balconies, working fireplaces, and private whirlpool baths are a few of the amenities that may be found here on Cape Cod's picturesque south shore. The intimate restaurant features superb cuisine, and pursuits to beguile quiet hours or to engage the energetic are all around. (*Traditional, Victorian, Village, Inn-Resort. Member since 1981*)

Rte. 6 (E) to Exit 11, R. on Rte. 137 and L. on Rte. 28 for 3.5 mi. to light and R. fork to Queen Anne Rd. and up hill to inn.
TEL. 508-945-0394
RES. 800-545-INNS
FAX 508-945-4884
70 Queen Anne Rd.
Chatham, MA 02633
Guenther Weinkopf,
Innkeeper

THORNCROFT INN

🛏	14 Rooms, $150/$450 B&B
💳	Visa, MC, Amex, Discov, DC
🛁	All Private Baths
🌳🍸	Open Year-round
🐕	Children over 12; No Pets
⚡R	Beaches, Boating, Golf, Tennis, Bicycling, Fishing
☕	Breakfast
🚭	No Smoking
🏨	Confrernce Facilities (10)
♿	Wheelchair Access (1 rm.)

18 Thorncroft Inn is situated in two restored buildings on 3 1/2 acres of quiet, treed grounds on the Island of Martha's Vineyard. It is secluded, exclusively couples oriented and first class, with Mobil★★★★ and AAA◆◆◆◆ ratings. Most rooms have working, wood burning fireplaces and canopied beds. Some have 2 person whirlpool bathtubs or private 300 gallon hot tubs. Thorncroft Inn is an ideal honeymoon, anniversary or special couples getaway. (*Elegant, Colonial, Village, Breakfast Inn. Member since 1994*)

Woods Hole/Martha's Vineyard Ferry (Car & Passenger, year 'round) from Cape Cod. Take R. at first stop sign; take next R. onto Main St. Inn 1 mile on L.
TEL. 508-693-3333
800-332-1236
FAX: 508-693-5419
E-mail: kgb@tiac.net
460 Main St.
Vineyard Haven
Martha's Vineyard, MA 02568
Karl & Lynn Buder,
Owners/Innkeepers

JARED COFFIN HOUSE

 60 Rooms, $100/$200
B&B

 Visa, MC, Amex, Diners,
Discov

All Private Baths

 Open Year-round

 Children & Pets Accepted
with prior approval

 Excellent Bike Paths, Conservation Walks, Swim-
ming, Sailing, Fishing
(none on premises)

All meals available on
premises; Wine & Liquor
available

Smoking Restrictions

Conference Facilities (24)
Wheelchair Access (6 rms.,
dining rm. & conf. fac.)

Flights from Newark, NYC, Boston,
New Bedford, & Hyannis. Or take
Hyannis ferry, leaving car in Hyannis
— cars unnecessary on Nantucket.
TEL. 508-228-2400
**Res: 800-248-2405 (M-F, 9-
5); FAX 508-325-7752**
29 Broad St., P.O. Box 1580
Nantucket, MA 02554-1580
Phil & Peg Read, Innkeepers
Jonathan Stoner, Gen. Mgr.

19 A collection of buildings from the mid-1800's tastefully re-stored to provide today's guest with the feeling of a gentler past. The inn is conveniently located in the Old Historic District near Main Street shops with easy access to island beaches and bike paths. The Tap Room and JARED's offer both casual and more formal dining featuring American cuisine. The inn is open for the Thanksgiving, Christmas, and New Year holidays and offers guests the friendly feeling of a home away from home. (*Historic, Island, Inn. Member since 1969*)

SEVEN SEA STREET INN

 9 Rooms, $75/$185 B&B
2 Suites, $125/$255 B&B

 Visa, MC, Amex

 All Private Baths

 Open Year-round

 Children 5 & up Welcome
in suites; No Pets

 Beaches, Bicycling, Boating,
Fishing, Tennis, Golf, Shopping, Museums

 Breakfast

 No Smoking

 N/A

Flights from Boston, NYC, Newark,
New Bedford & Hyannis Ferry, Leav-
ing car in Hyannis to steamboat
wharf, Nantucket. 2 min. walk from
wharf.
TEL. 508-228-3577
FAX 508-228-3578
E-mail: seast7@nantucket.net
7 Sea Street
Nantucket, MA 02554
Matthew & Mary Parker,
Innkeepers

20 Enjoy the warmth of our beautiful post and beam inn, located on a quiet side street just a short walk from the ferry, beach, and main street. An authentic early American ambiance combined with modern comforts in each of our rooms and suites provide a cozy respite for your stay with us on romantic Nantucket Island. We'll serve you an elegant continental breakfast and suggest you take in a spectacular view of the harbor from our widows walk or relax in our Jacuzzi whirlpool.

(*Traditional, Colonial, Island Village, Breakfast Inn. Member since 1996*)

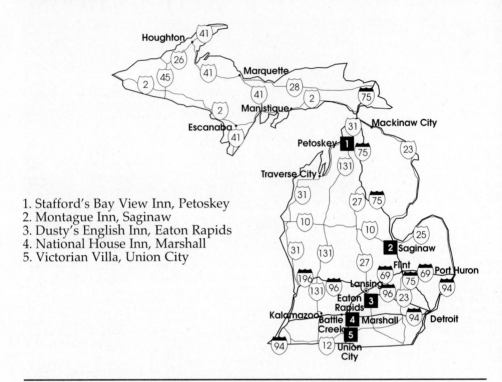

1. Stafford's Bay View Inn, Petoskey
2. Montague Inn, Saginaw
3. Dusty's English Inn, Eaton Rapids
4. National House Inn, Marshall
5. Victorian Villa, Union City

STAFFORD'S BAY VIEW INN

26 Rooms, $118/$218 B&B
5 Suites, $138/$218 B&B

Visa, MC, Amex

All Private Baths

Closed Mid-March—
Mother's Day

Children Welcome

No Pets; Kennel nearby

Driving Distance to
Mackinac Island, Ski &
Golf Resorts, and local his-
toric points of interest. On
Site Bike & Lawn Games

Breakfast, Lunch, Dinner
During May–Oct. & Winter
Weekends, Award Winning
Sun. Brunch

No Smoking

Conference Facilities (100)

Wheelchair Access (31 rms.,
dining rm., conf. fac.)

For more than 35 years the Stafford Smith family has owned, operated, and lovingly restored this grande dame Victorian Country Inn. Located on the shores of Lake Michigan's *Little Traverse Bay*, in the Historic Landmark District of Bay View, this inn sets the standard in fine dining, gracious service, and beautifully appointed bed chambers. Guests enjoy summer Chautauqua program and winter sleigh rides on the association grounds.
(*Traditional, Lake-side, Inn. Member since 1972*)

From Detroit, I-75 (N) to Gaylord exit,
Rte. 32 (W) to Rte. 131 (N) Petoskey.
From Chicago, I-94 to Rte. I96 (N) to
Rte. 131 (N) to Petoskey.
TEL. 616-347-2771
FAX 616-347-3413
E-mail: stafford@freeway.net
613 Woodland Ave.
P.O. Box 3
Petoskey, MI 49770
The Stafford Smith Family,
Innkeepers

MONTAGUE INN

17 Rooms, $65/$115 B&B
1 Suite, $150
Visa, MC, Amex
16 Private Baths
1 Shared Bath
Open Year-round

Children Accepted; No Pets
Cultural; Marshall Frederick Sculpture Gallery, Saginaw Art Museum, Japanese Tea House. Shopping: Antique Warehouse, Birch Run Outlet, Frankennuth ½ hr South. Winter & Summer sports

Breakfast; Lunch & Dinner Tues.–Sat. only
Wine & Liquor available
No Smoking in guest rooms

Conference Facilities (1) (max. 25 people)
Wheelchair Access (2 rms., dining rm. & conf. fac.)

From I-75 exit west on Holland Ave. (W) for approx. 3.5 mi. Go L. on Washington Ave., 2 blocks to inn.

TEL. 517-752-3939
FAX 517-752-3159
1581 S. Washington Ave.
Saginaw, MI 48601
Janet Hoffmann, Innkeeper

 This Georgian Mansion, restored to its original splendor, is surrounded by spacious lawns with flower and herb gardens. Summer evenings may be spent under the trees watching the sun set over the lake. Enjoy winter evenings curled up in front of a roaring fire in our library. Fine cuisine is offered in our intimate dining room overlooking the beautiful grounds. The Montague Inn provides a peaceful and elegant oasis in the heart of the city.
(*Elegant, Georgian/Colonial, In-Town, Inn. Member since 1989*)

DUSTY'S ENGLISH INN

7 Rooms, $75/$175 B&B
1 Suite, $125/$195 B&B
2 Cottage, $110/$175 B&B
Visa, MC, Discov

All Private Baths

Open Year-round
2 Persons per room limit
Children not encouraged; No Pet facilities

Golf, Fishing, Canoeing, Hiking, Biking, XC-Skiing, Antiquing

Breakfast, Lunch, Dinner; Authentic English pub; Wine, Beer, Ales, Liquor

Smoke-free Inn

Conference Facilities (50)

Wheelchair Access (4 rms., dining rm & conf. fac.)

From I-96 in Lansing, take M-99 (S) 8 mi. From I-94, take M-99 (N) 22 mi. Ninety miles west of Detroit. 20 miles south of State Capitol (Lansing) and Michigan State Univ. (E. Lansing).
TEL 517-663-2500
FAX 517-663-2643
728 S. Michigan Rd.
Lansing/Eaton Rapids, MI 48827
Dusty & Marcia Rhodes, Innkeepers

 A 1927 built Tudor-style riverside mansion on 15 acres. Rolling countryside with 2 miles of nature (xc-skiing in winter) trails along the Grand River and through woods. A 3 room suite and master bedroom are in the cottage complete with pool and fireplace sitting room. Six bedrooms in the inn find fireplaces, dining rooms, and walnut-paneled pub for cocktails, or pints of English ale.
(*Traditional, Country, Inn. Member since 1991*)

THE NATIONAL HOUSE INN

🛏	16 Rooms, $68/$130 B&B 2 Suites, $68/$130 B&B
💳	Visa, MC, Amex
🛁	All Private Baths
	Closed Dec. 25
🐕	Children Welcome No Pets
℞	Gift shop, Garden, Park, Tennis, Antiquing, XC Skiing, National Historic Landmark District Tours
⊙	Breakfast & Catered Dinners; Wine Available
🚭	No Smoking
	Conference facilities (36)
♿	Wheelchair Access (dining rm. & conf. fac.)

4 Marshall, a National Historic Landmark District and home of Win Schuler's restaurant, has many citations for its 850 structures of 19th-century architecture, including the National Register of Historic Places, on which this inn is also listed. Michigan's oldest operating inn, the first brick building in the county has been restored as a warm, hospitable inn, beautifully furnished, and lovely gardens. Afternoon Tea, Lectures, Candlelight Home Tours, Mystery Weekends.
(*Rustic, Village, Breakfast Inn. Member since 1978*)

I-94 to Exit 110; Rte. 27 (S) 2 mi. to Michigan Ave. Turn R. Marshall is halfway between Detroit & Chicago.

TEL. 616-781-7374
FAX: 616-781-4510
102 So. Parkview
Marshall, MI 49068

Barbara Bradley, Innkeeper

THE VICTORIAN VILLA INN

🛏	6 Rooms, $85/$95 B&B 4 Suites, $110/$145 B&B MAP rates available
💳	Visa, MC, Discov, Diners All Private Baths Open year-round
🐕	Children Accepted No Pets
℞	Antiquing, Hiking, Canoeing, Golf, Tandem Bicycles, Croquet, Fishing, Lawn Games, Special Weekends, Summertime Villa Dinner Theatre Productions
⊙	Breakfast, Afternoon Tea, Lunch (in Summer) Dinner, Picnic baskets, Victorian theme Dinners, Wine & Liquor available
🚭	No Smoking
	Conference Facilities (24)
♿	Wheelchair Access (1 rm., dining rm. Conf. Fac.)

5 A quiet and unhurried reflection of the 19th Century, the elegant and romantic Victorian Villa Inn offers distinctively furnished guest chambers, delicious hearty breakfasts, afternoon English Teas, and seasonal lunches. The Victorian Villa Inn also offers 19th Century gourmet 7-course Victorian dining, which has achieved national recognition in *Victoria Magazine, Midwest Living,* and *Wine Spectator.* Guests may also choose a special selection from over 200 wines from the Villa's own wine cellar, awarded *Wine Spectator*'s "Best of Award of Excellence." (*Elegant, Victorian, Village, Inn. Member since 1990*)

From I-69, exit M-60 (Exit 25); 7 mi. (W) to Union City & left on Broadway St. (the Main St. of town). Continue to inn on No. Broadway.

TEL. 517-741-7383; 800-34-VILLA; FAX 517-741-4002
601 No. Broadway St.
Union City, MI 49094
Ron Gibson, Cynthia Shattuck, Innkeepers

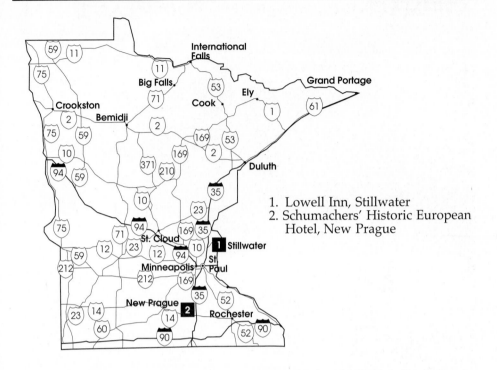

1. Lowell Inn, Stillwater
2. Schumachers' Historic European Hotel, New Prague

LOWELL INN

19 Rooms, $219/$299 MAP
2 Suites, $219/$299 MAP
Visa, MC

All Private Baths

Year-round

Children accepted; No Pets

Nearby Boating, Fishing, Cross-Country Skiing, Golf, Tennis, Historical Sights & Antique Shops

Breakfast, Lunch and Dinner

Smoking Restrictions

Conference Facilities (40)

Wheelcahair Access (dining rm. & conf. fac.)

Hwy. 94 to Hwy. 95 N. into downtown Stillwater. Turn L. onto Myrtle, R. on 2nd St. Inn on corner of Myrtle & 2nd.
TEL. 612-439-1100
FAX 612-439-4686
102 N. 2nd Street
Stillwater, MN 55082
Arthur & Maureen Palmer, Innkeepers

The Lowell Inn is a full-service, country inn featuring 21, individually styled lodging rooms—all with private bath as either conventional tub/shower combinations or jacuzzi-style, whirlpool baths for two. American dining fare is featured in the George Washington Room. An exotic tenderlion and jumbo shrimp Fondue Bourguigonne is featured in the Matterhorn Room. The Lowell Inn has been continuously owned and operated for over sixty years by four generations of the Palmer family. (*Elegant, Intown, Inn. (Member since 1996)*

SCHUMACHERS' HISTORIC EUROPEAN HOTEL

	11 Rooms, $109/$167 EP
	Visa, MC, Amex, Discov, DC
	All Private Baths 11 Whirlpool Tubs
	Year-round except Dec. 24–25
	No Pets
	18-hole Golf course, XC Skiing, Biking, Fishing, Casino
	Breakfast, Lunch, Dinner Wine, Beer & Liquor available
	Smoking Permitted; No Pipes or Cigars
	Conference Facilities (11)
	Wheelchair Access (dining rm.)

2 Named one of the "Ten Best Inns," 1992, one of the "Top Twelve Inns, 1991," and "National Pork Restaurant of the Year," 1992 and consistently named one of the favorite restaurants in Greater Minnesota, this charming Central European Inn is internationally known for its superb Czech and German cuisine by Chef/Proprietor John Schumacher. Bavarian folk painted furniture, eiderdown comforters, whirlpool tubs, gas fireplaces, Bavarian bar, and European gift shop add to the uniqueness of this inn. (*Elegant, Village, Inn. (Member since 1979)*

From Mpls., 35W (S) to Exit 76 Elko, New Market (County Rd. 2), W, turn R for 10 mi. At 13, turn L, S, follow 13 2 mi., merges w/19 W, follow 2 Hwys into New Prague. Hotel is on left hand side past center of New Prague.
TEL. 612-758-2133
FAX (612) 758-2400
212 W. Main St.
New Prague, MN 56071
Kathleen & John Schumacher, Innkeepers

FOR YOUR SPECIAL OCCASION

If you are planning a wedding, a birthday, anniversary, rehearsal dinner, shower, or any special celebration and want it to be the most memorable event ever, A Country Inn makes a perfect setting. If you picture a wedding in a lovely Victorian parlor, or beneath an arbor in a formal garden, or maybe beside a mirrored lake, you're holding a book that locates all those places and many more. Even the unique presentation of an engagement ring can become a singular dream for some romantics. By special arrangement at Country Inns, engagement rings have been served under silver domes at the dinner table or hidden in desserts or tied to a bottle of champagne. The special innovative requests made by hopeful grooms somehow spark the romance in all the staff. The event becomes special for everyone.

Innkeepers can make any occasion extraordinary, because most often that event is the primary focus of the entire Inn for that particular day. In planning the event, staff works one-on-one with the client to make sure that everything is exactly the way he or she wants it. The nature and size of Country Inns insures them the time and organization to see that every detail is perfect. Flowers, balloons, a limo, a carriage, a boat, maybe even a horse and sleigh: your request becomes the innkeeper's charge. There are Inns in this book where all of these things, and more, are available. The possibilities are only limited by the combined imaginations and talents of the client and the Innkeeper.

When you have a special occasion coming up, look around your area or thumb through this book, and select a Country Inn for the site. Let your imagination take control. Contact the Innkeeper and plan an event that will live in your memory forever.

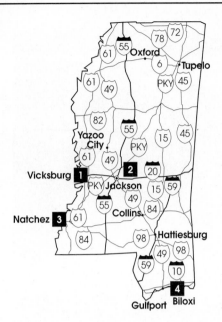

1. The Duff Green Mansion, Vicksburg
2. Fairview Inn, Jackson
3. Monmouth Plantation, Natchez
4. Father Ryan House Inn, Biloxi

THE DUFF GREEN MANSION

3 Rooms, $85/$110 B&B
2 Suites, $105/$160 B&B
8% Sales Tax
Visa, MC, Amex

Private Baths

Open Year-round

Children Welcome
Small Pets Accepted

Swimming pool on
grounds; Golf, Tennis,
Fishing, Hunting nearby;
many Historic Sites with-
in walking distance

Plantation Breakfast,
Wine & Liquor Available

Smoking in designated
areas only

Conference Facilities (75)

Wheelchair Access (2
rms)

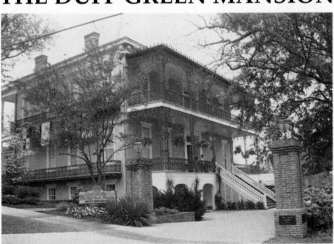

From I-20 Exit 4B to Clay St. Turn R.
on Adams. Turn right on First East St.
& continue on.

**TEL. 601-636-6968; 638-
6662; 800-992-0037; FAX
601-661-0079**

1114 First East St.
Vicksburg, MS 39180

Harry & Alicia Sharp,
Innkeepers

1 One of the finest examples of Palladian architecture in
the state (National Register of Historic Places), this 1856
mansion was pressed into service as a hospital for Confed-
erate, and later Union, soldiers during the famous siege of
Vicksburg. The 12,000-sq.-foot mansion in the historic Old
Town was restored in 1985 and is luxuriously furnished in
period antiques and reproductions.
(Traditional, In-town, Inn. Member since 1991)

79

MISSISSIPPI
FAIRVIEW INN

	3 Rooms, $115/$165 B&B 5 Suites, $165 B&B
	Visa, MC, Amex, Discov, Personal Checks
	All Private Baths Open Year-round
	Inappropriate for Children No Pets
	Walking/jogging, exercise equipment on property. Nearby: golf, tennis, baseball stadium, Agricultural Museum, Art Museum, Old Capitol Museum, Manship House, New Stage Theatre, Shopping
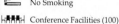	
	Breakfast, Dinner (by arrangement); BYOB No Smoking
	Conference Facilities (100)
	Wheelchair Access (3 rms., dining rm. & conf. fac)

2 In the heart of Mississippi's capital city stands Fairview, a National Register Colonial Revival mansion whose owners welcome guests in the hospitable tradition of the Old South. Guests may relax in the comfort of individually decorated bedrooms or suites or enjoy the eclectic interior design, various objets d'art, the oak-panelled library with its Civil War book collection, or stroll the extensive grounds and garden. Cover Feature and "Inn of the Month," Country Inns Magazine, October 1994. AAA 4-diamond award.

(*Elegant, Traditional, In-town Breakfast Inn. Member since 1994*)

I-55 Exit #98A on Woodrow Wilson, L. first traffic light at North State, L. one block past second traffic light at Fairview Street. Fairview is first property on L.

TEL. 601-948-3429
TOLL FREE 888-948-1908
FAX 601-948-1203
734 Fairview St.
Jackson, MS 39202
Carol & William Simmons, Innkeepers

MONMOUTH PLANTATION

	12 Rooms, $115/$160 13 Suites, $150/$225 AAA Four Diamond
	Visa, MC, Amex, Dicovr, Diners, Optima All Private Baths
	Open Year-round
	No Pets; Children over 14
	Croquet course, Fishing, and Walking Trails; Golf & Tennis 1/2 mi. from property. Gamble boat 1 mi. away on Miss. river.
	Breakfast and Dinner, Lunch for private parties only
	No Smoking; Smoking is allowed outside the rooms
	Conference Facility (100)
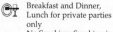	Wheelchair Access (4 rms., dining rm. & conf. fac.)

3 Monmouth Plantation, a National Historic Landmark circa 1818, a glorious return to the antebellum South. Rated "One of the ten most romantic places in the USA" by *Glamour Magazine* and *USA*. Today it tranquilly waits to enfold you in luxury and service. Walk our 26 beautifully landscaped acres. Twenty-seven rooms and suites in the mansion and the 5 other historic buildings hold priceless art and antiques while providing every modern comfort. Mornings begin with a delightful complimentary Southern breakfast. Nights sparkle under candlelight and crystal during 5-course dinners.

(*Elegant, Country, Inn. Member since 1993*)

East on State Street, 1 mile from downtown Natchez on the corner of John Quitmen Parkway and Melrose Avenue.

TEL. 601-442-5852
800-828-4531
FAX 601-446-7762
36 Melrose Avenue
Natchez, MS 39120
Lani & Ron Riches, Owner

FATHER RYAN HOUSE INN

 8 Rooms, $90/$115 B&B
3 Suites, $125/$150 B&B

 Visa, MC, Amex, Discov

 All Private Baths; 4 with
whirlpools

 Open Year-round

 Children Welcome; No
Pets

Beach across from Inn,
Pool, Historic Sites, Antique Shops, Shrimpboat
& Schooner Tours, Museums, Golf, Charter Fishing, Coastal Islands

 Gourmet Breakfast, Afternoon refreshments

 Smoking Restrictions
(outside only)

Wheelchair Access (1 rm.,
dining rm.)

Centrally located betw. New Orleans, LA & Mobile, AL. From I-10, Exit 46A on scenic Hwy 90, 6 blocks W. of I-110 off ramp.

TEL. 601-435-1189
800-295-1189
FAX 601-436-3063
1196 Beach Blvd.
Biloxi, MS 39530
Dina Davis & Rosanne McKenny, Innkeepers

4 A romantic 1841 beach front inn located on the Gulf Coast of Mississippi. The one time home of Father Abram Ryan, Poet Laureate and Chaplain of the Confederacy. All rooms include a private bath with bathrobes, cable television, telephone and antique furnishings dating to the mid 1800's. Rooms have views of the Gulf of Mexico, the gardens or the courtyard and pool. Selected by "Travel and Leisure" as one of the best beach front resorts in the Country.

(Traditional, Victorian, In-town Breakfast Inn. Member since 1995)

Dining at a Country Inn

For a number of Country Inns, dining becomes the raison detre; the Inn being established as a showcase for the chef/owner's self expression. At Chef-owned Inns, the diner can be assured that each meal will be an individually created masterpiece (or nearly so) prepared especially for him. Since the quality and design of the comestibles from such a kitchen carry with them the reputation and perhaps even livelihood of their creator, guests are treated to outstanding, sometimes innovative examples of what man can create for the palate. The dining experience will often be the first thing mentioned in the guest's bragging about this Inn.

The typical Country Inn cuisine for Independent Innkeepers' Association members is created by a talented chef (sometimes the owner) working hand in hand with the innkeeper to complete the total hospitality experience for the guests of the Inn. Often he is well trained and widely experienced. Sometimes he has worked up through the ranks in the kitchen "learning from the school of hard knocks." Some Country Inn chefs formerly worked at larger hotels but simply do not enjoy impersonally produced cuisine. Whatever the route, Country Inn chefs usually feel they have finally found their niche.

It is the feeling of most Innkeepers that hospitality includes providing sustenance to meet their guests' needs. Whether this means hot cider in the parlor, the ever-ready coffee/hot chocolate pot, home-baked cookies, gourmet breakfast, a picnic lunch, or candlelit dinner in an intimate dining room, the hospitality associated with the fare offered at a country inn is usually given very careful consideration.

MISSOURI

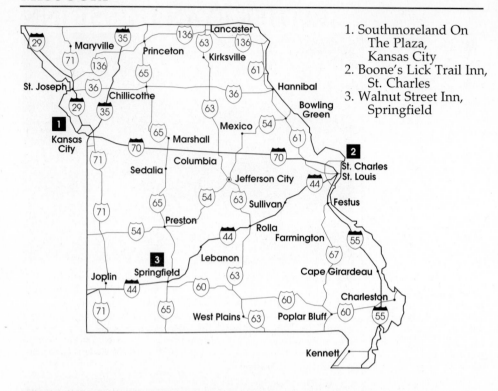

1. Southmoreland On
   The Plaza,
   Kansas City
2. Boone's Lick Trail Inn,
   St. Charles
3. Walnut Street Inn,
   Springfield

SOUTHMORELAND ON THE PLAZA

- 12 Rooms $100/$145 B&B
- Visa, MC, Amex
- All Private Baths
- Closed Christmas Eve & Christmas Day
- Children over 13; No Pets
- Nelson-Atkins Museum of Art, Country Club Plaza, Dining & Shopping, Theater, Dinner Playhouse, Tennis, Swimming, Royals Baseball, Chiefs Football, Crown Center, Historic Westport & River Market
- Breakfast, Wine & Hors d'oeuvres nightly
- Smoking areas designated
- Conference Facilities; A-V Equip. Available (14)
- Wheelchair Accessible First Floor

Award-winning Southmoreland's 1913 Colonial Revival styling brings New England to the heart of Kansas City's Historic, Arts, Entertainment and Shopping district—The Country Club Plaza. Business and leisure guests enjoy individually decorated rooms offering decks, fireplaces or double-Jacuzzi baths. Business travelers find respite at Southmoreland with its rare mix of business support services; in-room phones, FAX, message center, modem connections, 24-hour access and switchboard, and photocopier. Mobil Four-Star.

(*Traditional, Colonial, In-town, Breakfast Inn. Member since 1992*)

From I-70, I-35, I-29 in downtown Kansas City, Missouri, take the Main Street exit S. several miles to E 46th St., turn E (L), go 1 1/2 blocks to the Inn on the left.

TEL. (816) 531-7979
FAX (816) 531-2407
116 E. 46th St.
Kansas City, MO 64112
Susan Moehl &
Penni Johnson, Innkeepers

BOONE'S LICK TRAIL INN

  4 Rooms, $85/$135 B&B
1 Suite, $105/$175 B&B

 Visa, MC, Discov, Diners, Personal Checks

 All Private Baths

 Open Year-round; closed Xmas Eve

Children Accepted; No Pets; Kennels nearby

 Historic District, Winery Antiquing, Dining, Microbrewery, Goldernrod Showboat, Casinos, Katy Trail State Park: Biking/Hiking

  Full Breakfast, Lunches for Hikers/Bikers on Request

 No Smoking

Conference Facilities (10-16)

Wheelchair Access Limited (2 Rooms)

I-70 to exit 229 St. Charles Fifth St., (N) 3 blocks to Booneslick Rd. R. 4 blocks to Main St. Inn on SE corner of Main & Boonslick

TEL. (314) 947-7000
(800-366-2427 9-5 CST)

1000 South Main St.
St. Charles, MO 63301

V'Anne and Paul Mydler,
Innkeepers

　About 1840, our Federal-style building rose where Main Street met the Booneslick Trail, "THE" highway west, predating the Santa Fe and Oregon Trails. Today the inn, just six miles from the airport, 25 minutes to St. Louis sights, on the waterfront of "the Wide Missouri" River, is scented by rose and flower gardens facing the cobblestoned street of the eight-block Historic District. Folk Art, regional antique furniture and a working duck decoy collection color our rooms. Traditional breakfasts invite guests to linger peacefully over delicate lemon biscuits, fresh fruits and hot entrees in the dining and gathering rooms. Seasonal duck hunting available with Paul Mydler, MH guide.

(*Traditional, Federal, In-town, Breakfast Inn. Member since 1992*)

WALNUT STREET INN

 14 Rooms, $84/$139 B&B

 Visa, MC, Amex, Discov, Diners

 All Private Baths

 Open Year-round

No Pets; limited provisions for children

Nearby Lakes & Rivers, Golf, Tennis, Bass Pro, Caves, Bluffs, and Hiking Trails at the Nature Center. 45 min. from Branson, MO and Silver Dollar City

 Breakfast; Wine & Beer Available

 No Smoking except outside porches & balconies

Wheelchair Access (1 rm., dining rm.)

From I-44 take 65 S to Chestnut Expressway. West on Chestnut Expressway to Sherman Parkway; turn S 4 blocks to Walnut St.

TEL. 417-864-6346
FAX 417-864-6184

900 E. Walnut St.
Springfield, MO 65806

Gary & Paula Blankenship,
Innkeepers

　One of the "Top Twelve Inns in the Country" and recommended by *Glamour Magazine*, the 14-room luxury urban inn is in Springfield's Historic District and thirty minutes from Branson. Enjoy fireplaces, jacuzzis, private porches, and feather comforters for leisure travelers. In-room phones and fax for business travelers. Relax on the front porch swing, read a book by the fire, walk to the great Hall for the Performing Arts, museums, theaters and restaurants, or enjoy the Ozarks fine natural attractions.

(*Traditional, Victorian, In-Town, Breakfast Inn. Member since 1993*)

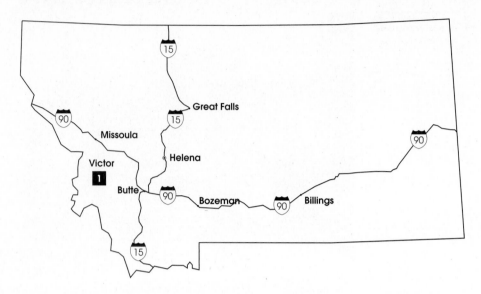

1. Bear Creek Lodge, Victor

BEAR CREEK LODGE

8 Rooms, $200/$250 AP
$150/$175 AP PP

Visa, MC, Amex, Discov

All Private Baths

Open Mar.–Dec.

Children under 13 with
prior approval only;
Pets considered

Horseback Riding, Hik-
ing, Fly Fishing, Rafting,
Mountain Biking, White
Water Rafting

Breakfast, Lunch, Dinner;
Wine & Liquor Available

Smoking outside only

Conference facilities (16)

N/A

1 Bear Creek Lodge is nestled on 74 scenic acres adjacent to the Selway Bitteroot Wilderness complex in southwest Montana. The inn features 8 rooms with private bath, each decorated with a mixture of old and new. Our mountain location enables us to offer our guests literally every type of mountain related recreation available.

(Western-rustic, Country, Retreat/Lodge. Member since 1994)

Go 2 mi. (S) of Victor on Rte. 93, (W) on Bear Creek Rd.; R then L on Red Crow. Straight on Bear Creek Trail (gravel rd.).

TEL. 406-642-3750
800-270-5550
FAX 406-642-6847
E-mail: bearcrik@montananet.com
HomePage:
http://www.recreate.com/bcl/
1184 Bear Creek Trail
Victor, MT 59875
Elizabeth & Roland Turney,
Owners

1. Philbrook Farm Inn, Shelburne
2. Adair, Bethlehem
3. The Notchland Inn, Hart's Location
4. Christmas Farm Inn, Jackson
5. Darby Field Inn, Conway
6. Stafford's in the Field, Chocorua
7. Corner House Inn, Center Sandwich
8. Moose Mountain Lodge, Etna
9. The Manor on Golden Pond, Holderness
10. Dexter's Inn and Tennis Club, Sunapee
11. Colby Hill Inn, Henniker
12. Inn at Crotched Mountain, Francestown
13. The Hancock Inn, Hancock
14. Chesterfield Inn, West Chesterfield

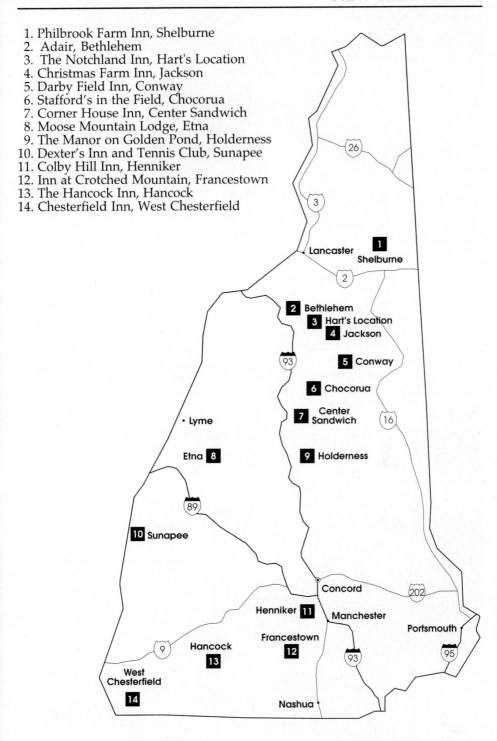

NEW HAMPSHIRE
PHILBROOK FARM INN

	18 Rooms, $110/$140 MAP DBL OCC
	5 Cottages $575/week (Summer only)
	No Credit Cards
	Private & Shared Baths
	Closed April 1 to May 1; Nov. 1 to Dec. 26
	Children Welcome
	Pets Accepted in Cottages
	Swimming pool, Game room, Major Ski areas, Nat'l. forest Hiking, Golf
	Full Breakfast, Trail Lunches to order, Dinner; B&B rates avail. BYOB
	No Smoking in dining room
	Conference Facilities (45)
	Wheelchair Access (Dining rm.)

1 The latchstring has been out at this venerable (National Register of Historic Places) inn since 1861 and 5 generations of the Philbrook family have been dispensing New England hospitality and wholesome, hearty, home-cooked New England meals ever since. As they say, "you will find simplicity rather than luxury, genuineness rather than pretension" at this peaceful retreat.

(*Traditional, Country, Mountain Inn. Member since 1978*)

U.S. Rte. 2 (W—20 mi.) from Bethel, ME. or (E—6 mi.) from Gorham, NH. At inn sign turn on Meadow Rd. for 1 mi. to R. at North Rd. for .5 mi. to inn.
TEL. 603-466-3831
603-466-3428
881 North Rd.
Shelburne, NH 03581

The Philbrook & Leger Families, Innkeepers

ADAIR

	7 Rooms, $135/$155 B&B; $205/$255 MAP
	2 Suites, $185/$220 B&B; $255/$290 MAP
	Visa, MC, Amex
	All Private Baths
	Open year-round
	Older children welcome; No Pets
	Tennis, Hiking, Golf, Shuffleboard, Billiards, Biking, Antiques, X-country and Downhill Skiing
	Breakfast, Dinner, in season (Wed.–Sun.)
	No Smoking
	Conference Facilities (16)
	N/A

2 A country estate built on 200 acres offering quiet elegance in the heart of the White Mountains. Built in 1927 as a wedding gift for Dorothy Adair Hogan, it has hosted many prominent politicians and Hollywood legends. Of classic Georgian Colonial Revival design, Adair offers extensive gardens and landscaping by the Olmsted Brothers of Boston's Emerald Necklace and Central Park fame. Dramatic views of the Presidential and Dalton Mountain ranges in addition to memorable dining. AAA ◆◆◆◆.

(*Elegant; Mountain, Inn. Member since 1995*)

From I-93, take Exit 40 onto Rte. 302E. Take 1st L at the Adair sign & continue to follow signs.
TEL. 603-444-2600
TOLL FREE 888-444-2600
Fax 603-444-4823
80 Guider Lane
Bethlehem, NH 03574

Hardy, Pat & Nancy Banfield, Innkeepers

THE NOTCHLAND INN

 7 Rooms, $170/$200 MAP

 4 Suites, $190/$250 MAP
Visa, MC, Amex, Discovr

All Private Baths

Open year-round

Appropriate for children over 12
No Pets

 Hiking, Birdwatching, River Swimming, Rock Climbing, Skiing, X-Country Skiing, Canoeing, Golf, Antiques, Crafts, Shopping Outlets, Ice Climbing

Breakfast & Dinner

No Smoking

Conference Facilities (12-25)

N/A

Rt. 93, Exit 35, Rt. 3 to Rt. 302; turn R., continue on Rt.302 toward Bartlett for 15.5 mi. to Inn on R.
TEL. 603-374-6131
800-866-6131
FAX 603-374-6168
E-mail: notchland@aol.com
Rt. 302
Hart's Location, NH 03812
Les Schoof & Ed Butler, Innkeepers

3 Get away from it all, relax and rejuvenate at our comfortable 1862 granite mansion in the midst of the White Mountain National Forest. Settle into one of eleven spacious guest rooms, individually appointed and all with working fireplaces. Notchland's wonderful 5-course dinner and hearty country breakfast are served in a romantic fireplaced dining room. Visit with our llamas and horses. Hiking, biking, swimming, skiing, skating, antiques, crafts and outlet shopping are close at hand. Notchland . . . a magical location. (*Traditional, Mountain, Inn. Member since 1996*)

CHRISTMAS FARM INN

 22 Rooms, $130/$160 MAP

10 Suites, $160/190 MAP
Visa, MC, Amex

All Private Baths, 5 Jacuzzis

Open Year-round

Children Most Welcome
No Pets

 Swimming Pool, Putting Green, Game Room, Shuffleboard, XC & Down-hill Skiing, Golf, Tennis in area

Breakfast & Dinner
Wine & Liquor available

Non-Smoking Dining & Living Rooms, some guest rooms

Conference Facilities (50)

 Wheelchair Access (dining rm. & conf. fac.)

From Rte. 16 to Rte. 16A across covered bridge .5 mi. to schoolhouse. R. on Rte. 16B for .5 mi. to inn on R.
TEL. 603-383-4313
800-HI-ELVES
FAX 603-383-6495
Box CC, Route 16B
Jackson, NH 03846

The Zeliff Family, Innkeepers

4 In a setting of majestic mountains, crystal-clear rivers and leafy woods, the cluster of buildings that make up this rambling inn invite you to share the good life. Whether inside in cozily decorated rooms, outside at the garden swimming pool, or in the candlelit dining room feasting on delectable, fresh meals, guests enjoy the at-home feeling. (*Traditional, Village, Inn. Member since 1988*)

THE DARBY FIELD INN

	14 Rooms, $80/$140 B&B $130/$170 MAP DBL. OCC.
	2 Suites, $180/$200 MAP
	Visa, MC, Amex
	14 Private, 2 Shared Bath
	Open Year-round exc. April
	Children over 2 Accepted No Pets
	Swimming pool, XC ski trails, Canoeing, Golf, Tennis, Hiking, Rock climbing
	Breakfast & Dinner Wine & Liquor available
	Smoking Restricted
	Wheelchair Access (dining rm.)

5 Beguiling guests with a spectacular view of distant mountains from its dining room, many guest rooms, and terrace swimming pool, this 1830 inn on the edge of the White Mountain National Forest is a favorite with outdoor enthusiasts. Well-groomed ski and hiking trails past rivers and waterfalls, a cozy pub, a massive stone fireplace, and hearty, delicious food are part of the picture.
(*Traditional, Mountain, Inn. Member since 1981*)

Rte. 16 (N) toward Conway. Turn L. .5 mi. before Conway at inn sign. 1 mi. to 2nd inn sign. Turn R. & continue 1 mi. to inn.
TEL. 800-426-4147
603-447-2181
FAX 603-447-5726
P.O. Box D, Bald Hill
Conway, NH 03818
Marc & Maria Donaldson, Innkeepers

STAFFORDS-IN-THE-FIELD

	11 Rooms, $60/$110 MAP–PP
	3 Cotts, $95/$110 MAP–PP Visa, MC
	8 Private, 3 Shared Baths
	Open Year-round Inquire Regarding Children; No Pets, Kennel Nearby
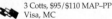	Walking Trails, Tennis, Croquet, XC Skiing, Golf, Swimming, Climbing, Antiques, Wedding Receptions in Restored Barn
	Breakfast & Dinner, Picnic Lunches; Wine & Liquor Available
	No Smoking
	Conference Facility (250)
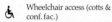	Wheelchair access (cotts & conf. fac.)

6 This New England farmhouse circa 1778, set amidst rolling fields & hidden from view by the surrounding forest. Known the world over for its gourmet country dining. The herbs from Ramona's kitchen garden flavor the scrumptious dishes served in the lantern-lit dining room. Walk in the woods, sleep under down filled quilts, enjoy the peace and quiet of the country.
(*Traditional, Federal, Country, Inn. Member since 1972*)

From Chocorua Village & Rte. 16, take Rte. 113 (W) 1 mi. to inn sign. From Rte. 93, Exit 23 to Rtes. 104 & 25 (E) to Rte. 16 (N) to village & Rte. 113 as above.
TEL. 603-323-7766
800-833-9509
FAX 603-323-7531
Box 270
Chocorua, NH 03817
Fred & Ramona Stafford, Innkeepers

CORNER HOUSE INN

 3 rooms, $80 B&B

 Visa, MC, Amex, Discov

 All Private Baths

 Open Year-round
exc.Thanksgiving, Dec. 25

 Children over 4
Well-behaved Pets allowed

 Crafts & Antique Shops,
Museum, Art Gallery,
Squam Lake, Tennis,
Hiking, Skiing

 Breakfast, Lunch, Dinner
Wine & Liquor available

 Smoking discouraged
including dining rm.

 Conference Facilities (70)

Wheelchair Access (din-
ing rm. & conf. fac.)

I-93, Exit 23 & Rt. 104 (E) to Meredith. R. at light on Rt. 25 (E) to Ctr. Harbor. L. at 2nd light to Bean Rd. for 7 mi. to blinker. R. onto Main St. to inn.
TEL. 603-284-6219
800-501-6219
FAX 603-284-6220
Main St., P.O. Box 204
Ctr. Sandwich, NH 03227
Jane & Don Brown,
Innkeepers

The picturesque village of Center Sandwich and the surrounding lakes and mountain area, near "Golden Pond" (Squam Lake), offer delightful diversions in any season. A warm welcome awaits at the intimate 150-year-old Corner House, sparkling with country antiques and beautiful crafts made by many local artisans. The Inn boasts one of the area's most widely acclaimed restaurants. (*Traditional, Village, Inn. Member since 1987*)

MOOSE MOUNTAIN LODGE

 12 rooms, $160/$180 B&B,
$60 B&B PP $80/$90
MAP PP PD; $90 AP PP
Visa, MC

5 Shared Baths

Open June 1–Oct 30,
Dec 26–Mar 10

Children Welcome;
No Pets

Hiking & Skiing Trails,
Swimming Pond, Large
Porch, Appalachian Trail,
Connecticut River,
Dartmouth College

Breakfast, Lunch & Din-
ner in winter; Breakfast &
Dinner summer & fall

No Smoking

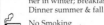 Conf. Fac. (10-12)

 N/A

I-89, Exit 18 (N) to Rte. 120 for 0.5 mi. to R. at Etna Rd. for 3.6 mi. to R. on Rudsboro Rd. for 2 mi. to L. on Old Dana Rd. for 0.4 mi. up mtn. to lodge.
TEL. 603-643-3529
FAX 603-643-4119
E-mail: meeze@aol.com
Hanover, NH
Moose Mountain Rd.
P.O.Box 272
Etna, NH 03750
Peter & Kay Shumway,
Innkeepers

Perched high on the side of Moose Mountain, with hiking and ski trails threading through 350 acres of woods and meadows, this big, old, comfortable lodge offers ever-changing views of the Connecticut River Valley. Meals are healthy, plentiful and delicious; the welcome is warm and friendly. Far from the sounds of civilization, peace and quiet reign. (*Rustic, Mountain, Lodge. Member since 1984*)

89

THE MANOR ON GOLDEN POND

🛏	17 rooms, $190/$325 MAP 6 suites/cottages, $950/ $1,750 weekly EP
💳	Visa, MC, Amex
🛁	All Private Baths
🛋	Manor House—Open year-round; Suites/ Cottages—June–Oct.
🐕	Children Welcome No Pets
R	Lakes, Canoes, Fishing, Beach, Pool, Tennis, Lawn Games, Golf, Hik- ing, Antiquing, Downhill & X-country Skiing, Sleigh Rides, Relaxing
🍽	Breakfast, Dinner, After- noon Tea; Wine & Liquer Available
🚭	No Smoking
♿	Conf. Facilities (40) N/A

9 Overlooking Squam Lake, this turn of the century estate provides the warmth and charm of a country home. Beauty and allure are reflected in the individually decorated bedrooms; most have wood burning fireplaces and views, and some whirlpools for two. Magnificently carved moldings and rich wood panelling in the dining rooms provide a setting of classical elegance for the nationally acclaimed cuisine. The Manor on Golden Pond is an unforgettable romantic getaway. AAA ♦♦♦♦ Restaurant, Award of Excellence, Wine Spectator Magazine. (*Elegant, Waterside, Country Inn. Member since 1995*)

I-93, Exit 24, (E) on Rte. 3, proceed for 4.7 mi., turn R at our sign (Less than 2 hrs from Boston)

TEL. 603-968-3348
800-545-2141
FAX 603-968-2116
P.O. Box T, Rte. 3
Holderness, NH 03245

David & Bambi Arnold,
Innkeepers

DEXTER'S INN & TENNIS CLUB

🛏	17 Rooms, $67.50/$87.50 MAP–PP
💳	1 Cottage, $95 MAP–PP DO Visa, MC, Discover
🛁	All Private Baths
🛋	Closed Nov. 1 to May 1
🐕	Children Accepted Pets Accepted
R	3 Tennis Courts, Pool, Lawn Games, Lake activities, Hiking, Golf
🍽	Breakfast, Dinner Wine & Liquor available
🚭	Non-smoking Rooms & Dining area
🏠	Conference Facilities (25)
♿	Wheelchair Access (1 rm., dining rm. & conf. fac.)

10 Tennis buffs love Dexter's, but so do all the guests who come for the breathtaking views, idyllic gardens, green lawns, bright guest rooms and excellent, bountiful food. The Simpson-Durfor family runs the inn like a well-appointed private estate, which provides a perfect setting for weddings and family reunions. In addition to the outstanding tennis program and 3 excellent golf courses nearby, they offer friendly service and advice on the myriad diversions available in the area.
(*Country, Inn/Resort. Member since 1978*)

I-89 (N), Exit 12 & Rte. 11 (W) for 5.5 mi. to L. on Winn Hill Rd. for 1.5 mi. From I-91 (N), Exit 8 & Rte. 11/103 (E) for 18 mi. to Newport & Rte. 103 for .1 mi. to L. on Young Hill Rd. for 1.2 mi.
TEL. 800-232-5571
603-763-5571
Box 703IIA, Stagecoach Rd.
Sunapee, NH 03782
Michael Durfor & Holly
Simpson-Durfor, Innkeepers

COLBY HILL INN

 16 Rooms, $85/$165 B&B

 Visa, MC, Amex, Diners, Discov, CB

 All Private Baths

 Open Year-round

 Appropriate for children over 7; No Pets, enjoy ours

 Swimming, Games, Ice Skating, Skiing, Fishing, Books, Tennis, Antiques, and Canterbury Shaker Village

Full Breakfast Daily (for inn guests), Dinner Daily for everyone. Wine & Liquor Available

No Smoking except outside

Conference Facility (32)

N/A

17 miles west of Concord off Route 202/9. South 1/2 miles on Rt. 114 to blinking light and Pharmacy. Turn right. Inn is 1/2 mile on the right.
TEL. 603-428-3281
800-531-0330
FAX 603-428-9218
The Oaks, PO Box 779
Henniker NH 03242
Ellie, John, and Laurel Day, Innkeepers

 Congenial inn-dogs Bertha and Delilah await with a handshake and the cookie jar beckons at this rambling 1795 inn, a complex of farmhouse, carriage house, and barns on five village acres. 16 antique-filled guestrooms, some with working fireplaces, all with private baths and phones. Now all fully air conditioned. And the food is memorable—from the bountiful breakfasts to the acclaimed candlelit dinners served in the gardenside dining room. Classic New England scenery abounds around this village on the river.
(*Traditional, Village, Inn. Member since 1993*)

INN AT CROTCHED MOUNTAIN

 13 Rooms, $60/$70 B&B $120/$140 MAP

 No Credit Cards

 8 Private Baths

 Closed end of ski season to mid-May; late Oct. to Thanksgiving

 Children Accepted
Pets Accepted

Swimming pool, Tennis courts, XC and walking trails, Downhill Skiing, Ice Skating, Antique shops, Summer Theaters

Breakfast, Dinner
Wine & Liquor available
Cigars or Pipes restricted

 No smoking in Dining Room

Conference Facilities (26)

 Wheelchair Access (4 Rms., dining rm. conf. fac.)

From Manchester, Rte. 101 (W) to 114 (N) to Goffstown & 13 (S) to New Boston & 136 (W) to Francestown. R. at 47 (N) 2.5 mi. to L. on Mountain Rd. for 1 mi. to inn.
TEL. 603-588-6840
Mountain Rd.
Francestown, NH 03043

Rose & John Perry, Innkeepers

 This 170-year-old colonial house is located on the northern side of Crotched Mountain. An awe-inspiring setting and a spectacular view of Piscataquog Valley makes all the difference at this out-of-the-way Colonial inn. Walking and ski trails thread the woods; vegetable and flower gardens supply food and adornment for tables and rooms. Rose Perry's savory home cooking has the added zest of an occasional Indonesian dish. John and Rose, who have been operating the inn since 1973, look forward to welcoming you.
(*Traditional, Country, Inn. Member since 1981*)

THE HANCOCK INN

🛏	11 rooms, $98/$158 B&B
💳	Visa, MC, Amex, Discovr Diners
🛁	All Private Baths
🛋	Open Year-round Appropriate for Children over 12; No Pets
🐕	Canoeing, Kayaking, and Swimming our many lakes, Climbing Mouunt Monadnock, Skiing (Alpine and X-Country), Theater, Galleries, Antiquing
☕	Breakfast, house guests only; Dinner to the public; Wine & Liquor available
🚬	No Smoking
🪑	Conference Facilities (35)
♿	Wheelchair Access (dining rm.)

13 Built as an inn the first year of George Washingtons' Presidency. "The impeccably maintained classic house, with stately columns, provides an incentive for a passerby to stop. An even better reason is the imaginative food served . . . ." (U.S. Air Magazine) (Yankee Magazine's Travel Guide) 1996 Editors' Pick, calls it "one of the outstanding reasons to visit New England." All rooms have four poster or canopy beds, hand sewn quilts, private bath, telephones, air-conditioning and cable T.V. Some with fireplaces. Come experience the serenity. (*Traditional, Village, Inn. Member since 1971*)

From Keene, Rte. 9 (N) to Rte. 123 (E) to Hancock. From Peterborough, Rte. 202 (N) to L. on Rte. 123 to Hancock.
TEL. 603-525-3318
Outside N.H. **800-525-1789**
FAX 603-525-9301
E-mail:
innkeeper@hancockinn.mv.com
Main Street
Hancock, NH 03449
Linda & Joe Johnston,
Innkeepers

CHESTERFIELD INN

🛏	11 Rooms, $115/$180 B&B 2 Suites, $155/$190 B&B
💳	All Major Credit Cards
🛁	All Private Baths
🛋	Open Year-round except Christmas Day
🐕	Children & Pets Welcome
🎨	Arts, Crafts, Music in Keene & Brattleboro. Swimming & Boating on Spofford Lake
☕	Breakfast & Dinner Daily Wine & Liquor available
🚬	No Smoking
🪑	Conference Facilities (25)
♿	Wheelchair Access (2 rms. Dining & conf. fac.)

14 Serving since 1787 as a tavern, a farm, and a museum, the inn's guest rooms today are spacious; some with fireplaces, or outdoor balconies, all with private baths, air conditioning, TV & telephone. Outside, the meadow overlooks Vermont's Green Mountains. Guests enjoy the cuisine of chef Carl Warner, head chef since 1987. Chesterfield Inn is a wonderful place to relax in comfortable elegance. AAA 4-Diamond Award for 5 consecutive years. (*Elegant, Colonial, Country, Inn. Member since 1990*)

From I-91, take Exit 3 to Rte. 9 (E). Continue on Rte. 9 for 3 mi. to inn on L.
TEL. 800-365-5515
FAX: 603-256-6131
E-mail: chstinn@sover.net
Route 9, Box 155
Chesterfield, NH 03443

Judy & Phil Hueber,
Innkeepers

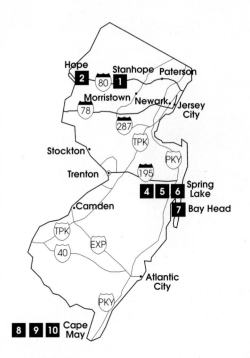

1. Whistling Swan Inn, Stanhope
2. Inn at Millrace Pond, Hope
4. Hamilton House Inn, Spring Lake
5. Normandy Inn, Spring Lake
6. Sea Crest By The Sea, Spring Lake
7. Conover's Bay Head Inn, Bay Head
8. Mainstay Inn & Cottage, Cape May
9. Manor House, Cape May
10. The Queen Victoria, Cape May

WHISTLING SWAN INN

10 Rooms, $85/$135 B&B

Visa, MC, Amex, Discov

All Private Baths

Open Year-round

Children over 12 are Welcome; No Pets Please

Near Waterloo Village, Wineries, Antiquing, Winter Sports, State forests, Shopping, Fairs, Shows, Flea Markets

Full Buffet Breakfast, Wine, Lemonade, Coffee, Tea, Cider

No Smoking

Conference (10-12)

N/A

Bus & Train via N.J. Transit to Netcong/Stanhope. Exit 27 off I-80 via route 183/206 one mile to Hess gasoline station. Turn on Main St. across from Hess.
TEL 201-347-6369
FAX 201-347-3391
E-mail: wswan@worldnet.att.net
Website: bbianj.com/ whistlingswan/
110 Main St.
Stanhope, NJ 07874
Joe Mulay and Paula Williams, Innkeepers

1 Nestled in northwestern New Jersey's Skylands Tourism region only 45 miles west of New York City, this 1905 Victorian home has been converted to a B&B and renovated in two major segments of time. Each room has a private bath, queen size bed and period furnishings. The house is air conditioned. Much of what is in the house is from Paula's grandmother's home in Oklahoma. Enjoy the porch swing, hammock and picnic table or sherry, movies, fireplaces and Tubs-for-Two bathroom. We work with any dietary requirements. Specialize in business travelers.
(*Traditional, Village, Breakfast Inn. Member since 1992*)

93

THE INN AT MILLRACE POND

🛏	17 Rooms, $85/$165 B&B Corp. Rate Sun.– Thurs.
💳	Visa, MC, Amex, Diners
🛁	All Private Baths
🍽	Open Year-round Dining Room Closed for Dinner Christmas Day
🐐	Children Accepted (limited); No Pets
☀️R	Tennis, Antiquing, Hiking, Fishing, Canoeing, Skiing, Golf, Bicycling, Winery tours, Waterloo Village.
☕	Breakfast; Dinner daily Sunday Lunch or Dinner served Noon- 8:00 p.m.
🚭	Wine & Liquor available No Smoking
⌐⌐⌐	Conference Facilities (40)
♿	Wheelchair Access (restaurant)

2 Originally a grist mill complex, Circa 1769, it's historic buildings were restored in 1986, creating a lovely inn along Beaver Brook. Authentically decorated rooms in the Grist Mill, Millrace House, and stone Wheelwright's Cottage blend the quiet elegance of Colonial America with modern amenities. The Mill's rich industrial heritage is evident while enjoying the restaurant's acclaimed seasonal menu. Colonial traditions of hospitality, value and gracious service highlight a visit to historic Hope. AAA ◆◆◆ Mobile ★★★ (*Rustic, Village, Inn. Member since 1988*)

From I-80, Exit 12, take Rte. 521 (S) 1 mi. to 4-way stop., L. on Rte. 519 (N), .2 mi. to inn. From the south, Rte. 78 to Rte. 22 to Rte. 519 (N), travel 18 mi., take R. at blinker/4-way .2 mi. to inn.
TEL. 908-459-4884
1-800-7-INNHOPE
FAX: 908-459-5276
Rte. 519, P.O. Box 359
Hope, NJ 07844
Cordie & Charles Puttkammer, Innkeepers

WE ASSURE QUALITY

When the innkeeper gave you this Association guidebook, *The Innkeepers' Register*, the intention of his generosity was, *Here is a guidebook of my fellow innkeepers' Inns. If you liked our Inn, you will probably like the others found in this book. We're all very different, but we hold the same very high standards of excellence.*

The reason this very bold statement can be made is the Quality Assurance Program adopted by the Independent Innkeepers' Association several years ago. The innkeepers' so strongly believed that they wanted to continue their quality protecting role in this industry, that a schedule was established under which every Inn in the Association will be inspected regularly to insure that they do not slip-up in their commitment to being ". . . the best at what we do."

You see, we realize that Inn-traveling has become very popular in recent years. As a matter of fact, so has it become popular "With this rapid growth in our industry, a plethora of guidebooks have become available from which the traveler must select from a plethora of Inns.

In protecting our own quality and the integrity of *The Register* in this growing market, we hopefully will be protecting the true tradition and spirit of American innkeeping. In 1966 Norman T. Simpson started us down the road toward "professional excellence and a genuine feeling of friendly welcome" for our guests. We are constantly aware of our need to protect our leadership position in the Country Inn industry as well as the integrity of *The Innkeepers' Register*. If you liked one of the Inns in this guidebook, we want to assure that you will like them all.

NEW JERSEY
HAMILTON HOUSE INN

 7 Rooms, S95/$165 B&B
1 Suite, $175/$225 B&B

 Visa, MC, Amex, Discovr, DC

 All Private Baths

 Open Year-round

 No Children or Pets

 Ocean Beach, On-premise pool, Theater, Tennis, Golf, Fishing, Racetrack (Thorobred), Antiquing, Shopping

 Breakfast

Smoking on porch only

Conference Facility (12)

N/A

From NY & N. Garden State Pkwy. to exit 98; Rte. 34 S. to 1st traffic circle. Proceed 3/4 around to Rte. 524. E. to ocean. Turn R., go 11 blocks. Turn R. onto Mercer Ave. From Phil. & S., Rte. I-195 E to exit to Rte. 34 S.; follow above directions.
TEL. 908-449-8282
Fax 908-449-0206
E-mail:
hamiltonhouse@worldnet.att.net
15 Mercer Ave.
Spring Lake, NJ 07762
Bud & Anne Benz, Innkeepers

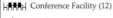 A Unique Seaside Experience. The aroma of fresh baked bread beckons you to our cheery dining room for a full breakfast at intimate tables. Sip iced tea by our backyard pool in summer, enjoy rooms with fireplaces in cooler weather. Ocean views, exquisitely decorated rooms with individual themes, antiques abound. Stroll the boardwalk, walk around the beautiful lake from which Spring Lake derives its name. A perfect getaway. Hospitality in the Old World Tradition.
(*Elegant, Victorian, Village, Breakfast Inn. Member since 1996*)

NORMANDY INN

 17 Rooms, $97–$121/ $146–$181 B&B
2 Suites, $212–$260/ $212–$286 B&B

 Visa, MC, Amex, Discovr, DC, CB

 All Private Baths
Open Year-round

 Children; No Pets

 Beach, Tennis, Golf, Fishing, Garden State Art Center, State Park, Local Theater

 Breakfast

 Restricted Smoking (front porch only)

 Conference facilities (30)

 N/A

N. Garden State Pkwy. S. to exit 98. Follow Rt. 34 S. to traffic circle. Go 3/4 way around & follow Rt. 524 E. Go straight until you get to the ocean. R. onto Ocean Ave. then 1st R. onto Tuttle Ave. 5th house on L.
TEL. 908-449-7172
FAX 908-449-1070
21 Tuttle Ave.
Spring Lake, NJ 07762
Michael & Susan Ingino, Innkeepers

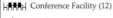 The Normandy Inn was originally built as a summer home and rental property in 1888 by the Audenreid family of Philadelphia. This Italianate villa with Queen Anne modifications has undergone and extensive and authentic renovation of both the interior and the exterior of the house. Included in this renovation were colors used from the pallet of "Century of Color" by Roger Moss. The prized furnishings of the common rooms as well as all of the guestrooms are original American Victorian antique. These furnishings are accented with reproduction wallpaper which reflects the elegance of the Inn's Victorian origins.
(*Traditional, Village, Breakfast Inn. Member since 1996*)

SEA CREST BY THE SEA

🛏	10 Rooms, $145 / $189 B&B 2 Suite, $235 / $259 B&B
💳	Visa, MC, Amex
🛁	All Private Baths
🛋	Open Year-round
🐕	No Children or Pets
Ⓡ	Ocean Beach, Tennis, Golf, Playhouse, Race Track, Antiquing, Biking, Fishing, Sailing
🍷	Breakfast, Afternoon Tea
🚬	Smoking Outdoors Only
⊢💺⊣	Conference Facility (11)
♿	N/A

6 Your romantic fantasy escape. A Spring Lake Bed & Breakfast Inn just for the two of you. Lovingly restored 1885 Queen Anne Victorian for ladies and gentlemen on seaside holiday. Ocean views, open fireplaces, luxurious linens, feather beds, antique filled rooms, sumptuous breakfast and afternoon tea. A *Gourmet Magazine* "top choice," one of *Country Inns Magazine* "Top Inns." *Victoria* magazine calls it "a perfect ocean refuge." John & Carol Kirby welcome you with old fashioned hospitality to an atmosphere that will soothe your weary body and soul.

(*Elegant, Victorian, Village, Breakfast Inn. Member since 1993*)

From NY & N Garden Pkwy to 34. From Phil. & S I-195 to 34. On 34 go south to first traffic circle and 3/4 around to 524 east to ocean. Go 1 blk. and turn right on Tuttle Avenue.
TEL. 908-449-9031
800-803-9031
Fax 908-974-0403
http://www.bbianj.com/seacrest
19 Tuttle Ave
Spring Lake, NJ 07762
John & Carol Kirby, Innkeepers

CONOVER'S BAY HEAD INN

🛏	12 Rooms, $100/$210 B&B
💳	Visa, MC, Amex
🛁	All Private Baths
🛋	Open Year-round
🐕	No Children or Pets
Ⓡ	Ocean beach, Croquet, Tennis, Golf, Antiquing, Biking, Fishing, Wind Surfing on bay & lake, Sailing, Race Track, Island Bch. State Park, Historic Site tours, weekly concerts in summer
🍷	Breakfast, Afternoon Tea
🚬	No Smoking
⊢💺⊣	Conference facilities (10)
♿	N/A

7 Come through the garden gate of romantic memories. Discover the antique-filled splendor of Conover's Bay Head Inn; recognized for fine accommodations and hospitality since 1970. Each bed chamber has been uniquely designed with views of the ocean, bay, English gardens or other shingle style Victorians. The aroma of Inn-baked biscuits, muffins or coffee cake and the "feature" of the day will awaken you each morning. Bay Head, with its weathered shingle style houses, captures the feeling of a late 19th century residential seaside village.

(*Traditional, Village, Breakfast Inn. Member since 1996*)

From NY & N. Garden State Pkwy. exit 98 to Rt. 34 S. to 35 S. From Pa- Pa. Tpke to NJ tpke to I-95 S. to Rt. 34. Rte. 35 S. to Bay Head; 7 blocks on R. to Inn.
TEL. 908-892-4664
800-956-9099
Fax 908-892-8748
646 Main Ave.
Bay Head, NJ 08742
Carl & Beverly, Timothy Conover, Innkeepers

MAINSTAY INN

 9 rooms, $105/$195 B&B
7 suites, $125/$275 B&B

 No Credit Cards; Personal Checks

All Private Baths

 Open Year-round

 Appropriate for children over six; No Pets

 Ocean Beach, Historic Tours, Shopping, Excellent Dining, Biking, Hiking, Tennis, Golf, and rocking on the Veranda

 Breakfast, Afternoon Tea

 No Smoking

 Conference facilities (12)

Wheelchair Access (1 unit)

Take Garden State Pkwy. (S). In Cape May, Pkwy. becomes Lafayette St. Take L. at first light onto Madison Ave. Go 3 blocks, R. at Columbia Ave. Inn on R.
TEL. 609-884-8690
635 Columbia Ave.
Cape May, NJ 08204

Tom & Sue Carroll,
Innkeepers

 Once an exclusive gambling club, the Mainstay is now an elegant Victorian inn furnished in splendid antiques. Breakfast and afternoon tea are served each day either in the formal dining room or on the wide veranda. Located in Cape May's famous historic district, the inn is within walking distance of beaches, interesting shops and a vast selection of fine restaurants.
(Traditional, Village, Breakfast Inn. Member since 1976)

MANOR HOUSE

 9 Rooms, $82/$186 B&B
1 Suite, $124/$199 B&B

 Visa, MC, Checks

 8 Private, 2 Shared Bath

 Open Feb. 1–Jan.1

 Appropriate for Children over 12; No Pets

 Ocean swimming, Beach walking, Porch sitting, Birding, Golf, Historic Homes Tours, Napping

 Breakfast, Afternoon Tea

 Smoking Restricted, outside only

 Conference Facilities (12)

N/A

From zero-mi. mark on Garden State Pkwy. to Rte. 109 South becoming Lafayette St., turn L. on Franklin for 2 blks. to R. on Hughes—612 Hughes on L.
TEL. 609-884-4710
FAX 609-898-0471
612 Hughes St.
Cape May, NJ 08204-2318
Nancy & Tom McDonald,
Innkeepers

 On a tree-lined residential street in the heart of the historic district, Manor House offers guests an exceptionally clean and comfortable turn of the century inn experience. Fluffy robes in the rooms and a generous cookie fairy are but a few of the fun touches found here. Relaxing on the porch, reading in the garden, or roaming the beaches and streets of Cape May occur with little effort. Traditional sticky buns and made-from-scratch full breakfasts and the innkeeper's good-humoredness give the inn its reputation for fine food and its character.
(Traditional, Village, Breakfast Inn. Member since 1991)

THE QUEEN VICTORIA®

🛏	17 Rooms, $100/$220 B&B
🗝	6 Suites, $160/260 B&B Personal checks
🛁	All Private Baths, 13 with Whirlpool Tubs
🛋	Open Year-round
🐕	Children Accepted No Pets
☀	Ocean swimming, Historic tours, Birding, Shopping, Dining, Biking (free inn bikes), Tennis, Golf, Fishing
🍷	Full Breakfast, Afternoon Tea, B.Y.O.B.
🚭	No Smoking Inside
🪑	Conference Facilities for 10-20
♿	Wheelchair Access (1 suite)

10 The Wells family welcome you to three restored Victorian homes in the center of the Historic District with warm hospitality and special services. Relax on porches overlooking Victorian gardens. Fortify yourself with a hearty breakfast and afternoon tea for bicycle riding, antique shopping, historic touring or nature walks. Dine at several of New Jersey's best restaurants. Victorian ambiance yet modern amenities—air conditioning and whirlpool tubs. December, devoted to Christmas.

(*Traditional, Victorian, Village, Breakfast Inn. Member since 1992*)

Garden State Parkway to southern end: continue straight over bridge, past marinas and onto Lafayette St. At second light turn left onto Ocean Street. Go 3 blocks. Turn right on Columbia and right into loading areas.

TEL. 609-884-8702
102 Ocean St.
Cape May, NJ 08204
Joan & Dane Wells,
Innkeepers

IT LOOKS SO EASY - LIKE DUCKS ON A POND

Many of our guests aspire to become Innkeepers once they have visited and experienced one our fine Inns. Many of them do indeed follow through and become part of the Innkeeping world. However, many more become discouraged when they sit down with someone who has had several years' experience or visit with a consultant or perhaps attend a seminar on Innkeeping. They are amazed about *everything* that goes into being an Innkeeper.

Innkeepers themselves are responsible for the perception that the business is an "easy, fun" way to spend one's time. Guests see them smiling as they greet their guests or pour coffee or chat about the local area while giving directions on interesting things to see and do. Guests never get to see their hosts dealing with leaky pipes, disgruntled employees, late food purveyors, obstinate suppliers, laundry equipment breakdowns, hours of bookwork, government regulations etc., etc. And that is as it should be.

Norm Kinney, the executive director of Independent Innkeepers' Association, always says that Innkeepers make it look too easy. He likens Innkeepers to ducks swimming on a pond. They are gliding along smoothly on the surface and paddling like crazy underneath.

So, is Innkeeping as easy as it looks? NO. Would most Innkeepers do it again? I think the majority of them would tell you, YES. Even with all the breathless paddling, innkeeping is an exciting, gratifying, challenging, and enviable way to *fully* live each day and *soundly* rest each night.

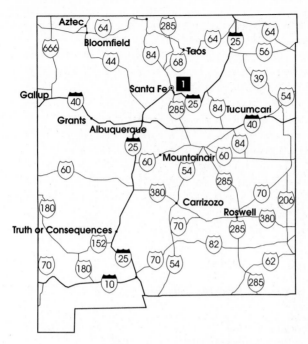

1. Grant Corner Inn, Santa Fe

GRANT CORNER INN

12 Rooms, $80/$155 B&B
Hacienda, $105/$130 B&B

Visa, MC

10 Private Baths, 2
Shared Baths

Open Year-round

Appropriate for Children
over 6; No Pets

Skiing, Hiking, Fishing,
Golf, Tennis, Swimming
(fee)

Complimentary Breakfast; Picnic Lunches, Catered Dinners, Restaurant
Serving Brunch to Public
Sat. & Sun. Complimentary Wine

Smoke-free inn

Conference Facilities (20)

Wheelchair Access (1 rm.)

From Albuquerque, I-25 (N) Exit St.
Francis L. (N) 3 mi.to R. at Alameda
(W).6blk.L.(N)on Guadalupe.1 mi.,
R. (W) on Johnson .1 blk., parking on
L.

TEL. 505-983-6678
FAX 505-983-1526

122 Grant Ave.
Santa Fe, NM 87501

Louise Stewart, Innkeeper

1 This delightful inn has an ideal location just two blocks from the historic plaza of downtown Santa Fe, among intriguing shops, galleries, and restaurants. Lush gardens, beautifully appointed guest rooms, fabulous gourmet breakfasts, and the gracious hospitality of Louise and her staff make this an experience not to be missed. Ample parking on the premises.

(*Traditional, In-Town, Breakfast Inn. Member since 1988*)

STAY A FEW DAYS - ENJOY THE COMMUNITY

Innkeepers are always happiest when a guest books a room for a few days rather than just one overnight. "We just can't begin to do our community justice when a guest arrives at dinnertime and has to leave shortly after breakfast," said innkeeper William Eberhardt, The Sherwood Inn, Skaneateles, NY.

Typically, country inns are located in small communities of either historic, architectural, natural, or recreational interest. Many times the inn has been a focal point of the community for years and years. As part of their hospitality emphasis, innkeepers are prepared to inform guests about the community as well as help them select activities and local sightseeing expeditions during their stay.

Many of these Americana experiences aren't written up in slick magazines and tourist brochures. They don't draw crowds (yet), and their names are not on the tip of every travel agent's tongue. Small community sights, events, festivities, museum, and natural features do, however, provide interesting and memorable experiences for those who take the time to seek them out and enjoy them.

The business-people and regular citizens in small communities, especially those who are accustomed to having out-of-town visitors who frequent the town's country inn, are all part of the whole experience, too. Often they will inquire about a "stranger's" visit to a community and consider themselves as part of an impromptu welcoming committee. Certainly the business community prospers from out of town "spenders", but somehow you don't get the feeling economics is the motivation behind their friendliness. Often, they just like being small town and somehow envied by those who come to take advantage of another way of life for a few days.

The following excerpt from an article in *USA Today* shows how the hospitality inherent at The Sherwood Inn for 188 years has spilled over into the thinking of the community.

In *recent days, signs have been going up throughout the village (Skaneateles, NY) declaring "Stress Free Zones." And Village clean-up crews have been donning aprons filled with brochures — sort of like roving information booths for visitors.*

Whether you've been there before or not, Skaneateles doesn't want you to fret about the little things. Forget to feed the parking meter? - not to worry. The city has people going around adding nickels if the little "expired" sign is showing. It's just that kind of place.

Most small communities have their own innovative ways of making visitors welcome. It is understandable, then, that the innkeeper is frustrated when he can't share that with the guest who arrives for dinner and leaves after breakfast. Next time you make a reservation at one of our country inns, ask about special attractions/events in the community . . . then stand by for a Chamber of Commerce run-down. Chances are you will end up booking for several days.

1. William Seward Inn, Westfield
2. White Inn, Fredonia
3. Asa Ransom House, Clarence
4. The Genesee Country Inn, Mumford
5. Oliver Loud's Inn, Pittsford
6. Morgan-Samuels B&B Inn, Canandaigua
7. Rose Inn, Ithaca
8. Benn Conger Inn, Groton
9. The Sherwood Inn, Skaneateles
10. Lincklaen House, Cazenovia
11. Chestnut Inn on Oquage Lake, Deposit
12. Overlook Mansion, Little Falls
13. Lake Placid Lodge, Lake Placid
14. Interlaken Inn, Lake Placid
15. Garnet Hill Lodge, North River
16. The Lamplight Inn B&B, Lake Luzerne
17. The Westchester House B&B, Saratoga Springs
18. The Sedgwick Inn, Berlin
19. Greenville Arms 1889 Inn, Greenville
20. Simmon's Way Village Inn, Millerton
21. Beekman Arms, Rhinebeck
22. Bird and Bottle Inn, Garrison

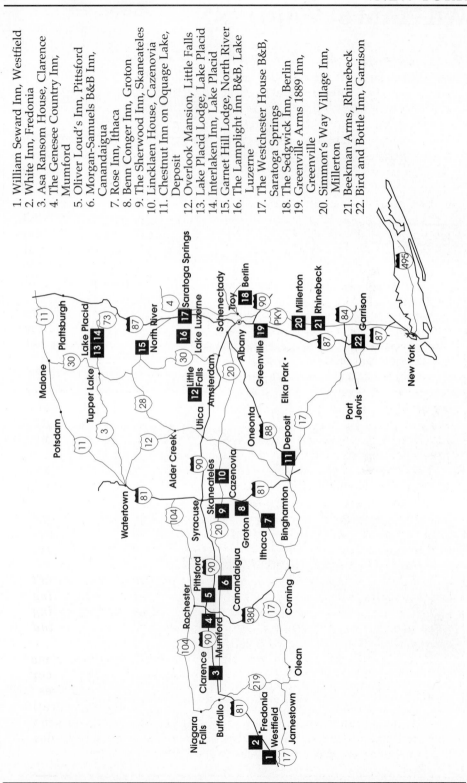

WILLIAM SEWARD INN

14 Rooms, $85/$165 B&B

Visa, MC, Discov.

All Private Baths
Open Year-round, except 12/24–25
Children over 10 are welcome; No Pets, Boarding available nearby
Chautauqua Institution, Lily Dale, Wineries, Antique & Speciality Shops, Skiing, Swimming, Boating, Tennis, Golf nearby.
Full Breakfast; Prix Fix Dinner available Thursday-Sunday by advance Reservation only; Wine available
No Smoking inside
Conference Facilities (15)
Wheelchair Access (2 Rms.)

 Although Chautauqua Institution is a major attraction, many travelers come specifically to stay at this 1821 antique-filled inn for rest and relaxation. The formal but comfortable ambiance created with period antiques (mid-1800s-early 1900s) in the 1821-1880 portion of Inn as well as the period reproduction setting in the new carriage house lend well to total relaxation for guests.
(*Traditional, Greek Revision, Country, Inn. Member since 1992*)

4 mi. S. on Rte. 394 from I-90, Exit 60. 2.5 hrs. NE of Cleveland, OH; 2.5 hrs. N of Pittsburgh, PA; 1.5 hrs. SW of Buffalo, NY; 3 hrs. SW of Toronto, Canada
TEL. 716-326-4151
FAX 716-326-4163
6645 S. Portage Rd.
Westfield, NY 14787
Jim and Debbie Dahlberg, Innkeepers

THE WHITE INN

12 Rooms, $59/$99 B&B
11 Suites, $99/$169 B&B

Visa, MC, Amex, DC, Discov.

All Private Baths

Open Year-round

Children welcome
No Pets

Antiquing, Wineries, Chautauqua Institution, SUNY college activities, Golf, Bicycling, XC/alpine skiing
Breakfast included; Lunch, Dinner, Wine & Liquor available
Some Non-smoking rms. Non-smoking Dining area
Conference Facilities (65)
Wheelchair access (dining rm. & conf. fac.)

 Built on the 1868 homesite of the county's first physician, The White Inn features period antiques and reproductions in beautifully restored guest rooms and public spaces. Superb cuisine has gained an enthusiastic following among guests and area residents. A charter member of the Duncan Hines "Family of Fine Restaurants," the Inn offers fine dining and banquets as well as cocktails and casual fare in our lounge.
(*Traditional, In-Town, Inn. Member since 1989*)

NY Thruwy. (I-90) Exit 59. At traffic light L. on Rte. 60 (S) to 2nd traffic light, R. on Rte. 20 (W), Main St. Inn on R.
TEL. 716-672-2103
FAX 716-672-2107
52 East Main St.
Fredonia, NY 14063
Robert Contiguglia & Kathleen Dennison, Innkeepers

ASA RANSOM HOUSE

 6 Rooms, $95/$125 B&B
3 Suites, $145 B&B
Sat. MAP only

 Visa, MC, Discov

 All Private Baths

 Closed Fri.; month of Jan.

 Well-supervised Children welcome; No Pets

 Niagara Falls—28 mi., many Antique Shops within walking distance

 Breakfast for House-guests; Dinner Sun. thru Thurs. (Sat.-Houseguests only); Wine & Liquor available

No Smoking

Conference Facilities (40)

Wheelchair Access

Traveling (E): I-90, Exit 49, L. on Rte. 78 for 1 mi. to R. on Rte. 5 for 5.3 mi. Traveling (W): I-90, Exit 48A & R. on Rte. 77 for 1 mi. to R. on Rte. 5 for 10 mi. to inn.
TEL. 716-759-2315
FAX 716-759-2791
E-mail: asaransom@a01.com
10529 Main St. (Rte. 5)
Clarence, NY 14031-1684
Robert Lenz & Judy Lenz, Innkeepers

3 On the site of the first gristmill built in Erie County (1803), this historic village inn offers country gourmet dining and fine New York State wines. Guests are romanced in the winter by the glowing fireplaces in the guest rooms, and enchanted in the summer by spacious grounds full of herbs and flowers. Some rooms have porches and balconies and a full country breakfast is included for all guests. Clarence is known throughout the East for its antiques and treasures. Only 25 miles from Niagara Falls. (*Traditional, Village Inn. Member since 1976*)

THE GENESEE COUNTRY INN

 9 Rooms, $85/$130 B&B
2 nite min (some wkends)

 Visa, MC, Amex, DC

 All Private Baths

 Closed Dec. 24 & 25

 No Pets; Inn has pets in residence

Trout fishing, Walking, Biking, Genesee Country Museum, Letchworth St. Pk., Rochester, Discount shopping, Gift Shop

 Breakfast houseguests; Luncheon for conferences; Tea, Cheese & Crackers; BYOB

 No Smoking

Conference Facilities (14)

Wheelchair Access (1 rm)

From NY Thrwy. (I-90) take Exit 47 and Rte. 19 S. to LeRoy. Go (E) on Rte. 5 to Caledonia, (N) on Rte. 36 to Mumford. L. on George St. 1 1/2 blocks—Inn on R.
TEL. 716-538-2500
FAX 716-538-4565
Res. only 1-800-NYSTAYS
948 George St.,
Mumford, NY 14511-0340
Glenda Barcklow, Proprietor, Kim Rasmussen, Innkeeper

4 GIVE YOURSELF A HIDEAWAY BREAK... Savor the magic quiet of our award-winning historic storybook stonemill in the century village of Mumford. See blue heron as you flyfish secluded "A-rated" troutstreams, visit nearby village-museum, our "19th century Williamsburg of Western NY," or Letchworth Park known as "The Grand Canyon of the East," then just relax and enjoy our hospitality. Tea, breakfast, some fireplaces, canopy beds, giftshop. Near fine restaurants. AAA, MOBIL, *Country Inns and Backroads*. 20 minutes Rochester, NY.
(*Traditional, Colonial, Village, Breakfast Inn. Member since 1988*)

OLIVER LOUD'S INN

🛏	8 Rooms, $135/$155 B&B
💳	Visa, MC, Amex, CB, Diners Club
🛁	All Private Baths
🏡	Open Year-round
🐕	Children 13 & over welcome; No Pets; kennel nearby
☀R	Erie Canal towpath for hiking, Jogging, XC Skiing, Biking, Boating, Golf, Tennis, Museums, Sight-seeing
☕	Cont. Breakfast hamper, Richardson's Canal House rest.; Wine & Liquor available
🚭	Smoking/non-smoking rms.
⊢⊣	Conference Facilities (20)
♿	Wheelchair Access (1 rm.)

5 Feeding ducks, building snowmen, visiting nearby shops, or rocking on the porch over-looking the Erie Canal, are some ways to relax at this circa 1810 stagecoach inn. Authentically furnished with antiques and period artwork, guests are pampered with V.I.P. welcome trays, as well as a breakfast hamper delivered to your room. King sized and canopy beds available. (*Elegant, Village, Inn. Member since 1989*)

NY Thruwy. (I-90) Exit 45, to I-490 (W) for 3 mi. to Bushnell's Basin exit (#27), turn R. & continue to Marsh Rd. signal & bear R. to inn.
TEL. 716-248-5200
FAX 716-248-9970
1474 Marsh Rd.
Pittsford, NY 14534

Vivienne Tellier, Innkeeper

MORGAN-SAMUELS B&B INN

🛏	5 Rooms, $109/$195 B&B 1 Suite, $195/$225 B&B Business Rate/$69–$99
💳	All rms. have fireplaces Visa, MC, Discov
🛁	All Private Baths Open Year-round exc. Dec. 24–25
🏡	Children under 3 or over 10; Pets outdoors only
🐕	Tennis, Golf, Nearby Lake, Wineries, Outdoor Symphonies & Concerts,
☀R	Sonnerberg Gardens, Horse drawn Sleigh Rides, 2100-ft. elevation downhill skiing (11 m.)
☕	Candlelit Gourmet Brkfast w/ Mozart, Dinner prix fixe by Reservation Fri.–Sat. or special request of 8+;
🚭	BYOB No Smoking
⊢⊣	Conference Facilities (15)
♿	Wheelchair Access (dining rm.)

6 As you travel the 2,000-ft. tree-lined drive to the secluded 1810 English style mansion you sense the difference between ordinary and legendary. The Inn sits like a plantation on a rise surrounded by 46 acres. Four patios, a lily pond with waterfall, five acres of lawn and gardens are canopied by 250 noble trees. Three rooms with French doors and balconies, ten active fireplaces, and a tea room with stone wall with 6-ft. glass window and pot-bellied stove. Library, common room, large screened and furnished porch, 2 jacuzzis, museum quality antiques, oil paintings. Mobil ★★★ AAA ◆◆◆◆
(*Elegant, Victorian, Village, Breakfast Inn. Member since 1992*)

I-90 from E Exit 43 R. on 21 to 488; L. 1st R. to stop sign continue 3/4 mile to Inn on R.
TEL. (716) 394-9232
FAX (716) 394-8044
2920 Smith Rd.
Canandaigua, N.Y. 14424

Julie & John Sullivan, Innkeepers

ROSE INN

 10 Rooms, $100/$175 B&B
5 Suites, $175/$275 B&B

 Visa, MC

 All Private Baths

 Open Year-round
Children over 10 or prior
arrangements; No Pets,
kennel next door

 Cayuga Lake Sports, X-
Country Skiing, near
Downhill Skiing, Golf,
Fishing, Wineries, Cornell
University, Antiques

 Breakfast, Dinner prix
fixe by reservation
Tues.–Sat.; Wine &
Liquor available
No smoking

Conference Facilities (60)
Wheelchair Access (conf.
fac.)

10 m. N of Ithaca on 34 N. From
Ithaca 13 exit, 34 N, 6 m. to "T" (red
flashing light). R. for .5 m. to fork, stay
L., Inn is 3.5 m. on R.
TEL. 607-533-7905
FAX 607-533-7908
E-mail: roseinn@clarityconnect.com
Rte. 34 North, P.O. Box 6576
Ithaca, NY 14851-6576
Charles & Sherry Rosemann,
Innkeepers
Patricia Cain, Manager

7 A spectacular Inn in a lovely country setting. Located halfway between NYC and Niagara Falls, in the heart of the Finger Lakes. This 1850 Italianate mansion is a gem of woodcraft, with a stunning circular staircase of Honduran Mahogany. Large, high ceilinged rooms are luxuriously furnished with antiques from around the world accented by lush colors and fabrics. Extraordinary cuisine is romantically served in elegant private dining rooms. Sherry and Charles welcome you to New York's only Mobil **** and AAA ◆◆◆◆ inn.

(Elegant, Country, Inn. Member since 1986)

BENN CONGER INN

 2 Rooms, $110/$130 B&B
3 Suites, $120/$220 B&B

 Visa, MC, Amex, Diners

 All Private Baths

Open Year-round

 Children Welcome
No Pets—Kennel nearby

 Hiking, Biking, XC Skiing,
Golf, Tennis, all Lake
Sports, Antiques, Wineries

 Breakfast, Dinner
Wine & Liquor available

 Smoking limited

Conference Facilities (40)

N/A

From I-81, Exit 12 (Homer) (S) on Rte.
281 for 2 mi. R. (W) on Rte. 222 for 9
mi. to Groton. Cross Rte. 38, making
no turns. Inn is up hill on R.
TEL. 607-898-5817
206 W. Cortland St.
Groton, NY 13073

Alison & Peter Van der
Meulen, Innkeepers

8 A revival mansion built for industrialist Benn Conger, the Inn is best known as a hideaway for mobster Dutch Schultz. Eighteen pastoral acres, gracious public rooms, including a library and conservatory, oversized suites, antiques, imported linens, amenities, Mediterranean-inspired cuisine and over 100 fine wines will please the most discriminating traveler. ("Wine Spectator" Award 1987-96).

(Elegant, Village, Inn. Member since 1991)

THE SHERWOOD INN

🛏	13 Rooms, $75/$145 B&B 6 Suites, $225 B&B
🗝	3 Bedroom Hospitality Suite W/Fully Equipped Kitchen
🛁	Visa, MC, Amex, Diners, CB
🛋	All Private Baths Open Year-round Peak rates effective Fri. & Sat. nights year-round
🐕	Children Accepted No Pets
☀R	Swimming, Boating, Golf, Downhill and XC Skiing, Fishing, Bicycling, Hiking, Antiquing
☕	Continental Breakfast, Lunch, Dinner; Dining room closed 12/24 & 25; Wine & Liquor available
🚬	No Smoking in Hotel; Non-smoking dining area
⌂	Conference/Banquet Facilities for 25/250
♿	N/A

9 From the handsome lobby with its fireplace and gift shop to the pleasant guest rooms, many of which overlook beautiful Skaneateles Lake, gracious service and comfort are the keynotes here. American cuisine with a Continental touch has been featured in *Bon Appetit*, and is served in the dining rooms and the friendly, casual tavern. Cocktail Cruises aboard our restored vintage Chris Craft. Featured in USAIR Magazine as one of the ten top historic country inns. The lovely village of Skaneateles offers many activities including the sights, sounds and aromas of a Dickens' Christmas.

(*Traditional, Village, Inn. Member since 1979*)

From N. Y. Thruwy: Exit
Weedsport, Rte. 34 (S) to Auburn.
(E) on Rte. 20, 7 mi. to Skaneateles.
From (S): Rte. 81 (N) to Cortland,
Rte. 41 (N) to Skaneateles. L. on Rte.
20 for 1 mi.
TEL. 315-685-3405
1-800-3-SHERWOOD
FAX 315-685-8983
26 West Genesee St.
Skaneateles, NY 13152
William Eberhardt, Innkeeper

LINCKLAEN HOUSE

🛏	18 rooms, $94/$109 B&B 3 suites, $120/$140 B&B
🗝	Visa, MC,
🛁	All Private Baths
🛋	Open Year-round
🐕	Children accepted Pets accepted
☀R	Swimming, Golf, Tennis, Downhill & XC Skiing
☕	Lunch, Dinner; Afternoon Tea Wine & Liquor available
🚬	Smoking accepted
⌂	Conference facilities (50) Banquet facilities (200)
♿	N/A

10 Built in 1835 as a luxurious stopover for 19th century travelers, the Lincklaen House has long been a local landmark and has hosted such luminaries as President Grover Cleveland and John D. Rockefeller. The old-world atmosphere is now combined with modern comfort and gracious service, offering guests a return to an era of elegant hospitality. (*Traditional, Village, Inn. Member since 1968*)

From NY Thruwy. (I-90): Exit 34, take
Rte. 13 (S) to Cazenovia. R. on Rte. 20,
1 block. From I-81: Exit 15 (La Fayette),
E. on Rte. 20. 18 mi. to Cazenovia.
TEL. 315-655-3461
FAX 315-655-5443
79 Albany St., Box 36
Cazenovia, NY 13035

The Tobin Family,
Innkeepers

CHESTNUT INN AT OQUAGA LAKE

24 Rooms, $69/$199
6 Suites, 1 Cottage, $1000/$1250 wkly

Visa, MC, Amex, Discovr, DC

10 private baths

Open Year-round

Children Welcome
No Pets

Summer-Hiking, Biking, Boating, Water Skiing, Fishing, Games. Winter-Skating, XC-Skiing, hiking, Games

Lunch (seasonal), Dinner

Smoking restricted to tavern & outside only

Conference Facilities (1)

Wheelchair Access (dining rm.)

From Rte. 17E., exit 82, R. off exit.
From Rte. 17W., exit 82, L. off exit.
At stop, L. for .5 mi., R. at Sun Diner, up hill for 2.5 mi, turn on the L.

TEL. 607-467-2500
800-467-7676
FAX 607-467-5911

498 Oquaga Lake Rd.
Deposit, NY 13754

Tom Spaulding, Innkeeper

Built in 1928, The Chestnut Inn at Oquaga Lake is a classic example of architecture and building construction at its best. The inn is almost totally constructed of the now extinct North American chestnut wood. Enjoy the amenities of a lakeside resort. Guests can also delight in the ultimate dining experience in a relaxed elegance in the main diningroom, or casual dining in the lakeside sunroom. Take a ride on the inn's replica launch, *PICKLES*, that once graced the waters of Oquaga Lake.
(*Traditional, Waterside, Inn. Member since 1996*)

OVERLOOK MANSION

5 rooms, $87/$120 B&B

Visa, MC, Amex

3 Private Baths

Open 2/97–12/97

Children Welcome
No Pets

General Herkimer Home, dock 17 of the Barge Canal, Herkimer Diamond, Cooperstown, Glimmergloss Opera, House & Baseball Hall of Fame

Breakfast and Dinner;

Smoking restrictions

Conference facilities (10)

N/A

From Albany, I-90 N. to exit 29A, Rte. SW to Little Falls.

TEL. 315-823-4222
FAX 315-823-4760

1 Overlook Lane
Little Falls, NY 13365

Carin Carolina Mei, Innkeeper

Nestled on a natural bluff overlooking the picturesque city of Little Falls, the Overlook Mansion is an architectural treasure that recalls a time of grace and elegance. Stained Glass Windows, Hardwood Floors, ceramic tiles, fruitwood trim and hand carved fireplaces are among the beautiful features to be found. Today, Overlook mansion is a haven for guests seeking the quiet, warmth, hospitality and visual delights usually associated with a bygone era. We will give you a wonderful welcome!
(*Victorian, Town, Inn. Member since 1997*)

NEW YORK
LAKE PLACID LODGE

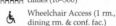

17 Rooms, $175/$450 B&B
5 Suites, $175/$450 B&B
16 Cabins, $175/$450 B&B
All Major Credit Cards

All Private Baths

Open Year-round
Children in Cabins, Pets in 2 designated lodge rooms—extra charge
Boating, Canoeing, Golf, Tennis, Hiking, Mt. Biking, X-country Skiing, Downhill Skiing, Horseback Riding, Swimming
Breakfast, complimentary afternoon tea included

No Smoking
Conference/Wedding Facilities (10–300)
Wheelchair Access (1 rm., dining rm. & conf. fac.)

13 Lake Placid Lodge embodies both the spirit of the North Woods and its venerable tradition of lakeshore summer cottages. It is, above all, a very personal place, romantic and private, a century-old camp restored to its rightful Adirondack heritage. Set alongside a pristine mountain lake amidst a vast wilderness of six million acres, the Lodge is committed to providing you with sumptuously comfortable accommodations, breathtaking views, memorable meals and a friendly, obliging staff to anticipate all your needs.

(*Adirondack. Rustic, Mountain Waterside, Lodge. Member since 1996*)

From Albany: I-87 N. to exit 30. Rt. 73 to Rt. 86. 1½ mi. to Whiteface Inn Rd. R. 1½ mi to lodge sign. ¼ mi. thru golf course to lodge. From Montreal: Canadian Rt. 15/I-87 S. to Veeseville exit 34, Rt. 9 N. to Rt. 86 to Lake Placid. 1½ mi. to Whiteface Inn Rd. Turn R., 1½ mi to lodge sign, go ¼ mi. thru golf course to lodge.
TEL. 518-523-2700
FAX 518-523-1124
P.O. Box 550/Whiteface Inn Rd.
Lake Placid, NY 12946
Kathryn Kincannon, Innkeeper

INTERLAKEN INN

10 Rooms, $120/$180 MAP
1 Suite, $180 MAP
Visa, MC, Amex
All Private Baths
Open Year-round; B&B only Apr. & Nov.
Children accepted over 5 small pets
Skiing, Golf, Tennis, Boating, Hiking, Fishing, Skating, Bicycling, Sight Seeing, Bobsledding, Lugging, Antiques
Full Breakfast, Dinner, Afternoon Tea, Sherry in each room, Wine & Liquor Available
Smoking limited to 1st floor only, non smoking dining room
Conference Facilities (20)
N/A

14 In the heart of the Adirondack Mountains, site of the 1932 and 1980 winter Olympics, this 1906 Victorian Inn offers a wonderfully romantic setting with uniquely decorated, antique furnished rooms. Enjoy a peaceful setting and four seasons of outdoor activities. The Inn offers fine dining using the season's freshest bounty to provide guests with a unique dining experience.

(*Traditional, Village, Inn. Member since 1992*)

I-87 to Rt. 73 to Lake Placid, at 1st stoplight turn L. (Main St.) to Mirror Lake Dr. to Interlaken on L.
TEL. 518-523-3180
800-428-4369
FAX 518-523-0117

15 Interlaken Ave.
Lake Placid, NY 12946

Roy and Carol Johnson, Jim & Kathy Gonzales, Kevin Gregg, Innkeepers

GARNET HILL LODGE

	24 Rooms, $65/$105 MAP-pp
	Visa, MC
	All private baths
	Open year-round
	Children Welcome; No Pets
	Swimming, Tennis, Hiking, Boating, Fishing, XC Skiing, Museums, Downhill Skiing
	Breakfast, Lunch, Dinner Wine & Liquor Available
	No smoking
	Conference Facilities (60)
	Wheelchair Access (1 rm)

From Albany on I-87 Exit 23 (Warrensburg). (N) on Rte. 9 to Rte. 28. (W) on Rte. 28, 22 mi. to North River. L. on 13th Lake Rd. 4.5 mi. to inn.

TEL. 518-251-2444
FAX 518-251-3089
13th Lake Rd.
North River, NY 12856

George & Mary Heim,
Innkeepers

15 Built in the tradition of the Adirondack Great Camps, Garnet Hill offers warm and welcoming hospitality in an informal and relaxing atmosphere, outstanding continental cuisine, specializing in "heart healthy" and vegetarian dishes. Nestled in the heart of Adirondacks, a destination resort, guests enjoy miles of hiking and cross country ski trails which start at the front door; boating, and swimming.

(Rustic, Mountain, Resort. Member since 1980)

THE LAMPLIGHT INN BED & BREAKFAST

	10 Rooms, $89/$140 B&B 7 Suites, $125/$165 B&B
	Visa, MC, Amex
	All Private Baths, 4 Jacuzzi jet tubs
	Open Year-round; (Closed Christmas Eve & Christmas Day)
	Children accepted over 12 No Pets
	Nearby Lake, Swimming, White Water Rafting, Horseback Riding, Golf, Tennis, Antiquing, Hiking, Mountain Biking, near Saratoga Springs & Lake George, Winter Sports
	Breakfast, Wine & Beer available
	Smoking on porch of main building only non-smoking carriagehouse & guesthouse
	Conference Facilities (50)
	Wheelchair Access (1 rm., dining rm. & conf. fac.)

From NYC—I-87—NY State thruway to Exit 24, Albany to entrance 1N—Northway (87) to Exit 21—Lk Luzerne/Lk George Exit. Route 9N South 11 miles. Inn is on Right.

TEL. 518-696-5294
800-262-4668

E-mail: lampinfo@adirondack.net

231 Lake Ave., P.O. Box 70
Lake Luzerne, NY 12846

Gene & Linda Merlino, Innkeepers

16 Active Saratoga Springs/Lake George area. 1890 Victorian built as the vacation home of a wealthy playboy/lumberman. Nestled in the foothills of the Southern Adirondacks on 10 acres surrounded by towering pines and just a short walk to crystal clear Lake Luzerne. Year round activity. Romantic getaway, fireplaces, memorable breakfast. Carriage House with fireplaces, Jacuzzi jet tubs and TV's. AAA ◆◆◆. 1992 Inn of the Year—Laniers—"Complete Guide to Bed & Breakfasts, Inns & Guest Houses of US & Canada."

(Victorian, Traditional, Village, Breakfast Inn. Member since 1996)

THE WESTCHESTER HOUSE B&B

🛏	7 Rooms, $85/$95–$150/$250
💳	Visa, MC, Amex
🛁	All Private Baths
🛋	Open Feb. thru. Nov.
🐕	Well-behaved children by prior arrangement No Pets
☀R	Saratoga Performing Arts Center, Throughbred racing, Antiques, Tennis, Golf, Swimming, Biking, Fishing, Hiking, Skidmore College
❦🍷	Breakfast
🚬	Smoking Permitted on porch or in gardens
🛏🛏	Conference Facilities (12)
♿	N/A

17 Saratoga's hidden jewel. Nestled in a residential tree lined street and surrounded by exuberant gardens this whimsical Queen Anne "painted lady" offers old-world ambience, up-to-date comforts and gracious hospitality. Lace curtains, oriental carpets, high ceilings and the rich luster of natural woods combine with king or queen size beds and tiled baths to provide elegance and comfort. The charm and excitement of Saratoga is at our doorstep. AAA ◆◆◆

(*Traditional, Victorian, Inn-Town, Breakfast Inn. Member since 1996*)

30 mi. N. of Albany: I-87 to exit 13N. 4 mi. N. of 5th traffic light. Right (E.) on Lincoln to number 102.

TEL. 518-587-7613

102 Lincoln Ave.
P.O. Box 944
Saratoga Springs, NY 12866
Bob & Stephanie Melvin,
Innkeepers

THE SEDGWICK INN

🛏	4 Rooms, $85/$95 B&B 1 Ste, $100/$120 B&B Annex $65/$75
💳	Visa, MC, Amex, Diners, Discov
🛁	All Private Baths
🛋	Open Year-round
🐕	Children accepted in annex; Pets accepted in annex
☀R	Library, Gift & Gourmet shops, Downhill & XC Skiing, Swimming, Theatre, Tanglewood Music Festival, Art Museums
❦🍷	Breakfast, Light lunches, Gourmet Dinners Wine & Liquor available
🚬	No Smoking in Inn bedrooms
🛏🛏	Conference Facilities (25)
♿	Wheelchair Access (annex, dining rm.)

18 This historic inn, once a stagecoach stop, sits on 12 acres in the beautiful Taconic Valley on the New York side of the Berkshires, within easy access to Albany, Western Massachussets and Southern Vermont. Comfortable, yet elegant, it has been described as "the quintessential country inn." Rooms are furnished in antiques. Fireplaces, fine art and interesting artifacts grace both the handsome living room and the well-stocked library where the original indentures, date 1791, are displayed. The restaurant is renowned for its fine food and the carriage house features unusual gifts.

(*Traditional, Country, Inn. Member since 1985*)

From Albany: Rte. 787 N to Troy. Exit Rte. 7 E to Rte. 278. R. on 278 to Rte. 2, L. on Rte. 2 for approx. 15 m. to Rte. 22. R. on 22 S, 6 m. to inn. From N.Y.C.: Taconic Pkwy N, Exit Rte. 295 E to Rte. 22. L. on Rte. 22 N for 22 m.
TEL. 518-658-2334
800-845-4886
FAX 518-658-3998
Rte. 22, Box 250
Berlin, NY 12022
Edie Evans, Innkeeper

GREENVILLE ARMS 1889 INN

	12 Rooms, $110/$145 B&B 1 Suite, $145 B&B
	Visa, MC, Discov
	All Private Baths
	Closed Dec. 1–28
	Not appropriate for children under 12; No Pets
	Swimming pool, Tennis, Golf, Bicycling, Hiking, Hudson Valley & Catskill Sightseeing
	Breakfast for houseguests Candlelight dining by advance reservation
	Wine & Beer available
	No Smoking Conference Facilities (30)
	N/A

From NYC: 2 hrs. (N) on I-87 to Exit 21 & Rte. 23(W) for 9 mi. Then (N) on Rte. 32 for 9 mi. to Greenville. Inn is on L., before traffic light.

TEL. 518-966-5219
FAX 518-966-8754
E-Mail: NY1889inn@aol.com
P.O. Box 659, South St.
Greenville, NY 12083-0659
Tish Dalton & Eliot Dalton, Innkeepers

19 Built in 1889 in the foothills of the Northern Catskills, this lovely Queen Anne Victorian inn has welcomed guests for over 40 years. Two buildings are set on 6 acres of lawns, shade trees and gardens. Antiques, original artwork and Victorian details add to an atmosphere of warmth and relaxed comfort. After a full country breakfast, guests enjoy hiking, biking, sightseeing or relaxing by the inn's pool. In the evening, guests are treated to delicious seasonal American cuisine, completing a memorable experience. (*Traditional, Village, Inn. Member since 1991*)

SIMMONS' WAY VILLAGE INN & RESTAURANT

	9 Rooms, $145/$175 1 Suite, $320
	Visa, MC, Amex, Diners
	All Private Baths
	Open Year-round
	Children Accepted No Pets
	Skiing, Golf, Tennis, Swimming, Concerts, Summer Stock, Auto Racing, Antiquing, Historical sites
	Breakfast (guests only), Brunch, Dinner; MAP available
	Wine & Liquor available Smoking in restricted areas
	Conference Facilities (25)
	N/A

From N.Y.C. (90 mi.): Taconic Pkwy. to Rte. 44(E) or I-684 to Rte. 22 (N) to Rte. 44 (E) (Main St.). From Boston (160 mi.): Mass. Tpke., Exit 2, Rte. 102 (W) to Rte. 7 (S) to Rte. 44 (W). From Hartford: Rte. 44 (W) to Millerton.
TEL. 518-789-6235
FAX 518-789-6236
E-mail: swvi@taconic.net
33 Main St.
Millerton, NY 12546
The Carter Family, Owners & Innkeepers

20 Graceful retreat in grand Victorian elegance and civility. Located near CT border in Berkshire foothills. Antiques, fireplaces, porches and historic, candlelit silver service highlight memorable accommodations and internationally acclaimed cuisine and wine selections. Selected by American Express/Hertz as "Quintessential Country Inn 1991" for a national ad campaign. Simmons' Way has been awarded a rare distinction of 4-star rating at local, national and international levels. (*Victorian, Village, Inn. Member since 1990*)

BEEKMAN ARMS

	57 Rooms, $85/$125 EP 2 Suites, $125/$140 B&B
	Visa, MC, Amex, Diners
	All Private Baths
	Open Year-round
	Children under 3 free No Pets exc. motel unit
	Golf, Swimming, Fishing, XC Skiing, Tennis, Antiquing Nearby
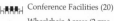	Breakfast, Lunch, Dinner Wine & Liquor available
	17 rooms Non-smoking Non-smoking Dining area
	Conference Facilities (20)
	Wheelchair Access (2 rms, dining rm. & conf. fac.)

21 Located in a historic walking village with exceptional attractions nearby; FDR Home & Library, Culinary Institute of America, Montgomery Place and a World War I Air Show. Each of the 59 rooms are uniquely decorated, many with working fireplaces. The 1766 Travern, rated excellent by *NY Times*, offers regional American Cuisine by Larry Forgione, noted chef and author who has been a James Beard Chef of the Year. Wide plank floors, overhead beams and a stone hearth beckon guests as they enter the lobby, recalling a simpler and more genuine way of life. "What a perfectly lovely Inn you have" M.J.R. 5/31/96 (*Traditional, Village, Inn. Member since 1967*)

NY Thruwy. (I-90) Rhinecliff Bridge Exit to Rte. 9 (S) 2 mi. to Rhinebeck Village. From Taconic Pkwy. take Rte. 199 (W) to L. on Rte. 308 to Rhinebeck Village.

TEL. 914-876-7077
FAX 914-876-7077
4 Mill St., Route 9
Rhinebeck, NY 12572

Chuck LaForge, Innkeeper

THE BIRD & BOTTLE INN

	2 Rooms, $210/$220 MAP 1 Suite, $240 MAP 1 Cottage, $240 MAP
	Visa, MC, Amex, Diners
	All Private Baths
	Open year-round
	Children 12 & over; No Pets
	Hiking, Nature walks, Golf, XC Skiing, Boating
	Lunch (Thur.-Sat.), Dinner, Sun. brunch; Wine & Liquor available
	Smoking restrictions
	Conference Facilities (50)
	Wheelchair Access (dining rm.)

22 A famed landmark on the old Albany-New York Post Road since 1761, this inn continues to welcome travelers with traditional Hudson River Valley hospitality. An authentic old country inn, it is internationally renowned for its gourmet cuisine, served in 3 dining rooms with woodburning fireplaces, and cozy overnight accommodations, also with working fireplaces, 4-poster or canopied beds, and Colonial furnishings. *Hudson Valley Magazine* voted . . . "Best Restaurant, Putnam County, NY 1993." (*Colonial, Country, Inn. Member since 1972*)

From Rte. I-84: Fishkill: (S) 8 mi. on Rte. 9. Inn on L. From NYC and Westchester: (N) on Rte. 9A and 9, past Croton and Peekskill. Inn 8 mi. beyond Peekskill on Rte. 9 in Garrison area.

TEL. 914-424-3000
FAX 914-424-3283
Old Albany Post Rd. (Rte. 9)
Garrison, NY 10524
Ira Boyar, Innkeeper

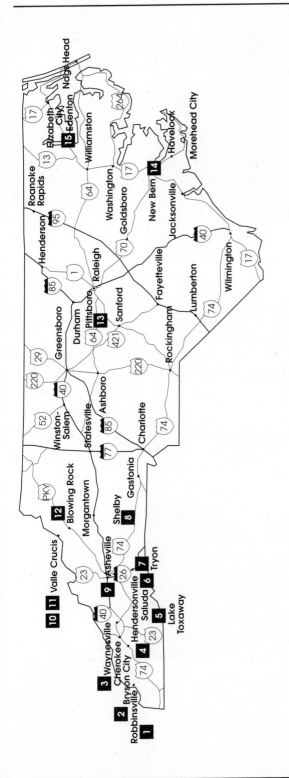

9. Richmond Hill Inn, Asheville
10. The Inn at Taylor House, Valle Crucis
11. Mast Farm Inn, Valle Crucis
12. Gideon Ridge Inn, Blowing Rock
13. The Fearrington House, Pittsboro
14. Harmony House Inn, New Bern
15. The Lords Proprietor's Inn, Edenton

1. Snowbird Mountain Lodge, Robbinsville
2. Hemlock Inn, Bryson City
3. The Swag Country Inn, Waynesville
4. The Waverly Inn, Hendersonville
5. The Greystone Inn, Lake Toxaway
6. The Orchard Inn, Saluda
7. Pine Crest Inn, Tryon
8. The Inn at Webbley, Shelby

SNOWBIRD MOUNTAIN LODGE

🛏	22 Rooms, $125/$185 AP
💳	Visa, MC
🛁	All Private Baths
🌳	Open April–Nov.
👪	Children over 11 welcome; No Pets
☀R	Hiking, Mtn. Biking, White Water Rafting, Fishing, Historic Indian Sites, Horseback Riding
☕🍴	Breakfast, Lunch, Dinner BYOB
🚭	No Smoking
♿	Wheelchair Access (2 rooms and dining room)

 High up in Santeetlah Gap, not far from the giant hardwood trees of the Joyce Kilmer virgin forest, is this secluded, rustic and picturesque mountain lodge, built of chestnut logs and native stone. Huge fireplaces, comfortable beds in pleasant rooms, a spectacular view and plentiful, delicious meals make this an exceptional vacation retreat. The lodge is on the National Register of Historic Places.
(*Rustic, Mountain, Lodge. Member since 1973*)

Robbinsville, at Hardees, Rte. 129 N for 1. 5 mi. to L. on Massey Branch Rd. for 3.3 mi. R. on Snowbird Rd., then R. on Santeetlah Rd..
TEL 704-479-3433
Fax 704-479-3473
E-mail: snbomtnldg@aol.com
275 Santeetlah Rd.
Robbinsville, NC 28771
Karen & Robert Rankin
Innkeepers

HEMLOCK INN

🛏	22 rooms, $125/$155 MAP 3 cotts., $160/$185 MAP Family Suites for 4 people, $193/$210
💳	Visa, MC, Discovr
🛁	All Private Baths
🌳	Open mid-April–Oct.
🐎	Children welcome No Pets
☀R	Hiking, Ping-pong, Shuffle-board, Skittles, Smoky Mtn. Natl. Park, Tubing, Cherokee Indian Res.
☕🍴	Breakfast at 8:30 A.M., Dinner at 6 P.M., Mon. to Sat. & 12:30 P.M. Sun.
🚭	Non-smoking dining room
♿	Wheelchair access (8 rms.)

 High, cool, quiet, and restful, this inn is beautifully situated on top of a small mountain on the edge of the Great Smoky Mountains National Park. There's a friendly informality in the family atmosphere and authentic country furniture. Honest-to-goodness home cooking and farm-fresh vegetables are served bountifully from Lazy Susan tables.
(*Rustic, Mountain, Inn. Member since 1973*)

Hwy. 74, Hyatt Creek Rd.- Ela exit & bear R. to L. turn on Hwy. 19 for approx. 1 mi. to R. turn at inn sign. Take country road 1 mi. to L. turn at next inn sign.
TEL. 704-488-2885
Galbreath Creek Rd.
P.O. Drawer EE,
Bryson City, NC 28713
Morris & Elaine White,
Innkeepers

THE SWAG COUNTRY INN

 13 rooms, $230/$380 AP
3 cabins, $325/$500 AP

 Visa, MC, Discovr

 All Private Baths

 Mid-May–End of October

 Children in cabins only; No Pets

 Hiking trails, Racquet-ball, Badminton, Croquet, Horseshoes, Pond with boat and dock

 All 3 Meals, hors d' oeuvres; Coffee beans & grinders in rooms; BYOB

 No inside Smoking

Conference Facilities (20)

Wheelchair Access (2 rms. & dining rm.)

NC I-40, Exit 20 to Hwy. 276 for 2.8 mi. to Swag sign. Just after sign, turn R. 4 mi. up blacktopped road to Swag gate. L. on gravel driveway 2.5 mi. to inn.
TEL. 704-926-0430
800-789-7672
FAX 704-926-2036
Hemphill Rd.,Rte. 2, Bx 280A
Waynesville, NC 28786
Deener Matthews, Innk.

3 This mountain hideaway is built of hand-hewn logs and is situated on 250 acres of secluded and unspoiled land. The Swag Country Inn is perched at 5,000 feet, with a private entrance into The Great Smoky Mountains National Park. Guests enjoy 50-mile breathtaking views. It offers countless amenities, such as a fine library, fireplaces, Jacuzzis, and exceptional cuisine.
(*Rustic, Mountain, Retreat. Member since 1991*)

THE WAVERLY INN

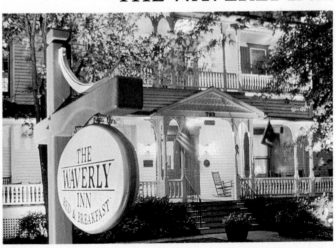

13 Rooms, $79/$139 B&B
1 Suite, $145/$195 B&B

Visa, MC, Amex, Discov.

 All Private Baths

 Open Year-round

 Children Welcome No Pets

 Biltmore Estate, Flat Rock Playhouse, Antiquing, Golf, Blue Ridge Pkwy., Hiking, Horseback Riding, Fishing

 Full Breakfast; Refreshments; Evening Social Hour; Arrangements for Private Parties, BYOB

 Smoking Limited

 Wheelchair Access (dining room)

From I-26, NC Exit 18B, US-64 (W); Continue 2 mi. into Hendersonville. Bear R. onto Rte. 25(N) for 800 yards. Inn is on L. at corner of 8th Ave. & N. Main.
TEL. 800-537-8195; 704-693-9193;
FAX 704-692-1010
E-MAIL INTERNET:
JSHEIRY@AOL.COM
783 N. Main St.
Hendersonville, NC 28792
John & Diane Sheiry, Darla Olmstead, Innkeepers

4 In an area rich with history and natural scenery, this National Register inn is the oldest surviving inn in Hendersonville's historic district. Walking distance to fine restaurants, exceptional shopping and antiquing. Polished wood, turn-of-the-century fittings, 4-poster beds, wide porches and rocking chairs are only part of the picture that brings guests back to this comfortable, friendly place. Join us for our daily social hour between 5 and 6 P.M. or just raid the cookie jar for one of Darla's famous inn house delectables.
(*Traditional, In-Town, Breakfast Inn. Member since 1991*)

THE GREYSTONE INN

🛏	30 Rooms, $245/$395 MAP
	3 suites $320/$495 MAP
💳	Visa, MC, Amex
🛁	All Private Baths
💡	Open Year-round
🐕	Children Welcome; No Pets
☀	Spa Facilities, Golf, Tennis, Swimming Pool, Croquet, Sailing, Water Skiing, Fishing, Hiking, Waterfalls, Champagne Cruise; Mountain Bikes
🍷	High-Country Breakfast, mid afternoon tea; Gourmet Dinner, Wine & Liquor Available
🚭	Non-smoking in public areas & Dining Room
🚻	Conference Facilities (35)
♿	Wheelchair Access (2 rms) (Dining Room)

5 With all the diversions of spectacularly beautiful Lake Toxaway at its doorstep, this intimate, historic (National Register) resort-inn combines the lure of its wild mountain setting with the comfort of modern luxuries and an exceptional cuisine. Romantic and tranquil. Excellent spa facilities. Complimentary tennis, sailboat, bassboat, ski boat, canoe and daily champagne cruise at all times and complimentary golf certain months. ◆◆◆◆

(*Elegant, Waterside, Resort. Member since 1991*)

From Asheville: I-40 to I-26 E., Rt. 280S (Exit #9) to Brevard. Us 64 W for 17 mi. to Lake Toxaway Country Club/Greystone Inn sign. Turn R. Approx. 3.5 mi. to inn.
TEL. 704-966-4700
800-824-5766 (in NC)
FAX 704-862-5689
Greystone Lane
Lake Toxaway, NC 28747
Tim & Boo Boo Lovelace, Inkps.

THE ORCHARD INN

🛏	9 Rooms, $105/$130 B&B
	3 Cottages $150/$175 B&B
💳	MC, Visa
🛁	All Private Baths
💡	Open Year-round except 3-5 days at Christmas
🐕	Appropriate for children over 12; No Pets
☀	Walking Paths, Birding, Antiquing, Biltmore Estate, Blue Ridge Parkway, Golf
🍷	Breakfast; Lunch-private groups of 12 or more only; Dinner (Summer—Tues.-Sat. Winter—Thurs–Sat.) BYOB
🚭	No Smoking
🚻	Conference Facilities (20)
♿	Wheelchair access (1 cottage)

6 "This turn of the century country house invites you to relax in its exceptional living room with large stone fireplace, oriental carpets, antiques, books, and folk art. Dine on the glassed in wraparound porch with breathtaking views of the Southern Blue Ridge Mountains. Stay in one of the nine comfortable guest rooms or in one of the three cozy fireplaced cottage suites, complete with whirlpool baths and decks."

(*Traditional, Country, Inn. Member since 1985*)

I-26, NC Exit 28 & turn toward Saluda for 1 mi. to L. on Hwy. 176 for .5 mi. to inn on R.
TEL. 800-581-3800
704-749-5471
Website: http://www.saluda.com/orchardinn
FAX 704-749-9805
E-mail: msdoty@aol.com
P.O. Box 725
Saluda, NC 28773
Veronica & Newell Doty, Innkeepers

PINE CREST INN

 22 Rooms, $135/$160 B&B
10 suites, $155/$185 B&B

 Visa, MC, Amex, Discov

 All Private Baths

 Open Feb. 1–Jan. 2
Children Welcome
No Pets
Golf, Tennis, Swimming,
Hiking, Horseback
riding, Biltmore House &
Gardens, Blue Ridge
Pkwy., Chimney Rock.,
Fence Equestrian & Na-
ture Ctr. Whitewater
Rafting, Waterfalls, Shops
& Antiques, Putting
green & Volleyball
Breakfast, Picnic Lunch &
Dinner Available; Beer,
wine & liquor available
Smoking Limited
Conference Facilities (up to
60)
Wheelchair Access (2 rm.,
dining rm. conf. fac.)

From I-26, Exit 36 to Tryon. Follow
Rte. 108/176 to town of Tryon. Turn
on New Market Rd. Follow signs to
inn.

TEL. 800-633-3001
704-859-9135

FAX: 704-859-9135

200 Pine Crest Lane
Tryon, NC 28782

Jeremy & Jennifer Wainwright,
Innkeepers

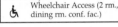 The famed hunt country and foothills of the Blue Ridge Moun-
tains are the setting for this classic Inn. Listed on the National Register,
the Pine Crest Inn features luxurious guest rooms, fireplaces, verandas, crisp mountain air, exceptional dining, and gracious service.
Fresh grilled seafood, Maryland crab cakes, rack of lamb, and roast
duck are the Chef's specialties. An extensive library, intimate bar, and
manicured grounds add to the atmosphere of casual elegance. Hiking
trails, nature walks, and natural waterfalls are nearby. AAA Four
Diamond Award.

(Elegant, Mountain, Inn. Member since 1991)

INN AT WEBBLEY

 8 Rooms, $125/$150 B&B

 Visa, MC, Discovr

 All Private Baths

 Open Year-round
Appropriate for children
over 12; No Pets

 Antique & Boutique
Shopping, State Parks for
Hiking, Gardner-Web
Univ., Historic Site

 Breakfast, Dinner by
prior arrangements only;
Dining nearby

 Smoking Restrictions—in
Courtyard and porches
only

 Conference Facilities (20)

 Wheelchair access (1 rm.,
dining rm., & conf. fac.)

I-85 S to exit 10B; proceed 15 mi to
stop light at Dekalb St. Turn R. at
light; go 7/10 mi., turn L. at Inn sign.
Next left is parking lot.

TEL. 704-481-1403

800-852-2346

FAX 704-487-0619

403 South Washington St.
Shelby, NC 28150

Max Gardner III & wife Victoria,
Innkeepers

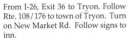 Webbley is a world removed from the ordinary. It invites romantic
interludes and magical memories. Convivial gatherings with friends.
Top-Level executive planning sessions. The Inn at Webbley offers the
ultimate retreat from the realities of everyday life, far removed from the
intrusions of everyday business. Webbley beckons with large, luxurious rooms lavishly furnished with imported French and English antiques, canopied beds, goose down duvets, fluffy robes, in-room
telephones, and remote cable television.

(Elegant, Colonial, In-Town, Breafast Inn. Member since 1996)

RICHMOND HILL INN

🛏	33 Rooms, $135/$290 B&B 3 Suites, $220/$375 B&B
💳	Visa, MC, Amex
🛁	All Private Baths
💡	Open Year-round
🐕	Children Welcome; Pets Not Permitted
⚡R	Croquet Lawn on site, Biltmore Estate tours, Blue Ridge Pkwy., Antiques & Crafts Shopping
🍷	Breakfast, Dinner; Sun. Brunch; Wine & Liquor Available
🚭	Non-Smoking Guest Rooms
👪	Conference Facilities (64)
♿	Wheelchair Access (1 rm., dining rm. & conf. fac.)

9 This 1889 Queen Anne mansion was one of the most elegant and innovative structures of its time. Now on the National Register, the Inn's rich oak paneling, handcarved fireplaces, and high ceilings provide an unusually luxurious setting in the Blue Ridge Mountains. Canopy and 4-poster beds, a highly acclaimed gourmet restaurant, and fresh mountain air are just a few of the attractions. (*Elegant, Mountain, Inn. Member since 1991*)

From I-240, take 19/23 Weaverville exit. Take exit 251 (UNC-A). L. at bottom of Ramp; L. onto Riverside Dr., R. on Pearson Bridge Rd., R. on Richmond Hill Dr.
TEL. 704-252-7313
FAX 704-252-8726
87 Richmond Hill Dr.
Asheville, NC 28806
Susan Michel, Innkeeper

THE INN AT THE TAYLOR HOUSE

🛏	5 Rooms, $125; 3 Suites, $165/$285 B&B; Outside Rentals, $105/$200 (b.fast not incl.)
💳	Visa, MC
🛁	All Private Baths
💡	Open Apr. 1–Early Dec.
🐕	Children by prior arrangement; No Pets
⚡R	Canoeing, Rafting, Golf, Horseback Riding, Hiking, Antique Shops, Theater
🍷	Breakfast; Arrangements for private parties, weddings & family reunions
🚬	Smoking on porch only
👪	
♿	Wheelchair Access (1 rm.) (dining room)

10 A bit of Europe in the peaceful, rural heart of the Blue Ridge Mountains, this charming farmhouse is decorated with fine antiques, oriental rugs, artwork, and European goose-down comforters on all the beds. Bright fabrics, wicker furniture and flowering plants invite guests to rock on the wide wraparound porch, while the friendly hospitality and memorable breakfasts add to their pleasure. (*Elegant, Country, Inn. Member since 1990*)

From Boone/Banner Elk, take Hwy. 105 to Broadstone Rd. (State Rd. 1112). Go 2.8 mi. past Mast Store Annex. Turn L. onto Hwy. 194. Just under a mile on R. side.
TEL. 704-963-5581
FAX 704-963-5818
Highway 194, P.O.Box 713
Valle Crucis, NC 28691
Chip Schwab, Innkeeper

MAST FARM INN

	9 Rooms, $75/$140 B&B 4 Cottages, $155/$205 B&B
	Visa, MC, Amex, Discovr
	11 Private, 1 Shared Bath
	Open Year-round, except Thanksgiving weekend & March
	Children welcome in cottages; No Pets
	Fishing, Hiking, Skiing, Golf, Canoeing
	Breakfast & Mon. dinner, houseguests only; Dinner Tues.-Sat., Sun. lunch; BYOB
	No Smoking
	Conference Facilities (10)
	Wheelchair Access (1 rm., dining rm.)

Boone/Blowing Rock/Banner Elk area. Watch for Valle Crucis sign at flashing light on NC 105 between Boone and Linville. Mast Farm Inn is 2.6 mi. from NC105 on SR1112 (Broadstone Rd.)
TEL. 704-963-5857
Toll-free: 1-888-963-5857
Web page: www.mastfarminn.com
FAX 704-963-6404
E-mail: stay@MastFarmInn.com
P.O.Box 704
Valle Crucis, NC 28691
Wanda Hinshaw & Kay Hinshaw Philipp, Innkeepers

11 The Mast Farm Inn continues a tradition of welcoming guests that began in the early 1900's. At that time, the 18-acre farm was not only producing its own food, but providing most other necessities as well. On the National Register of Historic Places, the 3-story farmhouse and the original outbuildings have been restored to accommodate guests year round. Nestled in the rural mountain valley community of Valle Crucis, near the Blue Ridge parkway and a variety of year-round activities, the Inn provides a peaceful retreat at the end of your day. (*Traditional, Country, Inn. Member since 1988*)

GIDEON RIDGE INN

	10 Rooms, $115/$170 B&B
	Visa, MC
	All Private Baths
	Open Year-round
	Appropriate for Children over 12; No Pets
	Hiking, Horseback Riding, Golf, Tennis, Village & Crafts shops, Blue Ridge Pkwy. Grandfather Mtn.
	Full breakfast, afternoon tea, Lunch & Dinner for groups by prior request; BYOB
	Smoking limited
	Conference Facilities (12-20)
	N/A

U.S. 321, 1.5 mi. (S) of village of Blowing Rock, turn (W) on Rock Rd., L. on Gideon Ridge Rd. at fork. Go to top of the ridge.
TEL. 704-295-3644
www.ridge-inn.com
FAX 704-295-4586
6148 Gideon Ridge Rd.
P.O. Box 1929
Blowing Rock, NC 28605
Cindy & Cobb Milner,
Jane & Cobb Milner, Innkeepers

12 Gideon Ridge Inn is ten delightful guest rooms with mountain breezes. French doors and stone terraces. Ceiling fans and wicker chairs. Antiques and good books. Fine breakfasts to linger over. Earl Grey Tea and shortbread cookies to savor. And a piano with a breathtaking view of the mountains. Really. (*Elegant, Mountain, Breakfast Inn. Member since 1990*)

THE FEARRINGTON HOUSE

🛏	17 Rooms, $165/$275 B&B
	11 Suites, $225/$275 B&B
💳	Visa, MC, Amex
🛁	All Private Baths
💡	Open Year-round
🐾	No children under 12; No Pets
☀R	Swimming, Biking, Walking, Bird watching, Golf, Tennis, Sailing, Fishing, Antique Shopping
🍷	Breakfast
🚬	Smoking limited
⊞	Conference facilities (40)
♿	Wheelchair Access (1 rm. & dining rm.)

13 In a cluster of low, attractive buildings surrounded by gardens and rolling countryside, this elegant inn offers luxurious quarters in a country setting. A member of Relais et Chateaux, the restaurant's sophisticated regional cuisine, prepared in the classical techniques, has received national acclaim, including AAA's ◆◆◆◆◆ award.
(*Elegant, Village, Inn. Member since 1987*)

Chapel Hill, U.S. 15-501 (S) 8 mi. to Fearrington Village.
TEL. 919-542-2121
FAX 919-542-4202
2000 Fearrington Village Center
Pittsboro, NC 27312

The Fitch Family, Innkeepers

HARMONY HOUSE INN

🛏	9 Rooms, $85/$95 B&B
	1 suite, $130 B&B
💳	Visa, MC, Discovr
🛁	All Private Baths
💡	Open Year-round
🐾	Well-behaved Children accepted; No Pets
☀R	Historic district, Tryon Palace, 2 rivers, Croatan Forest, Golf, Tennis, Boating, Museums, Antique Shops
🍷	Full Breakfast; Wine & Liquor Available
🚬	No Smoking
⊞	Conference facilities (10-12)
♿	N/A

14 As the Ellis family grew, so did their ca. 1850 home, with additions ca. 1860 (the Union troops were billeted in this home) and ca. 1880. In 1900, the home was sawed in half by the Ellis brothers, moved apart and rejoined with a second front door, hallway and staircase plus a wonderful front porch. Located in the historic district, this unusually spacious Greek Revival inn is decorated with antiques, locally made reproductions, Complimentary wine hour.
(*Greek Revival, Village, Breakfast Inn. Member since 1990*)

I-95 to Rte. 70 (E) to 4th New Bern exit to E. Front St., then L. on Pollock St. Hwy. 17 runs 1 blk. (N) of Pollock St.
TEL. 919-636-3810
800-636-3113
FAX: 919-636-3810
E-mail: harmony@nternet.net
215 Pollock St.
New Bern, NC 28560
Ed & Sooki Kirkpatrick, Innkeepers

THE LORDS PROPRIETORS' INN

20 Rooms, $185/$235
MAP; B&B (Sun. & Mon.)

None. We will bill.

All Private Baths

Open Year-round
Exc. Dec. 24 & 25

Children Welcome
No Pets

Swimming at owners'
country estate, Fishing,
Tennis nearby, Golf priv-
ileges, (two waterfront
courses)

Breakfast, Dinner (Tues.–
Sat.); Wine available with
dinner

Smoking in parlors and
on porches

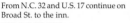 Conference Facilities (30)

Wheelchair Access (1 rm.,
dining rm. & conf. fac.)

From N.C. 32 and U.S. 17 continue on
Broad St. to the inn.
TEL 919-482-3641
Website:
web-www.Lordspropedenton.com
FAX 919-482-2432
E-mail:
reserv@lordspropedenton.com
300 No. Broad St.
Edenton, NC 27932
Arch & Jane Edwards,
Innkeepers

15 The Inn offers twenty spacious guest rooms in three restored homes on over an acre of grounds in Edenton's Historic District. Breakfast and dinner are served to guests in the Inn's dining room. Guest reactions: "We've enjoyed some fairly decent lodgings—Shepherds, the St. Francis, the George V. We have never felt as well cared for as at your Inn. The quality of the surroundings and management, the attention to detail, and the genuine friendliness you and your staff offer make the Lords Proprietors' Inn truly exceptional." "The food is unsurpassable."
(*Traditional Village Inn. Member since 1990*)

WHAT DID YOU DO BEFORE INNKEEPING?

"How did you happen to get into this innkeeping business?" That is the questions most often asked of innkeepers. And guests find the answers are as varied as the personalities of the innkeepers themselves.

One of the most common heroic replies is something about, "I got fed up with the impersonal corporate world (and/or the big city)." A few innkeepers just simply became disenchanted with their chosen vocations and "wanted a change." One gentleman, interested in historic restoration, discovered that the building he was so altruistically "returning to its original purpose, an 1835 stagecoach stop" was almost completed and *someone* was going to have to create a business for it. Suddenly he became an innkeeper.

And then there is the family that lived in a gracious and spacious southern plantation. By coincidence, one day when the father of the family was sitting at his desk looking at a $400.00 utilities bill, a prosperous acquaintance from a nearby city rang him to inquire if, just for a lark, he and his wife could bring another couple up to stay at his plantation while attending a nearby Saturday football game. The bill-paying plantation owner looked at the utilities bill and said, "Yes, of course you can. The charge will be $400, and we will serve you dinner" On that day his Inn was born, and he and his guests have been most pleased with that fortuitous decision ever since.

Each of the innkeepers in this book has a different background, a different story. Isn't that part of what makes inn-traveling such an adventure?

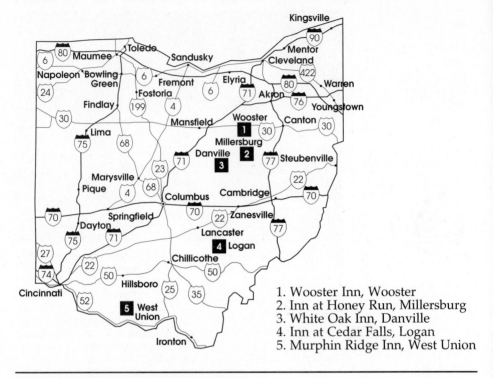

1. Wooster Inn, Wooster
2. Inn at Honey Run, Millersburg
3. White Oak Inn, Danville
4. Inn at Cedar Falls, Logan
5. Murphin Ridge Inn, West Union

THE WOOSTER INN

14 Rooms, $90/$100
2 Suites, $115/$130 EP

Visa, MC, Amex, Diners, Discov.

All Private Baths

Closed Dec. 25–26; 1st wk. Jan.

Well Supervised Children accepted; Pets Accepted

Golf, Tennis, Amish settlements, Football Hall of Fame in Canton, Wooster College activities

Breakfast, Lunch, Dinner, Wine & Beer available

Non-Smoking Dining Room

Conference Facilities (50)

Wheelchair Access (3 rms, dining rm. & conf. fac.)

1 The spacious campus of the College of Wooster is the setting for this pleasant inn, which overlooks the college golf course, where inn guests may play. Tastefully decorated rooms offer modern comfort and quiet, and cuisine in the attractive dining room is excellent and fresh. The Ohio Light Opera and college events provide cultural and recreational diversions.
(*Traditional, In-Town, Inn. Member since 1988*)

I-71 (S) to Burbank. L. on Rte. 83 (S), 18 mi. Wooster Exit, R. at Rte. 585 (S) for 200 ft. R. at Wayne Ave. Inn .7 mi. on L. I-71 (N) to US-30 E., 24 mi to Wooster Exit at Madison R. Follow to Bever to Wayne Ave. 2 mi. Turn R, 2 blks. to inn.
TEL. 330-264-2341
FAX 330-264-9951 (24 hr.)
801 E. Wayne Ave.
Wooster, OH 44691
Andrea Lazar, Innkeeper

THE INN AT HONEY RUN

	37 rooms, $65/$150 B&B 1 suite, 1 Guesthouse, $125/$280 B&B
	Visa, MC, Amex All Private Baths
	Open Jan. 10 (97)–Dec. 24; Dec. 26 (97)–Jan. 1 (98)
	Children accepted in Inn only, not Honeycombs or guest houses. No pets
	Birdwatching, Nat. trails, Game room, Amish Ctry, Cheese Factories, Craft Shops, Golf, Tennis, Hiking Trails
	Breakfast, Lunch (except Sun.), Dinner
	BYOB for guest rooms only
	Some Non-smoking rooms & areas, No smoking in dining room
	Conference Facilities (72)
	Wheelchair Access (1 rm., dining rm., conf. fac.)

From Millersburg: Rtes. 62/39 (E) for 2 blocks. L. on Rte. 241 (N) for 1.9 mi. R. (E) on County Rd. 203 for 1.5 mi.

TEL. 330-674-0011
800-468-6639
FAX. 330-674-2623
6920 County Road 203
Millersburg, OH 44654

Marge Stock, Innkeeper

2 Located on sixty acres of woods and pasture, this prize winning, contemporary inn offers a serene blend of nature and luxury. Stay in the INN and watch birds from your picture window. Enjoy an elaborate continental breakfast in your earth-sheltered Honeycomb Room with its stone fireplace and sliding glass door overlooking a wild flower meadow. Relax in a one- or two-bedroom Guest House with panoramic views of Holmes Country hills. Explore the sights, crafts and backroads of scenic Holmes County, home to the world's largest Amish population. (*Contemporary, County, Inn. Member since 1984*)

WHITE OAK INN

	10 Rooms, $75/$140 B&B (3 Rms. with Fireplaces)
	Visa, MC, Amex, Discov
	All Private Baths
	Closed Christmas
	Appropriate for Children over 12; No Pets
	Lawn games, Bicycling, Amish country touring, Antiquing, Golf, Fishing, Canoeing, Hiking
	Breakfast; Dinner by reservation; BYOB
	No Smoking
	Conference facilities (25)
	N/A

From I-71: Rte 36 (E) or Rtes. 95 (E) and 13 (S) to Mt. Vernon. Then U.S. Rte 36 (E) 13 mi. to Rte 715. From I-77: Rte. 36 (W) 43 mi. to Rte 715. Take Rte. 715 (E) 3 mi. to inn.
TEL. 614-599-6107
E-mail:
74627.3717@compuserve.com
29683 Walhonding (S.R. 715)
Danville, OH 43014

Ian & Yvonne Martin, Innkeepers

3 Turn-of-the-century farmhouse in a quiet, wooded country setting. Antiques and period decor, fireplace and square grand piano in the common room, front porch with swings and rockers, a screened house, and elegant meals, all make your stay a memorable one. Experience simple country pleasures. The Inn is close to Ohio's Amish area for quilts, oak furniture, antiques, and cheeses. We also offer guest participation in our onsite archaeological dig and other special event packages. (*Traditional, Country, Inn. Member since 1989*)

THE INN AT CEDAR FALLS

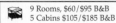	9 Rooms, $60/$95 B&B 5 Cabins $105/$185 B&B
	Visa, MC
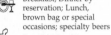	All Private Baths
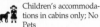	Open Year-round exc. Dec. 25
	Children's accommodations in cabins only; No Pets
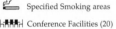	Hiking, Hammocks, Swimming, Canoeing, Riding, Antiquing, Artisans Shops
	Breakfast; Dinner by reservation; Lunch, brown bag or special occasions; specialty beers
	Specified Smoking areas
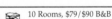	Conference Facilities (20)
	Wheelchair Access (2 rms., dining rm., & conf. fac.)

4 The restored and comfortably rustic 1840 Log House is an open kitchen-dining room, serving the most refined of gourmet dishes, prepared from home-grown produce. Guest rooms in the barn-shaped Inn building combine antique beds, private baths, and sweeping views of meadows, woods and wildlife. Fully-equipped 1800 log cabins, accommodating up to four, feature privacy. Facilities are appropriate for small business retreats, as well. The rugged and beautiful Hocking Hills State Park with glorious caves, waterfalls and forests flanks the Inn on three sides.
(*Rustic, Country, Inn. Member since 1989*)

From Columbus: Rte. 33 (S) to Logan exit, R. on Rte. 664, 9.5 mi. L. on Rte. 374. Inn is 1 mi. on L.
TEL. 614-385-7489
1-800-65-FALLS
FAX: 614-385-0820
E-mail:
www.n@cedarfalls.com
21190 State Route 374
Logan, OH 43138

Ellen Grinsfelder, Innkeeper

MURPHIN RIDGE INN

	10 Rooms, $79/$90 B&B
	No Credit Cards
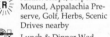	All Private Baths
	Open Feb. 16–Dec. 31 exc. Dec. 24–25, Jan. 1–Feb. 15; closed every Mon. & Tues.
	Children Welcome; No Pets
	Amish Shops, Serpent Mound, Appalachia Preserve, Golf, Herbs, Scenic Drives nearby
	Lunch & Dinner Wed. thru Sun.; BYOB for guest rooms only
	No Smoking
	Conference Facilities (25-30)
	Wheelchair Access (6 rms.)

5 An historic, tranquil 717-acre woodland farm is the setting for this prize-winning Inn. The brick farmhouse (1810) blends 3 attractive dining rooms, original fireplaces, unique Adams County crafted gifts and Art Gallery. Guests enjoy delicious entrees; homemade soups, made daily; luscious desserts from the professional kitchen staff. The custom furnished contemporary guesthouse includes fireplace rooms, porches, gathering room. Swimming, tennis, nature trails, horseshoes, shuffleboard, basketball, croquet boccie on premises.
(*Country, Inn. Member since 1992*)

Rte 32 E. Rte. 41 S. To Dunkinsville 6 mi, R. on Wheatridge 1 1/2 mi. R. on Murphin Ridge 1/2 mi.
TEL. (513) 544-2263
750 Murphin Ridge Rd.
West Union, OH 45693

Mary & Robert Crosset (CC.R), Innkeepers

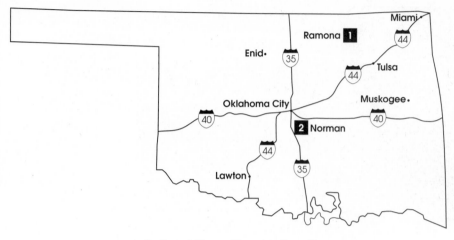

1. Jarret Farm Country Inn, Ramona
2. Montford Inn, Norman

JARRETT FARM COUNTRY INN

5 Suites, $135/$195 B&B

Visa, MC, Amex,

All Private Baths

Open Year-round

Children by prior Arrangement, No Pets

Swimming, Outdoor Spa, Walking Trails, Fishing, Picnics

Breakfast; & Dinner

Smoking on Patio & Porch Only

Conference facilities (8-10)

Wheelchair Access (dining rm ltd. & conf. fac., ltd)

20 mi. N of Tulsa on U.S. Hwy 75. West Side of Hwy.
TEL. 918-371-9868
FAX 918-371-4665
Rt. 2 Box 1480
Ramona, OK 74061
Jerry & Shauna Agnew, Innkeepers

1 You will be embraced by the casual, elegant appeal of this 115-acre hilltop retreat. Charming accomodations designed in a sophisticated county fashion offer secluded king and queen rooms, double jacuzzis and gaslog fireplaces, an outdoor pool and hot tub, closely mowed walking trails and superb evening dining that *Southern Living* called "Fabulous." Just 20 miles north of Tulsa, Jarrett Farm Country Inn is a must when visiting Oklahoma.
(*Contemporary, Country, Retreat, Lodge. Member since 1997*)

OKLAHOMA
MONTFORD INN

	10 Rooms, $70/$135 B&B 2 Suites, $95/$165 B&B
	Visa, MC, Amex, Discov
	All Private Baths
	Open Year-round
	Children Welcome, No Pets
	Private gym privileges, Golf, Tennis, Hiking, Horseback Riding, Sailing and Fishing nearby; Univ of Oklahoma Sporting & Cultural events
	Breakfast
	No Smoking
	Conference Facilities (20)
	Wheelchair Access (1 rm, dining rm. & Conf. fac.)

2 Nestled in the heart of Norman's historic district, this prairie style inn envelopes travelers in a relaxing and romantic atmosphere. Antiques and family heirlooms accent the individually decorated guestrooms and enchanting cottage. Fireplaces, private baths, canopied king-sized beds, jetted tubs and jacuzzis await the weary guest. Awaken to rich coffees and a gourmet country breakfast in the beautifully appointed dining room. Business travelers appreciate a private guest office, modem hookups, photocopier and fax service.

(*Traditional, In-Town, Breakfast Inn. Member since 1997*)

From I-35, take Main St., Downtown exit. Turn L. on University (about 2.2 mi from I-35). Go 2 blocks, turn R. ½ block on Tonhawa.
TEL 405-321-2200
800-321-8969
FAX 405-321-8347
322 W. Tonhawa
Norman OK 73069

Phyllis, Ron & William Murray, Innkeepers

THE STAFF AT A COUNTRY INN
PERSONAL INTEREST AND SERVICE

It doesn't take many visits along the Country Inn circuit to realize that a key ingredient for any hospitality recipe is the staff who "keep it all together". Since the size of most Inns limits the number of employees needed, the sometimes cumbersome employer/employee structure is usually not necessary. Staff members take personal interest in what they do, thereby losing that "employee" aura.

Many innkeepers very quickly and proudly introduce staff members to guests since they are often considered members of the Inn family. Sometimes they actually are members of the innkeeper's family. Besides the expected mother/father/offspring team found at many Inns, guests are sometimes surprised to have the innkeeper introduce the dishwasher or desk clerk as his mother. One very successful innkeeper employs his mother-in-law as a housekeeper; in another inn a retired gentleman is employed by his niece as a waiter.

Because Inns are usually very highly respected businesses in a community, they are often considered prestigious places to work. I recall overhearing one staff member tell her friend, "My friends *have* to work at other establishments in town. I *get* to work at the Inn." It is very difficult to hide this attitude from guests.

Every staff member from the lawn boy to the desk person to the housekeeper has an important role in providing consummate hospitality for every guest. The personal interest and service of staff members at an Inn is a big measure of what brings guests to enjoy their visits. Fortunately, in our Inns it is easy for staff to feel the importance of their contribution.   Certainly, guests perceive this Inn-family teamwork, and that makes all the difference . . . for everyone.

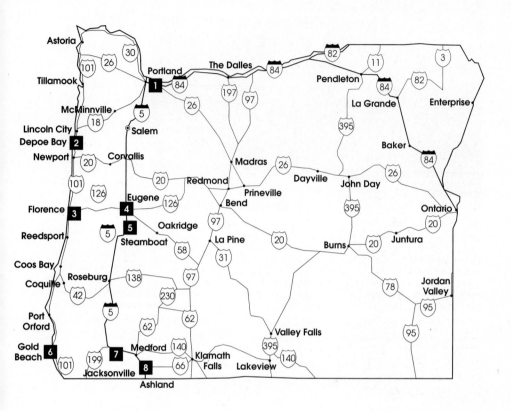

1. Heron Haus, Portland
2. The Channel House Inn, Depoe Bay
3. The Johnson House, Florence
4. The Campbell House, Eugene
5. Steamboat Inn, Steamboat
6. Tu Tu' Tun Lodge, Gold Beach
7. Jacksonville Inn, Jacksonville
8. The Winchester Country
   Inn, Ashland

OREGON
HERON HAUS

🛏	4 rooms, 2 Suites, $85/$250 B&B
	Visa, MC
	All Private Baths
	Open Year-round
	Children over 10 yr. old, No Pets
	Outside Pool, 1 1/2 hr to beach (Oregon Coast), 1 hr Mt Hood, Skiing, Hiking, 1 hr Touring Wine Country—Willamette Valley
	Breakfast; Continental
	No Smoking
♿	N/A

1 This elegant, three-story, turn of the century tudor sits high in the west hills, offering versatile accommodations for both the business traveler and romantic get-a-ways. Each room has sitting areas, work areas, phones with computer hook-ups, and TV's. All have queen or king size beds. The baths offer special extras—one has spa on windowed porch; another has shower with seven shower-heads. Off-street parking is provided. Two and a half blocks down the hill is the Nob Hill area with little boutiques, specialty shops and some of the best eating places in Portland.
(*Elegant, In-Town, Breakfast Inn. Member since 1994*)

Located in Northwest Portland, minutes from city center.
TEL. 503-274-1846
FAX 503-248-4055
E-mail: heronhai@aol.com
2545 N.W. Westover Rd.
Portland, OR 97210
Julie Keppeler, Innkeeper

CHANNEL HOUSE INN

🛏	5 rooms, $150 B&B 9 Suites, $195/$225 B&B
	Visa, MC, Discovr
	All Private Baths, 12 with whirlpools on deck
	Open Year-round
	Children over 16 welcome, No Pets
	Fishing, beachcomb, whale-watch, hike, golf, antiques, visit museums, galleries, historic lighthouses & covered bridges, Marine Science Center & Oregon Aquarium
	Breakfast
	No Smoking
♿	N/A

2 Amid the Oregon Coast's most magnificent scenery, Channel House combines the comforts of a first class hotel with the congeniality of a small country inn. Imagine fresh ocean breezes, sweeping panoramic views, unbelievable sunsets and whales within a stones throw. Nestled on an oceanfront perch, guestrooms have elegant contemporary decor including private whirlpools. One of the west coast's most renowned and romantic inns, it's the ideal honeymoon, anniversary or special couples getaway.
(*Contemporary, Village, Breakfast Inn. Member since 1997*)

Off Hwy 101, 1 block S. of the bridge in Depoe. Turn W. onto Ellingson.
TEL. 541-765-2140
    800-447-2140
FAX 541-765-2191
E-mail: cfinseth@newportnet.com
35 Ellingson
P.O. Box 56
Depoe Bay, OR 97347
Vickie L. Mix & Carl Finseth, Owners

THE JOHNSON HOUSE

6 rooms (including a
small garden cottage),
$95/$125 B&B
Visa, MC

3 Private Baths

Open Year-round

Appropriate for Children
over 12; No Pets

Ocean Beaches, Dunes,
Woods, Lakes, River,
Whale-watching, Horse-
back Riding, Hiking,
Fishing, Golf

Full Breakfast

Smoking on porches

N/A

1 block (N) of Siuslaw River; 2 blocks
(E) of Coast Hwy. 101; corner First &
Maple in Old Town.
TEL. 503-997-8000
1-800-768-9488
216 Maple St.
PO Box 1892
Florence, OR 97439

Ronald & Jayne Fraese,
Innkeepers

3 This is like "grandmother's house," with treasured heirlooms, amusing photographs and curios, where you are welcomed with a cup of tea. The faithfully restored 1892 Victorian
inn is in the center of Old Town, a waterfront community on
Oregon's scenic central coast. Just a block away from docks and
small commercial fishing fleet. Blue and ivory guest rooms
feature lace curtains, down comforters, and many books. Breakfasts are lavish and imaginative.
(*Traditional, Village, Breakfast Inn. Member since 1991*)

THE CAMPBELL HOUSE

12 Rooms, $79/$185 B&B
6 Suites, $225/$440 B&B

Visa, MC, Amex, Discovr

All Private Baths

Open Year-round
Children welcome; No Pets
Hiking, Bike riding, Fishing, Historic District of Eugene, Antiques & Shops,
White Water Rafting, Win-
ery Tours can be arranged
thru Campbell Inn
Breakfast, Room Service
Menu provided for Lunch
and Dinner
No Smoking (Smoking
allowed in outside
courtyard, private patios &
balconies)
Conference Facilities (100)
(50 for meetings)
Wheelchair Access (2 rms,
dining rm., conf. fac.)

From I-5 take exit 194-b to Eugene,take first
exit, Coburg Rd, road splits stay Left. Go
over river take first R. on E 3rd, 3 bloocks to
R. on Pearl. From airport: Hwy 99S to 7th
Ave. L. on High St. to E. 3rd to Pearl St.
TEL. 541-343-1119
800-264-2519
Web Site: http://www.campbellhouse.com
FAX 541-343-2258
E-mail: http: //www.campbellhouse.com
252 Pearl Street
Eugene, OR 97401
Roger & Myra Plant, Innkeepers
Judith Whipkey, General Manager

4 This beautiful estate, built in 1892, just a few blocks from downtown, has been restored as an elegant turn-of-the-century inn. Beautifully decorated with Waverly fabrics and wall coverings throughout,
the inn's European charm and elegance attracts both the leisure traveler
and business person as well. All rooms have private baths, telephones,
TV's with VCR's, and luxury amenities. Four-poster beds, fireplaces,
jetted tub for two and claw foot bathtubs available. Weddings; Recep-
tions; Meeting rooms.
(*Elegant, Victorian, Inn-Town, Inn. Member since 1997*)

OREGON
STEAMBOAT INN

🛏️	8 Cabins, $95 EP 5 Cotts./2 suites, 4 (3 bdrm) Houses $150/$225
💳	Visa, MC
🛁	All Private Baths
🛎️	Closed Jan.–Feb. & limited service Mar.–Apr.
🐕	Children Accepted No Pets
Ⓡ	Fishing for steelhead, 35 mi. of public water, Backpacking, Hiking
🍽️	Breakfast & Lunch, Dinner by reservation Wine Available
🚭	No Smoking
ⱨ⚹⚹⚹ⱨ	Conference facilities (70 day mtg. & 40 overnight)
♿	Wheelchair Access (2 rms., dining rm. & conf. fac.)

5 Nestled among towering firs, choose from cozy streamside cabins, cottages in the woods or luxurious suites on the river. You may want a picnic for a days outing to Crater Lake, local waterfalls, swimming holes, hiking trails or the wineries of Douglas County. Be sure to be back for the evening dinner. This creative meal, featuring fresh local ingredients and Oregon wine, will add the perfect finish to an already perfect day! (*Traditional, Waterside, Inn. Member since 1984*)

I-5 to Roseburg. Steamboat Inn is 38 mi. (E) on Rte. 138. Inn is 70 mi. (W) of Crater Lake and 40 mi. (W) of Diamond Lake, on Rte. 138.

TEL. 514-498-2411
1-800-840-8825
FAX 514-498-2411 (1 ring +*2)
42705 North Umpqua Hwy.
Steamboat, OR 97447-9703

Sharon & Jim Van Loan, Innkps.
Patricia Lee, Manager

TU TU' TUN LODGE

🛏️	16 rooms, $85/$165 EP 4 Suites, 1 cottage, 1 riverhouse, $175/$310 EP
💳	Visa, MC, Discovr
🛁	All Private Baths
🛎️	Full service May thru Oct. Limited service off-season
🐕	Children Welcome; No Pets Welcome
Ⓡ	Guided Fishing, White Water Boat Trips, Self-guided Hiking Trails, Beachcombing, 9-hole Golf Course, 4-hole Pitch & Putt, Horseshoes.
🍽️	Breakfast, Lunch (Reg. Guests Only), Dinner, MAP available; Wine & Liquor Available
🚭	No Smoking
ⱨ⚹⚹⚹ⱨ	Conference Facilities (40)
♿	Wheelchair Access (8 rms., dining rm. & conf. fac.)

6 Nestled on the banks of the Rogue River, Tu Tu' Tun Lodge combines the comforts of a first-class resort with the congeniality of a small hideaway. Guests enjoy hors d'oeuvre around the large stone fireplace, gourmet dining overlooking the river and madrone wood fires on the terrace at dusk. Come, partake in the serious challenge of the steelhead and salmon, experience the excitement of a white water excursion or simply enjoy some solitude.

(*Rustic, Waterside, Lodge. Member since 1989*)

Gold Beach, Hwy. 101 (E) 7 mi. along north side of Rogue River to Lodge.
TEL. 541-247-6664
Website: http:llwww.el.com/to/
tututunlodge
FAX 541-247-0672
E-mail: tututun@aol.com
96550 North Bank Rogue
Gold Beach, OR 97444

Dirk & Laurie Van Zante,
Innkeepers

JACKSONVILLE INN

   8 rooms, $90/$139 B&B
3 Suites, $195/$225 B&B

 Visa, MC, Discov, Amex, Diners

 All Private Baths

Open Year-round

Children Accepted
No Pets

 Museum, Antiques, Hiking, Wineries, Swimming, White Riv. Rafting, Shopping, Shakespeare Fest., Britt Music Festival

 Restaurant, Bistro
Sun. Brunch, Lounge
Wine & Liquor available
Non-smoking Rooms

 Conference Facilities (80)

N/A

I-5(N), Ex. 30, R. Crater Lk. Hwy (Hwy. 62) to Medford. R. on McAndrews, L. on Ross Lane, R. on W. Main (238), R. on Calif. St. I-5(S), Exit 27, L. on Barnett, R. on Riverside; L. on Main St. R. on Calif.
TEL. 541-899-1900
800-321-9344
FAX 541-899-1373
P.O. Box 359
Jacksonville, OR 97530
Jerry & Linda Evans, Innkps.

7 Housed in one of Jacksonville's early (1861) permanent structures, built during the gold rush, the inn has locally quarried sandstone walls flecked with bits of gold in the dining room and lounge. In addition to guest rooms furnished with restored antiques, the inn boasts one of Oregon's most award-winning restaurants, with superb dining and a connoisseur's wine cellar.
(*Traditional, Village, Inn. Member since 1991*)

THE WINCHESTER COUNTRY INN

 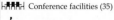 12 Rooms, $95/$130 B&B
6 suites, $130/$180 B&B

Visa, MC, Amex, Discovr.

All Private Baths

Open Year-round

Children Accepted
No Pets

  White water rafting, Hiking, XC & Downhill Skiing, Shakespeare Festival, Boating, Sailing, Britt Music Festival

  Breakfast, Sunday Brunch, Dinner; Wine & Liquor available

 Smoke-free Inn

  Conference facilities (35)

 Wheelchair Access (1 rm.)

From I-5 (S), 1st Ashland exit. R. on Valley View, L. on Hwy. 99 for 3 mi. to Ashland. R. on 2nd St. From I-5 (N), 1st Ashland exit, for 4 mi. to Ashland. L. on 2nd St.
TEL. 541-488-1113
800-972-4991
FAX: 541-488-4604
35 So. Second St.
Ashland, OR 97520
Michael and Laurie Gibbs, Innkeepers

8 A true country inn in the heart of the city, this handsomely restored, century-old Victorian home (National Register) invites you to enjoy an atmosphere of sophisticated country living. Beautiful tiered gardens and gazebo welcome guests each morning for breakfast. Guest rooms offer antiques, balconies and patios. Gourmet dinners and champagne Sunday brunch are served.
(*Traditional, Victorian, In-Town, Inn. Member since 1991*)

The Independent Innkeepers' Association Gift Certificate

A Lovely Gift for Someone Special

The gift of an overnight stay or a weekend at a country inn can be one of the most thoughtful and appreciated gifts you can give your parents or children, dear friends, or valued employees for Christmas, a birthday, an anniversary, or any special occasion. Innkeepers and other employers are discovering this is an excellent way of rewarding their employees, while at the same time giving them some much needed rest and relaxation.

An Independent Innkeepers' Association gift certificate means that you can give the gift of a stay at any one of over 300 member inns from Kennebunkport, Maine to Southern California; from Quebec, Canada to Key West, Florida; from Martha's Vineyard, Massachusetts to Seaview, Washington. We have inns in the Blue Ridge Mountains, on ranches in the western desert, near state parks and forests and nature preserves, in restored villages in historic districts, on lakes and by the sea. Choose your pleasure.

An Independent Innkeepers' Association gift certificate is good for two years and may be purchased through the Independent Innkeepers' Association office by personal check or Mastercard or Visa. With each gift certificate we send along a brand new copy of the *Innkeepers' Register.* For further information call **800-344-5244**.

A five dollar ($5) postage and handling fee will be added to all gift certificate purchases.

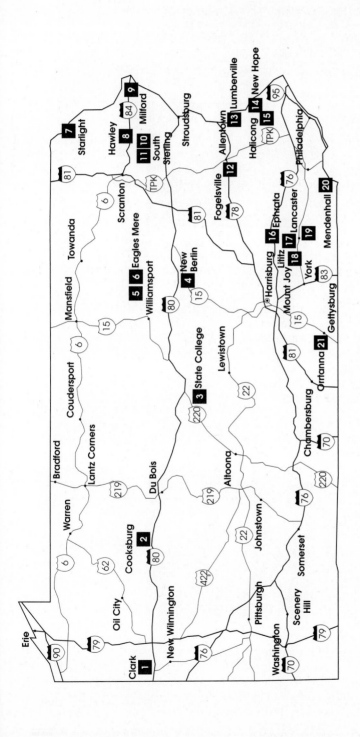

1. Tara—A Country Inn, Clark
2. Gateway Lodge, Cooksburg
3. Carnegie House, State College
4. The Inn at Olde New Berlin, New Berlin
5. Crestmont, Eagles Mere
6. Eagles Mere Inn, Eagles Mere
7. The Inn at Starlight Lake, Starlight
8. The Settlers Inn, Hawley
9. Cliff Park, Milford
10. The French Manor, South Sterling
11. Sterling Inn, South Sterling
12. Glasbern, Fogelsville
13. 1740 House, Lumberville
14. Whitehall Inn, New Hope
15. Barley Sheaf Farm, Holicong
16. Smithton Inn, Ephrata
17. Swiss Woods B&B, Lititz
18. Cameron Estate Inn, Mount Joy
19. The King's Cottage, Lancaster
20. Fairville Inn, Mendenhall
21. Hickory Bridge Farm, Orrtanna

TARA — A COUNTRY INN

24 Rooms, Sun.-Fri. $180/$355 MAP Sat. $250/$430

3 Suites, Sun.-Fri. $355/430 MAP Sat. $430

Visa, MC, Amex, Discov

All Private Baths

Open Year-round

Not appropriate for Children

Kennels nearby for Pets

Bocci, Croquet, Boating, Golf, Biking, Pool Table, Antiquing, XC Skiing, Swim Pools, Sauna, Steam

Breakfast, Lunch, Dinner, B&B rates available

Wine & Liquor available

Nonsmoking Facility

Conference Facilities (60)

Wheelchair Access (dining rm. & conf. fac.)

1 If you loved the movie *Gone With the Wind*, you will love Tara. Built in 1854, this magnificent mansion reflects the golden days of the antebellum South, with rooms charmingly decorated to recall the grace and grandeur of yesteryear. Delightfully different cuisine, from gourmet to family-style, is served in the three totally different restaurants. Mobil 4-star and AAA 4-diamond.

(*Elegant, Country, Inn. Member since 1986*)

From I-80, exit 1N, Rte. 18 (N) for 8 mi. Inn is located on (E) side overlooking Lake Shenango

TEL. 412-962-3535
800-782-2803

3665 Valley View, Box 475
Clark, PA 16113

Jim & Donna Winner, Innkeepers

GATEWAY LODGE

8 Rooms, $103/$115 EP, $128/$140 B&B, $188/$200 MAP; 2 Suites/8 Cottages, $167/$216 B&B $228/$276 MAP; 3 New Suites (Kingsize bed, fireplace & jacuzzi) $200/$212 EP; $230/$241 B&B; $290/$320 MAP

Visa, MC, Amex, Discov

13 Private Baths

Open Year-round exc. Wed. & Thur of Thanksgiving week & Dec. 24–25 (EP Cottages remain open)

Children over 8; No Pets

X-Country Skiing, Hiking, Biking, Tubing, Canoeing, Swimming, Hunting, Fishing, Antiquing, Arts & Crafts, Bird Watching

Breakfast; Lunch Limited (May–Oct.) Dinner

Wine & Liquor Available

Smoking on porch

Conference Facilities (40)

Wheelchair Access (3 cottages, dining rm. & conf. fac.)

2 Amid some of the most magnificent forest scenery east of the Rocky Mountains, this rustic log cabin inn has been awarded one of the ten best country inns in the U.S. Guests gather around the large stone fireplace in the living room and savor wonderful home-cooked meals by kerosene light. Main inn guests may enjoy the indoor swimming pool, sauna, tea time, and turn-down service.

(*Rustic, Country, Inn. Member since 1983*)

From W I-80 to Exit 9 (Clarion). Turn L, go to 3rd Light. Go Straight thru Light (Rte. 68), travel 10 mi. to stop sign. At stop Sign turn R on Rte. 36 (S) go 4 mi, cross over bridge. Continue 1/4 mi. S. Lodge on L. From E I-80 to Exit 13 (Brookville), R on Rte. 36 (N). Travel 16 mi. Lodge on R.

TEL. 814-744-8017
800-843-6862 (PA/MD)
FAX 814-744-8017

Route 36, Box 125
Cooksburg, PA 16217
Joe & Linda Burney, Innkps.

CARNEGIE HOUSE

 20 Rooms, $125/$175 B&B
2 Suites, $275 B&B

 Visa, MC, Amex

 All Private Baths

 Open Year-round

 Children & Pets by prior arrangement

 18 hole championship golf course, fitness trail, x-country skiing, biking, touring historic towns of Bellefonte and Boalsburg, Christopher Columbus Chapel, Penn State Athletic & Cultural Events, Palmer Museum of Art, Bryce Jordon Center events

Breakfast, Lunch, Dinner
No smoking except on verandah or the long porch

 Conference Facilities (16-44)

Wheelchair Access (8 rm., dining rm. & conf. fac.)

Mt. Nittany Express to Toftrees exit, Waddle Rd to Toftrees Ave. R. to stop sign (Cricklewood Dr.) Carnegie House is on this corner with entrance from Toftrees Ave. & Cricklewood Dr.

TEL. 814-234-2424
800-229-5033
FAX: 814-231-1299
E-mail: carnhouse@aol.com
100 Cricklewood Dr.
State College, PA 16803
Peter & Helga Schmid, Innkeepers

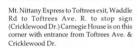 This old world style country house hotel, overlooks the 17th green of Toftrees championship golf course. The Carnegie House's library, with fireplace and comfortable furnishings, invites you to pause and delight in gracious conversation and pleasant libation with friends old and new. The verandah or long porch afford total relaxation. We offer a complete food fare…daily Continental breakfasts, Sunday cooked Scottish breakfast, leisurely luncheons and elegantly unhurried dinners. Perfect for holidays, reunions, and getaways.

(*Elegant, Colonial, Country, Inn. Member since 1997*)

THE INN AT OLDE NEW BERLIN

 5 Rooms, 1 Suite (2 Bdrm) $85/$110 B&B

 Visa, MC

 6 Private Baths

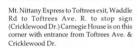 Open Year-round except 1st 2 wks of Jan.

 Children Wecome
No Pets

 Nearby State Parks for hiking & biking, Walnut Acres Organic Farm, Amish Culture (farms, shops, quilts)

 Breakfast; Lunch, Dinner

 Smoking Permitted on rear ramp of inn only

Conference Facilities (25)

Wheelchair Access (dining rm. & conf. fac.)

In Central PA, take Lewisburg exit off Rte. 80. At intersection of Rtes. 45 & 15, W. on Rte. 45 for appr. 4 mi. Turn L. onto Dreisbach Mtn. Rd. Continue for 5 mi. to Market St. R. on Market St., 2nd home on R.
TEL. 717-966-0321
FAX 717-966-9557
E-mail: newberln@postoffice.ptd.net
321 Market Street
New Berlin, PA 17855
John & Nancy Showers, Innkeepers

 "A luxurious base for indulging in a clutch of quiet pleasures"...The Philadelphia Inquirer. Inn memories are made from the inviting front porch swing to the herb garden where the restaurant's seasonings and garnishes are selected. Superb dining opportunities at Gabriel's Restaurant coupled with romantic lodging provide an uptown experience in a rural setting. Full line of romantic, unique gifts. Guests relay that they depart feeling nurtured, relaxed, and most of all inspired.

(*Traditional, Victorian, Village, Inn. Member since 1997*)

CRESTMONT INN

	15 Rooms, $89/$128 B&B 3 Suites, $138/$148 B&B 1 Apt., $750 for 6 nights, EP
	Visa, MC, Personal Checks
	All Private Baths
	Open May 1–Nov. 1
	Well behaved Children Welcome; No Pets
	Heated Swimming pool, Har-Tru Tennis, Golf, Lake Activities, Hiking & Bike trails, Entertainment & cultural activities, summer months
	Full country Breakfast; Gourmet Dinner Wine & Liquor available
	Smoking in limited areas Conference Facilities (30)
	Wheelchair Access (4 rms., dining rm. & Conf. fac.,)

5 Celebrating 21 years of innkeeping, the Oliver family warmly welcomes you to Eagles Mere's premier resort. On our inn's eight acres of manicured lawns and gardens are all the facilities for your vacation pleasure: 6 Har-Tru tennis courts; 60 x 30 heated swimming pool; shuffleboard courts; and miles of hiking and mountain biking trails adjacent to Wyoming State Forest. Guests may also enjoy swimming and boating on beautiful Lake Eagles Mere, or golf at Eagles Mere Country Club's 18 hole golf course. As Dr. and Mrs. Richard Oman of Pittsburgh, Pa., said, "Coming here every summer is the highlight of our year!". (*Traditional, Mountain, Inn. Member since 1989*)

From I-80, Exit 34 to 42 (N) for 33 mi. to Eagles Mere village. Continue thru town & follow Crestmont signs.

TEL. 717-525-3519
Res: 800-522-8767
Crestmont Dr.
Eagles Mere, PA 17731

Kathleen & Robert Oliver, Innkeepers
Karen Oliver, Manager

EAGLES MERE INN

	13 Rooms, $139/$175 MAP per couple
	4 Suites & Special, $175/$225 MAP per couple
	15% Serv Charge, 6% Tax
	Visa, MC, Pers. Checks
	All Private Baths
	Open Year-round
	Children accepted No Pets
	Swimming, Boating, Beautiful Scenery & Hiking Trails, Golf, Tennis, XC Skiing, Ice Toboggan
	Full Breakfast & 5 course Gourmet Dinner included; Wine and Liquor available
	Smoking allowed in Pub only
	Conference Facilities (30)
	N/A

6 Called: "The last unspoiled resort," this Mountain top Inn offers Ultimate Stress Relief! Peace & quiet 400 paces from a private, pristine lake and thousands of acres of Forest. Incredible Waterfalls & Vistas! Innkeeper has run 3 & 4 star Hotels & Restaurants and has made major renovations to this property. Guests enjoy personal attention, warm Hospitality, Gourmet meals, outstanding Wines and peaceful relaxation. Excellent for couples seeking a quiet & relaxing getaway or for small groups. **Gourmet meals included in rates.** Featured as a special vacation spot in numerous Travel Writer articles. Call for Brochure

(*Traditional, Mountain, Inn. Member since 1993*)

From East take Rte. 80 west to Exit #34 (Buckhorn) to Rte. 42 (N) From West take Rte. 80 to Rte. 220 (N) then to Rte. 42 (N)

TEL. 717-525-3273
800-426-3273
Mary & Sullivan Avenues
Eagles Mere, PA 17731

Susan & Peter Glaubitz & Greg Adams, Innkeepers

THE INN AT STARLIGHT LAKE

 26 Rooms, $110/$154 MAP

 Cottage Rooms $127/ $154 MAP
1 Suite, $170/$200 MAP
Visa, MC

 20 Private Baths

 Open Year-round

 Children Accepted
No Pets

 Swimming, Boating, Tennis, Ice Skating, XC Skiing, Lawn Sports, Fishing, Golf

Breakfast, Lunch, Dinner, Sunday Brunch
Wine & Liquor available

No Smoking in Dining Room

Conference facilities (20)

Wheelchair Access (dining rm.)

From N.Y. Rte. 17, Exit 87 (Hancock). On Rte. 191 (S) 1 mi. to Rte. 370 (W), turn R. 3 mi. to sign on R. take R. 1 mi. to inn. From I-81, Exit 62, local roads; map sent on request.
TEL. 717-798-2519
800-248-2519
FAX 717-798-2672
Starlight, PA 18461
Judy & Jack McMahon, Innkeepers

 Since 1909, guests have been drawn to this classic country inn on a clear lake in the rolling hills of northeastern Pennsylvania. The atmosphere is warm, congenial, and informal. Twenty-two Mainhouse and cottage rooms, (one w. fireplace), suite w. Jacuzzi, and a family house and conference center complete this delightful little universe. There are activities for all seasons: swimming, boating, fishing, tennis, cycling, hiking; in winter, x-c skiing and ice-skating. Lakeside dining offers outstanding cuisine with emphasis on fresh ingredients, baked goods, and homemade pastas.
(*Traditional, Waterside, Inn. Member since 1976*)

THE SETTLERS INN

15 Rooms, $75/$120 B&B
3 Suites, $120/$150 B&B

Visa, MC, Amex, Discovr

All Private Baths

Open Year-round
Appropriate for Children
No Pets

 Lake Wallenpaupack, Upper Delaware River, Promised Land State Park, Golf, Skiing, Horseback, Canoeing, Fishing, Glass Museum, Antique Shops

 Breakfast, Lunch, Dinner
Wine & Liquor available
No Smoking in guest rms or dining rm.

 Conference Facilities (100)

 Wheelchair Access (dining rm.)

I-84 Exit 7, Route 390N. to Route 507 N. to Rt. 6 W., then 2 1/2 miles to Inn
TEL. 717-226-2993
800-833-8527
FAX 717-226-1874
E-mail: settler@prolog.net
Four Main Avenue
Hawley, PA 18428

Jeanne & Grant Genzlinger, Innkeepers

 Reminiscent of a small European hotel, this Tudor Manor is in the small turn-of-the-century town of Hawley. Chestnut wood beams, a bluestone fireplace, leaded windows, outdoor patio & herb gardens add to the ambiance. The dining room is well known for a cuisine based on our region's food traditions highlighting products from local farms. Lake Wallenpaupack, the upper Delaware River, and Promised Land State Park are nearby providing many recreational activities. Antique shops and summer theatre in town. (*Traditional, Village, Inn. Member since 1992*)

CLIFF PARK INN & GOLF COURSE

	18 rooms, $93/$160 B&B MAP rates available
	Visa, MC, Amex, Diners, Discov
	All Private Baths
	Open Year-round
	Children Welcome; Sorry, No Pets
	On Premises: Golf, Hiking, XC Skiing, Off Premises: Delaware River for Swimming, Fishing, Rafting, Canoeing
	Breakfast, Lunch & Dinner; MAP rates available; Wine & Liquor Available
	Smoking Permitted
	Conference Facilities (60 day, 36 overnight)
	Wheelchair access (6 rms., dining rm. & conf. fac.)

9 Historic Country Inn (1820) on secluded 600-acre estate, surrounded by long-established golf course (1913). Spacious rooms, some with fireplaces. This historic inn offers old-fashioned hospitality, heirlooms reflecting the life and times of the Buchanan family. Antiques and lace grace the guest rooms and the maple-shaded veranda overlooks the golf course. Their master chef specializes in American, French and Cajun cuisine. Golf, Honeymoon and Country wedding packages.
(*Historic, Mountain, Inn. Member since 1990*)

I-80 to Ex. 34B; Rte. 15N becomes 206N, into Milford, PA. Thru traffic light, 2 blks. L. onto 7th & go 1.5 mi. to inn. From I-84, Ex. 10, Milford, (E) on Rte. 6 for 2 mi. R. on 7th St. for 1.5 mi. to inn.
TEL. 717-296-6491
800-225-6535
FAX 717-296-3982
E-mail: cpi@warwick.net
RR4, Box 7200
Milford, PA 18337-9708
Harry W. Buchanan III, Innkp.

THE FRENCH MANOR

	6 Rooms, $120/$180 B&B 3 suites, $160/$225 B&B
	Visa, MC, Amex, Discov
	All Private Baths
	Open Year-round
	Not suitable for Children No Pets
	Hiking, Croquet, Beautiful scenery, Swimming, Tennis, XC Skiing, Ice Skating nearby
	Breakfast, Lunch, Dinner; French restaurant; MAP rates available; Wine & Liquor available Non-smoking Dining
	Conference Facilities (18)
	Wheelchair Access (1 rm.)

10 The French Manor is an elegant country inn, secluded and private, like a secret lookout separate from the populace. You may choose from four spacious guest rooms in the Manor, three suites (one with jacuzzi and fireplace) or two comfortable rooms in the Carriage House. Enjoy a hearty breakfast with a view of the mountains from our dining room or in your room by request. Dinner is a celebration of authentic French cuisine in an atmosphere of elegance and refinement unmatched in the area.
(*Elegant, Country Inn. Member since 1991*)

From NYC: I-80(W), PA Exit 52 to Rte. 447(N) to Rte. 191(N) to S. Sterling. Turn L. on Huckleberry Rd. From Phila: NE extension of PA Tpke. to Pocono Exit 35. Follow Rtes. 940(E), 423(N) to 191(N) 2.5 mi. to Huckleberry Rd.
TEL. 717-676-3244
FAX: 717-676-9786
RES. 800-523-8200
Box 39, Huckleberry Rd.
South Sterling, PA 18460
Ron & Mary Kay Logan, Innkps.

THE STERLING INN

38 Rooms, $90/$120 B&B
16 Suites, $120/180 B&B
Visa, MC, Amex, Discov

All Private Baths

Open Year-round

Children Accepted;
No Pets

Indoor Pool, Lake, Tennis, Hiking, Horseback Riding, Golf, XC Skiing, Sleigh Rides, Antiquing

Breakfast, Lunch, Dinner
Wine & Liquor available
No Smoking in Dining area & all guestrooms in main inn

Conference facilities (10–100)

Wheelchair Access (3 rm., dining rm. & conf. fac.)

I-84, Exit 6, Rte. 507 (S), 3 mi. to Rte. 191 (S), 3 mi. to inn. I-80 (W) Exit 50, Rte. 191 (N) 25 mi. to inn. I-80 (E) Rte. 380 to Rte. 423 (N), to 191 (N), .5 mi. to inn.

TEL. 717-676-3311
RES: 800-523-8200
FAX: 717-676-9786
Rte. 191
South Sterling, PA 18460
The Logan Family, Innkeepers

11 The country inn you've always looked for, but never thought you'd find. A friendly, romantic atmosphere with beautiful gardens, crystal clear streams, a waterfall, Victorian suites with fireplaces, & horse-drawn sleigh rides. Attractive rooms, indoor pool & spa, & outstanding meals make this family operated, 130-year-old inn everything you thought a country inn should be. Honeymooners may enjoy the "Innkeeping with Romance" Package. Social groups and family reunions can be accommodated in the lodge or guest house. (*Traditional, Country, Inn. Member since 1974*)

GLASBERN

10 Rooms, $110/$185 B&B
14 Suites, $125/$300 B&B

Visa, MC

All Private Baths, 17 Whirlpools

Open Year-round

Limited accommodations for children
No Pets

Swimming pool, Trails thru 100 acres, Bicycling, Hot air ballooning, Fishing

Breakfast; Dinner Daily, Wine & Liquor Available

Smoking Restrictions

Conference Facilities (16)

Wheelchair Access (1 rm, dining rm. & conf. fac.)

From I-78 take Rte. 100(N) for .2 mi. to L. at light (W) for .3 mi. to R. on Church St. (N) for .6 mi. to R. on Pack House Rd. for .8 mi. to the inn.

TEL. 610-285-4723
www.glasbern.com
FAX 610-285-2862
E-mail: Innkeeper@glasbern.com
2141 Pack House Rd.
Fogelsville, PA 18051-9743
Beth & Al Granger, Owners

12 At the edge of Pennsylvania Dutch Country, a 20th Century country inn has evolved from a 19th century family farm. Small game and horses graze contentedly on the land, a reminder of nature's quiet treasure. Flowers and vegetables flourish amidst 100 acres of sloping paths, streams, and ponds. Inside, whirlpools and fireplaces enhance most guest rooms. All have private baths, phones, TV's and VCR's. Contemporary American Cuisine is offered under the Barn's timbered cathedral ceiling. Chosen by *The Discerning Traveler* as a "Romantic Hideaway" 1996; AAA 3 Diamonds; Mobil 3 Stars; ABBA 4 Crowns. (*Traditional, Country, Inn. Member since 1988*)

PENNSYLVANIA
1740 HOUSE

 23 Rooms, $75/$115 B&B
1 Suite, $100/$175 B&B

 Personal Checks Accepted

All Private Baths

 Open Year-round

 Well behaved Children 12 & over; No Pets

 Pool at inn, Canoeing, Riding, Golf, Individual A/C

 Breakfast, Daily to houseguests; Dinner, served on special occasions; BYOB

 Non-smoking Dining Room

 Conference facilities (22)

N/A

13 An intimate view of the river from a lovely room with a private terrace or balcony is only one of the pleasures at this 18th-century, restored farmhouse on the the banks of the Delaware River. *Newsweek, McCall's, Glamour, & Harper's Bazaar* have all listed The 1740 House as one of their 10 favorite inns.

(Traditional, Waterside, Breakfast Inn. Member since 1973)

From NY & NJ use 202 (S) to Rte. 32. From I-95 use New Hope/Yardley exit (N) to New Hope. Lumberville is 7 mi. (N) of New Hope on Rte. 32.
TEL. 215-297-5661
River Rd. (Hwy. 32)
Lumberville, PA 18933

Robert John Vris, Innkeeper

THE WHITEHALL INN

6 Rooms, $130/$190 B&B

Visa, MC, Amex, CB, Diners, Discov.

4 Private, 1 Shared Bath

Open Year-round

Appropriate for Children over 12; No Pets

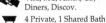 Swimming Pool, Horseback Riding, XC Skiing, Public & Private Golfing, Tennis, Hiking, Delaware River Water Sports

 4-Course Breakfast, Afternoon Tea

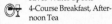 No Smoking on Property

 Conference Facilities (15)

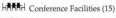 N/A

14 Experience a "Top 10 B&B Inn"! With heirloom sterling and European china and crystal, indulge in a four-course candlelight breakfast and afternoon high tea called "sumptuous" by *Bon Appetit*. The culinary genius of Suella abounds! Most rooms with fireplaces. Enjoy the pool, rose garden, and horses—all situated on the grounds of our 1794 estate. Evening turn-down service with our own Whitehall chocolate truffles. "After years in their niche, the Wasses continue to stand above the rest." It's all very special! Ask about our Spring Tea Concerts.

(Traditional, Country, Breakfast Inn. Member since 1990)

Hwy. 202 (S) from New Hope to Lahaska. L. on to Street Rd. to 2nd intersection, bear R. on Pineville Rd. Continue 1.5 mi. to inn on R.
TEL. 215-598-7945
888-37-WHITE
RD2, Box 250
1370 Pineville Rd.
New Hope, PA 18938
Mike and Suella Wass, Innkeepers

BARLEY SHEAF FARM

 8 Rooms, $105/$175 B&B
2 Suites, $145/$195 B&B

 Visa, MC, Amex

 All Private Baths

 Open Year-round

 Children 8 years & over;
No Pets

 Pool, Croquet, Flea
Markets, Shopping,
Historic touring,
Antiquing, Sports

Full Country Breakfast;
Wine & Cheese for after-
noon treat ocasionally

Smoking restricted to the
outside areas

Conference Facilities (35)

N/A

On Rte. 202, .5 mi. (W) of Lahaska.
From N.J. take Rte. 202. From Rte. 276
and south, take Rte. 263 (N) to
Buckingham and Rte. 202 to inn.

TEL. 215-794-5104
FAX 215-794-5332

Route 202, Box 10
Holicong, PA 18928

Veronika & Peter Süess,
Innkeepers

15 Barley Sheaf is an early Bucks County farm comfortably situated on 30 acres at the end of a long tree-lined drive. Once owned by the playwright George S. Kaufmann, it was the gathering place in the 30's and 40's for some of Broadway's brightest illuminaries, ie. Dorothy Parker, Mose Hart, the Marx brothers, etc. A park-like setting provides beauty and seclusion ideally suited for a romantic getaway. Lovely guest rooms, gracious common rooms, exceptional hospitality and an outstanding breakfast are Barley Sheaf hallmarks.
(*Traditional, Village, Breakfast Inn. Member since 1982*)

SMITHTON INN

 8 Rooms, $75/$150 B&B
1 Suite, $140/$170 B&B

 Visa, MC, Amex

 Private Baths, some
Whirlpools

 Open Year-round
Children and Pets by
prior arrangement

 Library, Gardens, Tour-
ing, Antiques, Epharta
Cloister, Farmers Country
Markets, Golf, Craft Cen-
ter, Museums, Art Galler-
ies

Full Breakfast

No Smoking

 Wheelchair Access (1 rm.)

From North, PA Turnpike. Exit 21 &
Rte. 222 (S). From South, Hwy. 30 to
Rte. 222 (N). From North or South,
Exit Rte. 222 at Rte. 322 (W) for 2.5 mi.
to inn.

TEL. 717-733-6094
900 W. Main St.
Ephrata, PA 17522

Dorothy Graybill, Innkeeper

16 A romantic 1763 stone inn located in Lancaster County among the Pennsylvania Dutch. Rooms are large, bright and cheerful with working fireplaces, canopy beds, desks, leather upholstered furniture, Penn. Dutch quilts, candles, chamber music, refrigeration, feather beds (by prior arrangement), books, reading lamps, fresh flowers and night shirts. Common rooms are warm and inviting with fireplaces. The Inn is located in the Penn Dutch farmlands where visiting the farm homes of Amish, Mennonites & Brethern people is an easy matter.
(*Colonial, Village, Breakfast Inn. Member since 1987*)

SWISS WOODS

	6 Rooms, $88/$145 B&B 1 Suite, $118/135
	Visa, MC, Amex, Discov
	All Private Baths (2 rms. have jacuzzi)
	Open Year-round except Dec. 24–26
	Well behaved Children accepted; No Pets
	Canoeing, Hiking, Birding, Farmers Markets, Hershey Park, PA Dutch Country
	Breakfast
	No Smoking
	N/A

17 Surrounded by meadows and gardens, Swiss Woods is a quiet retreat on 30 acres in Lancaster's Amish Country. All rooms here feature patios or balconies, some with views of the Speedwell Forge Lake, and are decorated with light furnishings so popular in Europe. Fabulous breakfasts in a sunlight common room highlight your stay. Take a hike, watch the birds and relax! German spoken.
(*Traditional, Country, Breakfast Inn. Member since 1993*)

From PA Tpk Exit 21 to 222 S. to 322 W. Follow to Rte. 501. Take 501 S. 1 mi. to first crossroads. Turn R. on Brubaker Valley Rd. Go 1 mi. to the lake. Turn R. on Blantz Rd. The Inn is on your left.
TEL. 717-627-3358; 800-594-8018; FAX 717-627-3483
E-mail: MREY889@prodigy.com
500 Blantz Rd.
Lititz, PA 17543
Werner & Debrah Mosimann, Innkeepers

CAMERON ESTATE INN

	17 Rooms, 1 Suite, $70/$80–$95/$120 B&B
	Visa, MC, Amex, Diners, Discov
	17 Private Baths
	Closed Christmas Day
	Children 12 yrs & older; No Pets
	Golf, Swimming & Tennis nearby
	Breakfast, Dinner, Sun. Brunch; Wine & Liquor available
	Smoking Restrictions
	Conference Facilities (60)
	Wheelchair access (dining rm. & conf. fac.)

18 The Inn & Restaurant occupy the rural Lancaster County estate of Simon Cameron, Abraham Lincoln's first Secretary of War. Rooms at Cameron are furnished in grand style and are individually decorated; 7 have fireplaces. The restaurant offers a fine selection of American and classic foods as well as the appropriate wines. Groff's Farm Restaurant, the county's finest, is also nearby.   Mobil Guide★★★
(*Elegant, Country, Inn. Member since 1982*)

Rte. 283 to Rte. 772(S) to 1st light in Mt. Joy and R. on Main, 2nd light L. (S. Angle St.), R. on Donegal Springs Rd. at stop turn, L. on Colebrook, R. back onto Donegal Springs Rd., 1/4 mile on R.
TEL. 717-653-1773
FAX 717-653-9432
1895 Donegal Springs Rd.
Mount Joy, PA 17552
Stephanie Seitz, Larry Hershey & Suzanne McKinnon, Innkeepers

THE KING'S COTTAGE, A BED & BREAKFAST INN

8 Rooms, $69/$145 B&B
1 Carriage House, $139/
$180 B&B

Visa, MC, Discover

All Private Baths
Open year-round
Children over 12; No Pets

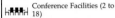
Tours of PA Dutch
Country, Amish dinners
arranged, Historic homes
(Wheatland, Rockford,
Hans Herr), Museums (PA
Railroad Museum, Landis
Valley Farm Museum . . .),
Central Market, Antiques,
Arts & Crafts, Breweries &
Wineries, Hershey, Golf,
Swimming & Tennis nearby
Breakfast, Afternoon tea from
4–7

Smoking restrictions—
outside only

Conference Facilities (2 to
18)

Wheelchair Access (Car-
riage House only)

Take Rte. 30 to Rte. 23 (W)/Walnut St.
Exit. Turn R at end of exit ramp, turn
L at 2nd light at Ranck Ave. At 2nd
stop sign turn L onto Orange St. go 1
block to Cottage Ave, turn R. Inn is
last building on R.

TEL. 717-397-1017
800-747-8717

FAX 717-397-3447

1049 East King St.
Lancaster, PA 17602
Karen & Jim Owens, Innkeepers

19 Escape to luxurious elegance and hospitality at the award winning Kings Cottage Bed and Breakfast. Snuggled in scenic Pennsylvania, Dutch Country, you'll enjoy Amish farmlands, historic sites and museums. Browse our farmers markets, antique shops, factory outlets, and craft stores. We'll pamper you with king/queen sized beds, gourmet breakfasts, evening cordials, fireplaces, and a jacuzzi. Enjoy personalized service including Amish dinner reservations, maps and activity recommendations. National Historic Register. AAA and Mobil 3 Diamonds—EXCELLENT!
(*Traditional, In-Town, Breakfast Inn. Member since 1995*)

FAIRVILLE INN

13 Rooms, $125/$175 B&B
2 Suites, $185 B&B

Visa, MC, Amex, Discovr

All Private Baths

Open Year-round

Not Suitable for Children
under 7; No Pets
Golf, Canoeing, Polo (in
Season), Museums
(Winterthur Longwood
Gardens, Hagley,
Nemours, Brandywine
River Museum) Great
Backroads for Walking/
Biking in the Brandywine
Valley
Continental Breakfast
No Smoking

Wheelchair Access (1 rm.,
Breakfast rm., living rm.)

8 mi. Rte. 52 (N) from I-95. Exit 7
Wilmington, DE 1 1/2 mi. Rte. 52 (S)
from US Rt 1 at Hamorton (Chadds
Ford/Longwood Gardens Area)

TEL. 610-388-5900
FAX 610-388-5902

Rte. 52
Mendenhall, PA 19357

Ole & Patricia Retlev,
Innkeepers

20 Located right between Winterthur, Longwood Gardens and the Brandywine River Museum, the Fairville Inn is surrounded by scenes from the Wyeth family paintings and the year-round, haunting beauty of the Brandywine Valley. Fifteen guestrooms in the Main House (c. 1820), Carriage House and restored Barn have TV/telephone, AC. Several have canopy bed, fireplace and private deck; all have fresh flowers and all the comforts of a country house inn!
(*Traditional, Village, Breakfast Inn. Member since 1995*)

PENNSYLVANIA
HICKORY BRIDGE FARM

	8 Rooms, $79/$115 B&B
	Visa, MC
	All Private Baths
	Open Year-round
	Children accepted; No Pets
	Gettysburg touring, Fishing, Swimming, Hiking, Bicycling, Golf, Skiing
	Breakfast (Houseguests), Dinner on weekends
	No Smoking
	Conference facilities (125) Wheelchair Access (conf. fac.)

21 A quaint country inn, offering 5-bedroom farmhouse accommodations (some with whirlpool baths) and four private cottages and a delightful restaurant in a restored barn, filled with antiques, located 8 miles west of Gettysburg on a family operated farm. Fine, family-style dining Friday, Saturday and Sunday. Inn open seven days a week with bountiful morning meals. A quiet, rural setting with a country store museum, gift shop . . . a wonderful "country place!"
(*Traditional, Country, Breakfast Inn. Member since 1978*)

Gettysburg, Rte. 116(W) to Fairfield and R. 3 mi.(N) to Orrtanna. Or Rte. 977 to Rte. 30(E) for 9 mi. Turn (S) at Cashtown for 3 mi. to inn.

TEL. 717-642-5261
96 Hickory Bridge Rd.
Orrtanna, PA 17353

Robert & Mary Lynn Martin, Innkeepers

INN ARCHITECTURE

The architecture of the Inns in this book is a good part of what makes them so interesting. The variations in vintage, style and design lend to the charm and ambiance that make each of them different and exciting.

Some Country Inns are housed in beautifully restored historic structures ranging from Colonial through Ante-bellum to Victorian. They encompass ornate woodwork, cut and stained glass, intricate detailing, even Doric columns and fanciful porches. Some are farmhouses and some are row houses. One Inn is made up of reclaimed century old log cabins. Another has guest rooms in the silo. Inn guests can encounter a contemporary structure that juts into the trees or a Scandinavian Inn that looks as if it has been transported from Europe. A couple of inns are in old stone mills, one with the mill stream running through the building.

If you are a lover of architecture and design, your fascination can be captured forever by going from one Inn to another enjoying the history and beauty of the buildings and appreciating the talent and ingenuity that went in to each of one of them. For many of the vintage structures, not only can one enjoy those features which were designed and created so long ago, but visitors also have the opportunity to appreciate the way in which our heritage is being preserved and protected by the careful restoration and adaptive use of these structures.

Certainly the grandeur and size of some historic edifices make them perfect for adaptation as overnight accommodations, Country Inns. And with each adaptation, architecture connoisseurs get to enjoy this win-win effort. Is it any wonder that a number of our Independent Innkeepers' Association innkeepers were once architects?

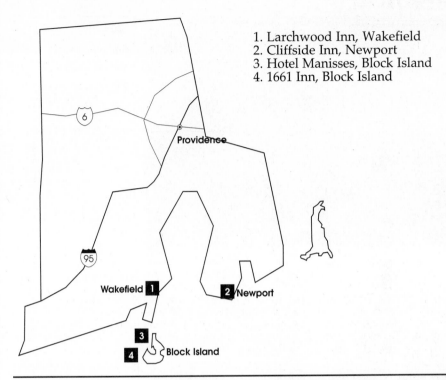

1. Larchwood Inn, Wakefield
2. Cliffside Inn, Newport
3. Hotel Manisses, Block Island
4. 1661 Inn, Block Island

LARCHWOOD INN

	18 Rooms, $50/$120 EP
	Visa, MC, Discov, DC
	11 Private Baths
	Open Year-round
	Children Accepted ($10) Pets Allowed ($5)
R	Ocean Swimming, Fishing, Golf, Tennis, Historic Touring, Bicycling, Boating
	Breakfast, Lunch, Dinner Wine and Liquor available
	Smoking restrictions
	Conference Facilities (125)
	Wheelchair Access (dining rm. & conf. fac.)

From the South—95 (N) to Rte. 78 at Westerly to Rte. 1, (N) to Pond St. in Wakefield. L onto Pond St. and continue until you are facing Inn. From the North—95 (S) to Rte. 4, then to Rte. 1, (S). At Pond St. exit, turn R and continue until you are facing the Inn.
TEL. 401-783-5454
1-800-275-5450
FAX 401-783-1800
521 Main St.
Wakefield, RI 02879
Francis & Diann Browning,
Innkeepers.

Watching over the main street of this quaint New England town for 160 years, this grand old house, surrounded by lawns and shaded by stately trees, dispenses hospitality along with good food and spirits from early morning to late night. Historic Newport, picturesque Mystic Seaport, Foxwood Casino, and salty Block Island are a short ride away. Conveniences such as telephones, computers, and fax are available within the confines of this country inn with Scottish flavor. If you've never stayed at the Larchwood Inn, you're in for a real treat! (*Traditional, In-Town, Colonial. Member since 1969*)

RHODE ISLAND
CLIFFSIDE INN

	8 Rooms, $175/$275 B&B 7 Suites, $275/$325 B&B
	Visa, MC, Amex, Discov
	All Private Baths, 11 with whirlpools, 1 steam bath
	Open year-round
	Children over 13 wel- come; No Pets
	Near Atlantic Ocean & Sand Beach, world fa- mous Cliff Walk Newport Mansion, fine dining & shopping, music festivals, year round culture events, sailing, fishing, golf, tennis
	Breakfast
	NonSmoking
	Conference Sp (15)
	N/A

 This historic second-Empire manor house was built in 1880 by Maryland Governor Thomas Swann and later owned by provocative artist Beatrice Turner. Located in a quiet neighborhood, it is steps from the famous Cliffwalk, a five minute walk to the beach and near Newport's renowned mansions. Romantic interiors include 15 fireplaces, 11 whirlpool tubs, antiques, 100 Turner artworks and architectural surprises. Cliffside is noted for it's gourmet breakfasts and afternoon Victorian tea served fireside. (*Elegant, Victorian, In-Town, Waterside, Breakfast Inn. Member since 1997*)

Boston: 1.5 hr. 93 S. to 24 S. to 114 S.
NY: 3.5 hr. 95 N. to R.I. Rt. 138 E.
TEL. 401-847-1811
800-845-1811
FAX 401-848-5850
2 Seaview Ave
Newport, RI 02840
Stephan Nicolas, Innkeeper

HOTEL MANISSES

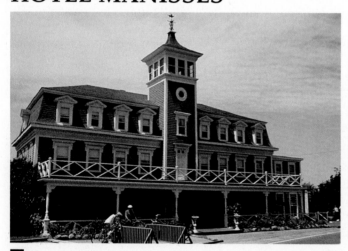

	17 Rooms, $75/$350 B&B
	Visa, MC, Amex
	All Private Baths; 4 Jacuzzis
	Open year-round
	Appropriate for Children over 10; No Pets
	Swimming, Yachting, Hiking, Biking, Horse- back Riding
	Breakfast, Lunch, Dinner Wine & Liquor available
	NonSmoking rooms available
	Conference Facilities (80)
	N/A

 Step into 19th Century yesteryear with a stay at this Romantic Victorian hotel featuring 17 meticulously appointed rooms with private baths and authentic Victorian furniture; some rooms with jacuzzis. The award-winning dining room serves dinner every evening. Sample delicious selections from our varied menu as featured in *Gourmet* magazine. Tableside flaming Coffees, After dinner drinks & Desserts served nightly in the upstairs parlour. (*Elegant, Victorian, Village, Inn. Member since 1982*)

By ferry: Providence, Pt. Judith, Newport, RI & New London, CT. By air: Newport, Westerly, Providence, RI & New London, Waterford, CT. Contact inn for schedules.
TEL. 401-466-2421;
401-466-2063
FAX 401-466-3162
Spring St.
Block Island, RI 02807
Joan & Justin Abrams,
Rita & Steve Draper, Innkeepers

THE 1661 INN

 21 Rooms, $75/$350 B&B
(3 w/fireplaces)

 Visa, MC, Amex

 16 Private Baths; 5 Jacuzzis

 Open Year-round

 Children of All Ages
No Pets

 Swings, Biking, Hiking,
Yachting, Swimming,
Shelling (9 mos of the yr)

 Breakfast, Lunch, Dinner
(available at Hotel
Manisses); Comp. Wine &
Nibble hr.; Wine & Liquor
Available

 Smoking restrictions

Conference Facilities (80)

 N/A

By Ferry: Providence, Pt. Judith, New-port, RI, and New London, CT. By air: Newport, Westerly, Providence, RI or charters. Contact inn for sched-ules.
TEL.401-466-2421
401-466-2063
FAX 401-466-2858
Spring Street
Block Island, RI 02807
Joan & Justin Abrams
Rita & Steve Draper, Innkeepers

4 Enjoy the spectacular views of the Atlantic ocean at The 1661 Inn. Most rooms feature ocean views, private decks, jacuzzis and some rooms have fireplaces. The ocean view dining deck with a canopy is a wonderful place to enjoy a relaxing buffet breakfast.
(*Elegant, Colonial, Waterside, Inn. Member since 1976*)

THE CHEF'S UNIFORM

Something there is about a chef's uniform that stirs interest for most of us. Whether we fancy ourselves designing and preparing gourmet meals or flipping sautéed vegetables over a leaping flame, many of us enjoy identifying with a chef in uniform.

Aside from the responsibilities of a chef, the uniform he wears has its own interesting story. The design and construction of the garment are both practical and utilitarian.

The white coat of the chef is double-breasted so that it can be re-buttoned to hide the stains if it becomes soiled during service. The double layer of fabric created by the overlap provides additional protection from scalds and burns during the chef's frequent juxtaposition with the stove. And, of course, since the word "chef" does not denote gender, the double-breasted jacket is equally appropriate for both men and women.

Checked trousers, traditionally worn by chefs, help to disguise the stains and spots which are sure to develop during a chef's active, time-driven preparation of the cuisine by which he is judged.

As most might surmise, the neckerchief which chefs usually wear tied cravat style originally served to absorb perspiration. Today it is usually worn as decoration just as a tie is worn with a business suit.

And topping all this, the most recognizable feature of a chef in uniform is his high topped white hat. Starched and pleated, the chef's hat represents a heritage that goes back to the chefs of royalty at the time of the Byzantine empire.

Together, these various items of a chef's uniform blend to create a visage that stirs excitement in the observer and prestige for the wearer. Perhaps underlying all this is the anticipation both enjoy for the end product, a well-prepared meal.

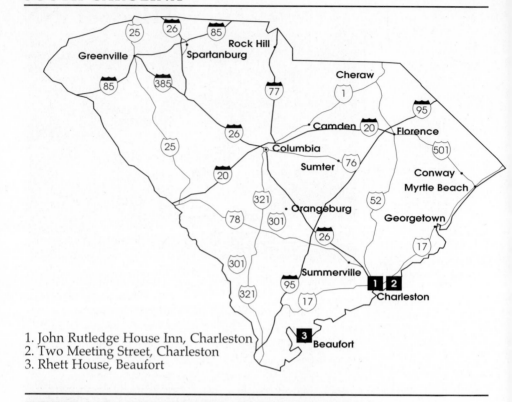

1. John Rutledge House Inn, Charleston
2. Two Meeting Street, Charleston
3. Rhett House, Beaufort

JOHN RUTLEDGE HOUSE INN

	16 Rooms $130/$260 B&B 3 Suites, $255/$310 B&B
	Visa, MC, Amex, Discovr, DC
	All Private Baths
	Open Year-round
	Appropriate for Children No Pets
	Historic District, Homes & Garden Tours, Market area & harbor within walking distance
R	Continental Bfkfast. incl., Full Brkfast. available.
	Walking distance to many restaurants for lunch and dinner. Afternoon tea w/ light refresh. Evening wine and sherry.
	Smoking Restrictions
	Conference Facilities (20)
	Wheelchair Access (2 rms.)

1 Built in 1763 by John Rutledge, a signer of the United States Constitution, this elegant home is now a bed and breakfast inn. All guests receive wine and sherry in the ballroom, evening turndown with chocolate at bedside and continental breakfast and newspaper delivered to the room each morning. AAA Four Diamond, Mobil Four Star & AB&BA 4 Crown. Historic Hotels of America. Andrew Harpers Hideway Report: "Charleston's Classiest Inn." (*Elegant, In-Town, Breakfast Inn. Member since 1992*)

From the Charleston Visitor's Center turn R. onto John St. then L. onto King St. Go one mi. to the Broad St. intersection. Turn R. onto Broad St. The John Rutledge House is the 4th house on the right.
TEL. 803-723-7999; 800-476-9741; FAX 803-720-2615
116 Broad St.
Charleston, SC 29401
Richard Widman, Owner &
Linda Bishop, Innkeeper

TWO MEETING STREET INN

 9 Rooms $135/$240 B&B

 No Credit Cards

 All Private Baths

 Closed Christmas (3 days)

 Appropriate for Children over 12 years; No Pets
Easy access to Shopping, Antiquing, World-class Golf, Tennis, Beaches, Plantations, Historic Houses, Museums, and Fine Dining
Continental Breakfast; Afternoon Tea and Sherry

No Smoking

♿ N/A

From 26E, exit Meeting Street. Travel south - Located on corner of Meeting and South Battery at White Point Garden.
TEL. 803-723-7322
2 Meeting Street
Charleston, SC 29401

Pete and Jean Spell,
Karen Spell Shaw
Innkeepers

2 Given as a wedding gift by a bride's loving father, this Queen Anne mansion welcomes all who are romantic at heart. From Southern rockers on the beautiful arched piazza, guests overlook White Point Gardens at Charleston's historic Battery. Family antiques, oriental rugs, Tiffany windows, and four-poster canopy beds create a most charming atmosphere. Share Texas size homemade muffins in the courtyard and enjoy a relaxing afternoon with sherry and tea on the wide veranda. For 55 years, the Spell family has graciously welcomed guests.
(*Elegant, Victorian, In-Town, Breakfast Inn. Member since 1992*)

THE RHETT HOUSE

17 Rooms, $125/$225
8 Jaccuzzis & 7 Fireplaces
Visa, MC, Amex

All Private Baths

Open Year-round
Appropriate for Children over 5; No Pets
Antiques, Historic Antebellum Mansions, Moss-draped Live Oaks, Fabulous Barrier Island Beaches, Tennis, Carriage and Sailboat Tours, Lovely Gardens, Golf
Breakfast, Afternoon tea; Picnic Lunch & Candlelit Dinners by Reservation, Wine & Liquor
Smoking–Verandah Patios Only
Conference Facilities (40)
♿ Wheelchair Access (3 rms.)

I-95, Exit 33 & follow signs to Beaufort, R. on Craven St. for 4 blks. Off street parking in back. From the South, Exit 8 and follow signs to Beaufort.
TEL 803-524-9030
FAX 803-524-1310
1009 Craven St.
Beaufort, SC 29902

Steve & Marianne Harrison,
Innkeepers

3 Located in historic Beaufort by the bay, The Rhett House Inn is a beautifully restored 1820 plantation house. Furnished with English and American antiques, oriental rugs, fresh flowers, fireplaces and spacious verandahs. Romantic candlelit dinners featuring gourmet regional cuisine are graciously served with an extensive California wine list. Film site for *Forrest Gump, Prince of Tides, The Big Chill*, and several upcoming productions. History laden Beaufort, Charleston and Savannah offer rich exploring. Mobil ★★★★, AAA ◆◆◆◆.
(*Elegant, Greek Revival, In-Town, Inn. Member since 1991*)

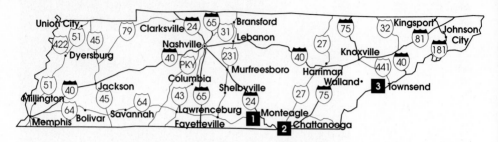

1. Adams Edgeworth Inn, Monteagle
2. Adams Hilborne, Chattanooga
3. Richmont Inn, Townsend

ADAMS EDGEWORTH INN

13 Rooms $70/$250 B&B
1 Suite, $150/$250 B&B
Visa, MC, Amex
All Private Baths
Open Year-round
Children welcome by prior arrangement;
No Pets, kennel nearby
Civil War, Jack Daniels, TN Aquarium, Sewanne University, Ocowee River, Music, Mountain Hiking, Caves, Tennis, Swim, Chautauqua
Breakfast, Dinner, 5 course gourmet candle lit dining with special evening with repertoire dining clubs
Smoking Restricted to Verandahs
Conference Facilities (18)
Wheelchair Access (4 rm., dining rm. & conf. fac.)

1 Nestled in a wilderness atop the Cumberland Mtns., Adams Edgeworth is an 1896 "Camelot" in a forest garden of brooks & tall trestle foot bridges. Come enjoy this National Register Inn featuring Chautaugua cottage decor, fine art, antiques, collector quilts, fireplaces and handmade mattresses on beautiful beds. Tour on bikes or our electric cart around the 150 Victorian cottages in our gated 96-acre private village. Fine candlelight dining by advance reservation. Musical & cultural events. Gift shop. Air conditioned. *(Country, Village, Inn. Member since 1992)*

I-24, Exit #134, R. 1/2 mi., L. under "Monteagle Assembly" archway. Thru stone gateway. Follow signs.

TEL. (615) 924-4000
FAX (615) 924-3236
Monteagle Assembly
Monteagle, TN 37356

Wendy & David Adams, Karen McFarland Innkeepers

THE ADAMS HILBORNE

  6 Rooms $95/$275 B&B
4 Suites, $95/$275 B&B

 Visa, MC, Amex

 All Private Baths

Open Year-round

 Children welcome by prior arrangement; No Pets

TN Aquarium, & I-Max theater; Lookout Mountain; Chickamauga Civil War Battlefield, Architectural & Historic Walking Tour

 Breakfast, Lunch, Dinner & Sun. Brunch available at our Restaurant, the Porch Café

Smoking Restricted to porches & backdeck

 Conference Facilities (80)

Wheelchair Access (1 rm., dining rm. & conf. fac.)

I-24 W. to 27N.-exit 1C (4th St.); 8 lights to Mable (by Roundhouse Arena)-R. on Mable; dead ends at a stop sign at Palmetto; R. on Palmetto; go to stop sign at Vine St. Turn L. on to Vine & immediately L. again into Inn parking lot.

TEL. 423-265-5000
FAX 423-265-5555

801 Vine St.
Chattanooga, TN 37403

David & Wendy Adams, Innkeepers

2 Huge oaks shelter this 1889 romantic National Register mayor's mansion featuring majestic 16 foot coffered ceilings, 12 foot pocket doors, hand-carved woodwork, and parquet floors. Hidden among imported fabrics, Oriental carpets, fine art and antiques are modern conveniences, cable TV's VCR's, private telephone lines, and office equipment. The Porch Cafe, a friendly Bistro restaurant, offers wines and spirits on the verandahs or in your room. Fine dining is available in the Ft. Wood Ballroom or the Tiffany Dining Room. (*Traditionally Elegant, In-Town, Full Service Inn. Member 1996*)

RICHMONT INN

 9 Rooms, $95/$130 B&B
1 Suite, $140/$150 B&B

 Cash or Check

All Private Baths

Open Year-round

Children 12 and over welcome. No Pets

 Hiking, Biking, Picnicking, Fishing, Horseback Riding, Golfing, Theatre, Antiques/Crafts Shopping

 Full Breakfast, Gourmet Desserts & Flavored coffees by candlelight. BYOB

 No Smoking Inside

 Wheelchair Access (1 rm. & dining rm.)

As you enter Townsend (Mi. Marker 26) from Maryville on US 321 N. take 1st R. on Old Tuckaleechee road. Turn R. on next paved road (Laurel Valley), go 0.8 mi. through stone wall entrance. Go to crest of hill, turn L.

TEL. 423-448-6751
FAX 423-448-6480

220 Winterberry Ln.
Townsend, TN 37882

Susan & Jim Hind, Innkeepers

3 Built in the architectural style of the historic Appalachian cantilever barn and beautifully furnished with 18th century English antiques and French paintings in the living-dining rooms. Room names honor eminent Appalachian people and the decor captures their mountain history and culture. Rated "Top Inn" by *Country Inns* magazine and awarded grand prize by *Gourmet* for its signature dessert. Breathtaking views, private balconies/spa tubs/woodburning fireplaces. Ten minutes to Great Smoky Mountains National Park.
(*Traditional Mountain, Breakfast Inn. Member since 1997*)

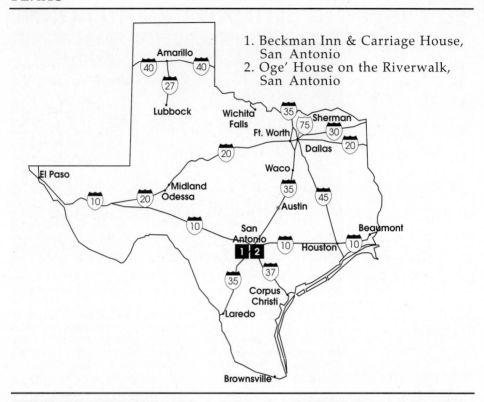

1. Beckman Inn & Carriage House, San Antonio
2. Oge' House on the Riverwalk, San Antonio

BECKMANN INN AND CARRIAGE HOUSE

3 rooms, $90/$130 B&B
2 Suites, $115/$130 B&B

Visa, MC, Amex, Discovr, DC

All Private Baths

Open Year-round

Appropriate for Children over 12; No Pets

Riverwalk, Alamo, Missions, Mexican Market, Zoo, Botanical Gardens, Sea World, Fiesta Texas, Golf, Horseback Riding, Museums, Theaters, Art Galleries, Antiquing and Shopping

Breakfast

Smoking outside on porches & patios

Conference Facilities (10)

N/A

1 Offering warm and gracious hospitality in a beautiful 1886 Victorian home and carriage house, it is perfectly located in the King William historic district. The Riverwalk starts across the street and the trolley stops at the corner, convenient to all San Antonio's festivities.

The wonderful wraparound porch welcomes guests to antique filled rooms featuring ornately carved, queen-size, Victorian beds, private baths, T.V.'s, phones, & guest refrigerators. A gourmet breakfast, with a breakfast dessert, is served in the dining room with china, crystal and silver. (*Elegant, In-Town, Breakfast Inn. Member since 1997*)

From airport, 281 S. to 37 S. Exit R. on Durango at 3rd stoplight. L. on S. St. Mary's St. R. on King William St., L. on E. Guenther Street
TEL. 210-229-1449
800-945-1449
FAX. 210-229-1061
San Antonio, TX 78204
Betty Jo & Don Schwartz, Innkeepers

OGE' HOUSE ON THE RIVERWALK

 5 rooms, $110/$135 B&B
4 Suite, $140/$195

 Visa, MC, Amex, Discovr, Diners

 All Private Baths

 Open Year-round

 No Facilities for children or pets

 Riverwalk, Alamo, Missions, Museums, Zoo, Botanical Gardens, 2 Theme Parks (Sea World), Fiesta Texas, Texas Convention Center, Golf, Tennis

 Breakfast

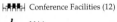 Smoking outside only

Conference Facilities (12)

N/A

From airport: Hwy. 37S to Durango Alamodome, exit R on Durango. Go thru 3 stop lights, turn L on Pancoast; Inn is 1st house on R with Black Historic marker at street.
TEL. 210-223-2353
1-800-242-2770
FAX. 210-226-5812
209 Washington St.
San Antonio, TX 78204
Sharrie & Patrick Magatagan, Innkeepers

2 Privately located on 1 1/2 landscaped acres along the famous San Antonio Riverwalk in The King William Historic District. This 1857 Antebellum Mansion with its grand verandas is known for its elegance, quiet comfort and luxury. Furnished in European and American Antiques, all rooms have King or Queen beds, telephones, cable tv, hospitality refrigerators and some with fireplaces and verandas. Conveniently located downtown within 6 blocks of Alamo, Convention Center, Alamodome, shopping, dining and entertainment. Fax and PC hookups. Mobil 3-Star rating.
(*Elegant, In-Town, Breakfast Inn. Member since 1994*)

THE CHEF'S HAT

Chefs have a highly recognizable uniform which has evolved over the years from necessity, tradition and perhaps a little showmanship. Most diners have come to savor the appearance of a chef, in uniform, as a portent of the cuisine that follows. Yet many do not know how various parts of the uniform came to be.

Usually the most recognizable part of the uniform is the chef's hat, called the *Toque Blanche*. There are several explanations for the shape of the hat. One which many believe is that the tall white hat may have originated at the time of the Byzantine empire when it was under siege by the barbarians.

At that time, philosophers, artists, chefs to royalty, and others fled to Greek Orthodox monasteries for protection. While in hiding, these "tradesmen" wore the same headgear as the priests so they would not be recognized. That headgear of priests at that time was a tall black hat.

After the threat of persecution diminished, the chefs differentiated themselves from the ordained priests by changing from tall black hats to tall white hats.

Traditionally, there are 100 pleats in a chef's hat. It is believed that they represent the one hundred ways a good chef can prepare eggs.

Through the years, the chef's hat has become a symbol of accomplishment and prestige for those who wear it. And for others it has become a recognizable signal that a master creator of cuisine is at hand.

SPECIAL EVENTS AND
GETAWAY PACKAGES

Almost every inn listed in this book has Special Events and Getaway Packages with great appeal for inn-goers. Usually these Events and Packages focus on local natural resources, talents, festivals, and innkeepers' interests. And many times, after a guest "happens on" to an inn's Special, he becomes a great fan and returns year after year for succeeding events.

When planning a trip, always call inns in an area and inquire about the Specials which will coincide with your travels. The innkeeper will be happy to send you a brochure with details about events, dates, and prices.

Because they are too numerous (each inn may have half-a-dozen or so) to mention individually, and because times and dates are so varied, we will pique your interest with the following as a partial list of the activities and festivities you can enjoy at inns in this book.

Kite Flying
Garden Walks
Photography Seminar
Grape Harvesting / Wine Making
Art Workshops
Antique Seminars
Hiking
Whale Watching
Dinner Theater
Trail Riding
Murder Mystery Weekends
Tours
Golf
Bicycling
Nature Hikes
Herb Presentations

Historic Home Tour
Holiday Celebrations
Archaeological Dig
Skiing
Cooking Classes
Quilting
Bird Watching
Boating Cruises
Spa / Stress Relief
Tennis
Local Winery / Brewery
Fishing and Hunting
Wild Flower Hikes
Wild Game Dinners
Poetry / Literary Readings
Music Festivals

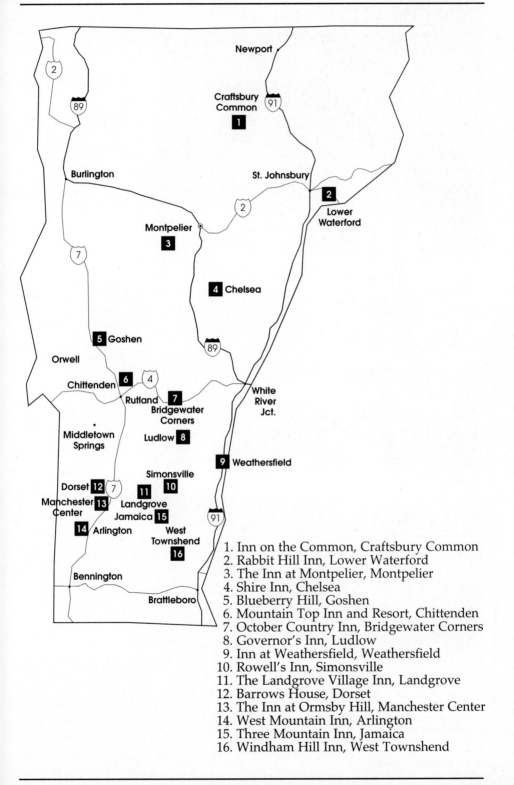

1. Inn on the Common, Craftsbury Common
2. Rabbit Hill Inn, Lower Waterford
3. The Inn at Montpelier, Montpelier
4. Shire Inn, Chelsea
5. Blueberry Hill, Goshen
6. Mountain Top Inn and Resort, Chittenden
7. October Country Inn, Bridgewater Corners
8. Governor's Inn, Ludlow
9. Inn at Weathersfield, Weathersfield
10. Rowell's Inn, Simonsville
11. The Landgrove Village Inn, Landgrove
12. Barrows House, Dorset
13. The Inn at Ormsby Hill, Manchester Center
14. West Mountain Inn, Arlington
15. Three Mountain Inn, Jamaica
16. Windham Hill Inn, West Townshend

INN ON THE COMMON

	14 Rooms, $200/$270 MAP 2 suites, $240/$270
	Visa, MC
	All Private Baths
	Open Year-round
	Children Accepted Pets Accepted
	Pool, Tennis Court, Gardens, XC Skiing, Golf, Lake, Trails
	Breakfast & Dinner Wine & Liquor available
	No Smoking in Dining Room
	Conference Facilities (20)
	N/A

1 With the ambiance of a sophisticated country house hotel, this inn offers outstanding cuisine and an award-winning wine cellar. With beautiful gardens and wonderful views, the lovely and comfortable guest rooms elegantly decorated with antiques and artworks, some with fireplaces, are spread among a compound of 3 meticulously restored Federal houses. (AAA◆◆◆◆)

(*Elegant, Federal, Country, Inn. Member since 1976*)

From I-91 (N), Exit 21, Rte. 2 (W) to Rte. 15 (W),. In Hardwick, Rte. 14 (N) 7 mi. turn R., 3 mi. to inn. From I-91 (S) Exit 26, Rte. 58 (W). Rte. 14 (S) 12 mi. to marked L. turn.
TEL. 802-586-9619; RES. 800 521-2233; FAX 802-586-2249
Main Street
Craftsbury Common, VT 05827
Michael & Penny Schmitt, Innkeepers

RABBIT HILL INN

	16 Rooms $179/$269 MAP 4 Suites $219/$269 MAP
	Visa, MC, Amex
	All Private Baths
	Closed April & Nov. 1-16
	Appropriate for Children over 12; No Pets
	Downhill & XC Skiing, Hiking, Canoeing, Iceskating, Swimming, Golf, Antiquing, Fishing, Lawn Games.
	Full Breakfast, Dinner, Teatime, Picnics Wine & Liquor available
	No Smoking
	Conference Facilities (20) Wheelchair Access (1 rm., 1 dining rm. & conf. fac.)

2 Full of whimsical and charming surprises, this 1795 Federal-period inn has been lavished with love and attention. Many rooms with fireplaces, canopy beds, jacuzzis for 2. Candlelit 4-Diamond dining, unique turn-down service and a sense of pampered relaxation make this an enchanting hideaway. Set in a tiny hamlet that is an Historic District overlooking mountains, the Inn is elegantly stylish and romantic, renowned for exceptional service and detail; personal, caring touches above all! On of the nation's "10 Best Inns" 3 years in a row. AAA ◆◆◆◆ Inn and ◆◆◆◆ Restaurant Mobil ★★★★. Air conditioned.

(*Elegant, Country, Federal. Member since 1990*)

From I-91 (N or S), Exit 19 to I-93 (S). Exit 1 R. on Rte. 18 (S), 7 mi. to inn. From I-93 (N), Exit 44, L. on Rte. 18 (N), 2 mi. to inn.
TEL. 802-748-5168
Reserv. 800-76-BUNNY
FAX 802-748-8342
E-mail: rabbit.hill.inn@Counriver.net
Route 18
Lower Waterford, VT 05848
John & Maureen Magee, Innkeepers

THE INN AT MONTPELIER

13 Rooms, $99/$155 B&B
(6 Suites w/fireplaces)

Visa, MC, Amex, Diners,
CB, Discovr

All Private Baths

Open Year-round

Children Welcome
No Pets
Downhill Skiing, 25
miles. State Capitol,
Shops, & 100 acre park a
short walk.
Generous Continental
Breakfast; Dinner daily;
Restaurant closed Mon-
day eves.
Wine & Liquor available
Smoking Restrictions—
All public rooms are non-
smoking
Conference Facilities (16)
Wheelchair Access (din-
ing rm. & conf. fac.)

I-89 to exit 8 Montpelier. Go to 4th
light, turn L onto Main St. Inn ap-
proximately 3 blocks on right.
TEL. (802) 223-2727
FAX (802) 223-0722
147 Main St.
Montpelier, VT 05602

Maureen & Bill Russell,
Innkeepers

 An elegant, comfortable historic inn where fine dining and caring service are our specialties. Enjoy fireside dining or relax on Vermont's grandest porch. Each guest room is uniquely decorated with antiques, reproductions, fine art and many have fireplaces. Guest pantries offer at-home convenience and warmth with refreshments at any time. TV, telephone and air-conditioning. AAA ◆◆◆◆ for both the Inn and Restaurant, 1st of only three in the state.
(*Elegant, Village, Inn. Member since 1992*)

SHIRE INN

6 Rooms, $90/$130 B&B
$140/$210 MAP
1 Cottage, $50/$110 EP

Visa, MC, Discovr,
Personal Checks
All Private Baths

Open Year-round

Appropriate for Children
over 6; under 6 ok in
cottage only; No Pets

XC & downhill Skiing,
Skating, Sleigh Rides, Bi-
cycling, Swimming, Ca-
noeing, Antiquing, Lawn
Games, Nature Trails
Breakfast & Dinner
Wine & Beer available
Afternoon Tea
No Smoking

Conference Facilities (10)
Wheelchair Access (1 rm.,
dining rm. & conf. rm.)

I-89, Vt. Exit 2 (Sharon) L. for 300 yds.,
R. on Rte. 14 (N). R. onto Rte. 110 (N).
13 mi. to Chelsea. From I-91 Exit 14, L.
onto Rte. 113 (N/W) to Chelsea.
TEL. 802-685-3031
800-441-6908
E-mail: Shireinn@sover.net
Main Street, Box 37
Chelsea, VT 05038

Jay & Karen Keller, Innkeepers

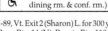 Centrally located for easy day trips to the best rural attractions in both Vermont and New Hampshire, this Inn and Chelsea Village (National Register) provide "just the kind of withdrawn New England atmosphere you hoped to find." (Norman Simpson) The traditional 1832 Adams-style brick and granite home on 25 acres offers large guest rooms with high ceilings, tall windows, canopied queen-sized beds and wood-burning fireplaces. The antique laden parlor is well stocked with books, puzzles and games. Exceptional meals start and end a day of genial relaxation.
(*Traditional, Village, Inn. Member since 1986*)

VERMONT
BLUEBERRY HILL

	12 rooms, 84/$120 MAP PP
	Visa, MC
	All Private Baths
	Open Year-round
	Children Welcome No Pets
	Cross country Skiing, Mountain biking, Walks & Hikes, Fishing
	Breakfast, Lunch (Boxed Lunch), Dinner; BYOB
	No Smoking
	Conference Facilities (50)
	Wheelchair Access (1 rm., dining rm. & conf. fac.)

5 Located in the tranquility of the Green Mountain National Forest, the Inn is artistically fashioned with antiques and warm quilts. A greenhouse adjacent to the kitchen, with brick walkway and ever blooming plants, brings the outdoors inside even during the height of winter. Step out the door in Winter for some of the most scenic Cross country skiing in New England or in summer, bike or hike your way around Romance Mountain. Come share our special way of life.
(*Colonial, Mountain, Inn. Member since 1994*)

From Brandon: Rte 73 East to Forest Road 32 on left, follow signs. From East Middlebury: Rte 125 East thru Ripton, to Forest Road 32 on right, follow signs.
TEL. 802-247-6735
800-448-0707
Website: http://www.sover.net/bbhill
FAX 802-247-3983
E-mail: Clarktg@vbi.champlain.edu
RD 3
Goshen, VT 05733
Tony Clark & Shari Brown, Innkeepers

MOUNTAIN TOP INN AND RESORT

	35 Rooms $103/$196 B&B 22 Chalets $176/$246 B&B
	Visa, MC, Amex
	All Private Baths
	Open Year-round
	Children Welcome No Pets
	Full resort — XC Skiing, Skating, Horseback & Sleigh Rides, Swimming, Sailing, Boating, Golf, Tennis
	Breakfast, Lunch, Dinner Wine & Liquor available
	No Smoking
	Conference Facilities (5–150)
	N/A

6 Commanding a spectacular lake & mountain view on a 1,000-acre estate, this inn offers a complete resort experience. Included in the rates are tennis, heated pool, pitch 'n' putt golf, sailing, fishing, trap shooting, mountain biking, and fly fishing. Special horseback riding vacations with instructions in riding, jumping, dressage and introductory polo and golf school are available. In winter cross country skiing, horsedrawn sleigh rides, sledding, ice skating and winter horseback riding. Attractive, congenial surroundings, and fine dining complete the picture.
(*Rustic, Mountain, Resort. Member since 1987*)

Chittenden is 10 mi. (NE) of Rutland. (N) on Rte. 7 or (E) on Rte. 4 from Rutland. Follow state signs to "Mountain Top Inn."
TEL 802-483-2311
or 800-445-2100
FAX 802-483-6373
E-mail: mttop@vermontel.com
Mountain Top Rd.
Chittenden, VT 05737
Mike & Maggie Gehan, Innkeepers

OCTOBER COUNTRY INN

 10 Rooms, $120/$158
MAP (2)

 Visa, MC, Amex

 Private and Shared Baths

 Closed early Nov., Re-opening for Thanksgiving, Closed April

 Children Accepted
No Pets

 Skiing, Tennis, Golf, Summer Theater, Coolidge Homestead, Swimming Pool, Games, Books

 Full Breakfasts; Family-style Dinners; Wine & Liquor Available

 No-smoking Inn

 Conference Facility (18)

N/A

From Woodstock continue 8 miles west on Rte 4 to junction of Rte 100A. Continue on 4 for 200 yards. Take 1st rt. then rt. again.

TEL. 802-672-3412; 800-648-8421

Upper Road, P.O. Box 66
Bridgewater Corners, VT 05035

Richard Sims & Patrick Runkel, Innkeepers

7 Relaxed and comfortable, this converted 19th century farmhouse on five acres near Woodstock offers warmth and intimacy in the finest innkeeping tradition. The scents of baking breads, fresh herbs and homemade desserts fill the inn as Chef Patrick works magic in Mexican, Italian, French Country, Greek and American motifs. Swim in the pool, bicycle, hike, ski, shop, sightsee or simply relax by the fire—then dine by candlelight. Away from the crowds, yet close to Killington, Woodstock and Dartmouth.
(*Traditional, Country, Inn. Member since 1992*)

THE GOVERNOR'S INN

 7 Rooms, $170/$230 MAP
1 Suite, $300/$325 MAP
B&B Rates Available

 Visa, MC, Pers. Checks

 All Private Baths

 Open Year-round
Fully Air conditioned

Not appropriate for young Children; No Pets

 Downhill & XC Skiing, Antiquing, Golf, Boating, Fishing, Hiking, Winery, Summer Theater, Priory Cooking Classes

Full Breakfast, Picnic Baskets, Dinner, Afternoon Tea, Wine & Liquor available

No Smoking

 Conference Facilities (16)

N/A

Ludlow is located at junction of Rtes. 100 & 103. Inn is (S) on Rte. 103, just off village green.

TEL. 802-228-8830; 800-GOVERNOR (468-3766)

86 Main Street
Ludlow, VT 05149

Charlie & Deedy Marble, Innkeepers

8 Three times judged one of the Nation's Ten Best Inns and awarded ★★★★ by Mobil. This may be the ultimate experience at a Victorian country inn. From potpourri scented air to soft strains of classical music, to beautifully kept heirlooms, attention is given to every detail insuring pleasure and comfort. Seventeen culinary awards, including "Vermont's Best Apple Pie," and recognition for excellence in innkeeping, service, and ambiance only add to the warm and generous hospitality intended to delight and surprise. Public dining by reservation.
(*Elegant, Victorian, Village, Inn. Member since 1987*)

VERMONT
THE INN AT WEATHERSFIELD

🛏	9 Rooms, $175/$195 MAP 3 Suites, $175/$225 MAP
💳	Visa, MC, Amex, Discov, CB, Diners
🛁	All Private Baths
🏠	Open Year-round
🐑	Appropriate for children over 8; No Pets
Ⓡ	Golf, Skiing, Hiking, Bik- ing, Fishing, Sleigh & Car- riage Rides, Sauna, Aerobics Equipment
☕	High Tea, Dinner & Breakfast included with stay; Wine & Liquor Available
🚭	No Smoking except outside porches (VT State Law)
🏠	Conference Facilities (40)
♿	Wheelchair Access (1 rm.)

9 Congeniality and caring have made this gracious "Colonial Sampler," woven with romance, tradition, music and poetry, one of America's "Ten Best Inns." The 21-acre Country Inn is nestled in the lap of Vermont history with skiing, golf, biking, swimming and horse-draw sleigh/carriage rides. Many of the twelve individually decorated suites and guest rooms feature canopy beds, fireplaces, and all have private baths. Award Winning Wine List, English high tea, five-course dinners with grand piano entertainment and bountiful breakfast buffet round out the ultimate inn experience. Mobil ★★★★ (*Traditional, Colonial, Mountain, Inn. Member since 1982*)

From I-91 (N), Exit 7 (Springfield), Rte. 11 (W) to Rte. 106 (N). Inn 5 mi. on left. From I-91 (S), Exit 8, Rte. 131 (W) to Rte. 106 (S). Inn is 4 mi. on right. **TEL. 802-263-9217; 800-477-4828; FAX 802-263-9219**
Rt 106 (Nr Perkinsville), Bx 165 **Weathersfield, VT 05151**

Terry and Mary Carter, Innkeepers

ROWELL'S INN

🛏	5 Rooms, $235 MAP (Includes all charges, tax gratuity & dinner wine)
💳	Visa, MC, Checks preferred
🛁	All Private Baths
🏠	Open Mid-May thru Oct.; Dec. thru March— Weekends; Res. advisable
🐑	Not Suitable for Children No Pets
Ⓡ	Skiing, Golf, Antiquing, Flyfishing, Biking, Hiking, Summer Theater, Priory
☕	Breakfast for Inn Guests; Dinner by Res., to public, Tues.–Sat. Wine, Beer, Ales, Liquor
🚭	Smoking Restricted to Tavern Room
🏠	
♿	N/A

10 CHARACTER, COMFORT, & GOOD FOOD describe this authentic 1820 stagecoach Inn (National Register). Filled with antiques, memorabilia, and the types of things that are sure to give that real Vermont Inn experience. Enjoy canopy beds, cozy fireplaces, relaxing library, and your own English-style pub. Inn features Nationally Recognized and Award Winning Traditional New England cuisine, prepared and served by your Innkeepers. Afternoon Tea, locally made cheeses. Five course Dinners, & "pick" of the Wine cellar are all included. Ideally located to explore all Vermont's attractions. AAA ◆◆◆ rated. Air conditioned in summer.

(*Traditional, Country, Inn. Member since 1985*)

The inn is on Rte. 11 (an east/west rte.) connecting Rtes. 7 & I-91. *The inn is 7 mi. (W) of Chester and 7 mi. (E) of Londonderry.*
TEL. 802-875-3658
RES. 800-728-0842
FAX 802-875-3680
RR #1, Box 267-D
Simonsville, VT 05143

Beth & Lee Davis
Innkeepers

THE LANDGROVE INN

 16 Rooms, $85/$110 B&B;
$160 MAP

 Visa, MC, Discov, Amex

 All Private Baths

 Open May 25–Oct. 25
Dec. 15–Apr. 1

 Children Welcome
No Pets

 Tennis Courts, Heated
Pool, Platform Tennis,
Hay & Sleigh Rides, XC
& Downhill Skiing,
Stocked Pond

 Breakfast & Dinner
Wine & Liquor available

 No Smoking

 Conference Facilities (40)

 Limited

I-91 (N), Exit 2 (Brattleboro). Rte. 30 (N), R. onto Rte. 11. L. at signs for Landgrove Inn, bear L. in village of Peru. From Rte. 7 (N), (E) in Manchester on Rte. 11. Continue as above.
TEL. 802-824-6673
800-669-8466
E-mail: vtinn@sover.net
R.D. 1, Box 215, Landgrove Rd.
Landgrove, VT 05148
Jay & Kathy Snyder
Innkeepers

 The principle of "Vermont continous architecture" extended this original 1840 farmhouse into the rambling inn it is today. It is in a true country inn setting, tucked into a valley in the mountains, with gravel roads and a town population of 200. Sumptuous dining by candlelight, superb breakfasts, and a mix of activities and fun for all ages at this informal, engaging country inn. Three generations of the Snyder family define the meaning of "family run country inn." The kind of place where relaxation and recreation come together in a most idyllic and secluded setting. (*Colonial, Country, Inn. Member since 1977*)

BARROWS HOUSE

 18 Rooms, $145/$205
MAP
10 Suites, $145/$240 MAP

 Visa, MC, Amex, Discov

 All Private Baths

 Open Year-round

 Children Welcome
Dogs in 3 Cottages only

 Heated Pool, Sauna, Tennis Courts, Bike, Skiing, Hiking, Historic & Fine Arts centers, Shopping, Game & Puzzle Room

Breakfast, Dinner, B&B available, Liquor & Wine available

No Smoking in restaurant & 25 of 28 rooms

Conference Facilities (20)

Wheelchair Access (1 rm., dining rm. & conf. fac.)

Manchester, Rte. 30 (N) 6 mi. to inn on R. Accessible from Vt. Rtes. 7, 4, 11, 30 and I-91 & 87.
TEL. 802-867-4455
800-639-1620
(Outside VT)
FAX 802-867-0132
E-mail: barhouse@vermontel.com
Route 30
Dorset, VT 05251
Linda & Jim McGinnis,
Innkeepers

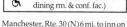

 The Barrows House is a collection of white clapboard buildings situated on 11 acres in the heart of a small picturebook Vermont town. Guests have a choice of 28 accommodations in eight different buildings, each with a history and style of its own. Dining at the Barrows House is an informal and delicious adventure in American regional cuisine. Whether with iced tea in the gazebo and English garden or mulled cider in front of a warm fire and historic stenciling, the Barrows House extends its welcome. (*Traditional, Federal, Village, Inn. Member since 1974*)

VERMONT
THE INN AT ORMSBY HILL

🛏	10 Rooms, $110/$210 B&B
💳	Visa, MC, Amex
🛁	All Private Baths
🛋	Open year-round
🐕	Appropriate for older well-behaved Children; No Pets
☀R	Nearby-walking, hiking, fishing, golf, swimming, x-country & downhill skiing, bicycling, summer theatre, museums, antiques, outlet shopping, canoeing
🍽	Breakfast; Dinner Fri. & Sat.
🚭	NoSmoking
🏛	Conference Facilities (12)
♿	Wheelchair Access (1 rm., dining rm. & conf. fac.)

13 A restored manor house, circa 1764, listed on the Register of Historic Places, with a spectacular setting. Romantic bed chambers with canopies, fireplaces and air-conditioning. Luxurious bathrooms with jacuzzis for two. Acclaimed dining served in the magnificent Conservatory/Dining Room. A patio and porch, with breathtaking views of the Battenkill Valley and the Green Mountains, just inviting you to relax and renew. Renowned for comfort, heartfelt hospitality, and profound attention to detail. (*Elegant, Colonial, Village, Breakfast Inn. Member since 1996*)

In Manchester Center, at junction of Rtes. 11/30 & 7A, take Historic Rte. 7A S. Approx. 3 mi. Inn on L.
TEL. 802-362-1163
800-670-2841
FAX 802-362-5176
Historic Route 7A
Manchester Center, VT. 05255

Ted & Chris Sprague, Innkeepers

WEST MOUNTAIN INN

🛏	10 Rooms $145/$199 MAP 6 Suites, $209/$229 MAP 2 Cottages, $145/$189
💳	Visa, MC, Amex, Discov
🛁	All Private Baths
	Open Year-round
🛋	Children Welcome No Pets
🐕	Hiking, Canoeing, Tubing, Flyfishing, Wilderness X-Country Skiing, Sledding, Skating and Golf and Tennis nearby. Downhill Skiing also nearby.
☀R	
🍽	Breakfast & Dinner; Lunch by special arrangement
🚭	Wine & Liquor available NoSmoking
🏛	Conference Facilities (40)
♿	Wheelchair Access (1 rm., dining rm. & conf. fac.)

14 Llamas and African violets are only two of the delightful surprises at this happy, relaxed country inn, nestled on a mountainside overlooking the Battenkill River. In addition to Wes Carlson's herd of treking llamas and the custom of presenting guests with a lovely African violet, there are cheerful rooms and a rich outdoor world to explore. Miles of trails for hiking or wilderness x-country skiing, and river sport opportunities abound. Guests dine on exceptional New England country cuisine in an atmosphere filled with a spirit of genuine warmth and hospitality. (*Traditional, Country, Inn. Member since 1984*)

Rt. 7 (N), Exit 3. Take access road to end, R. on Rte. 7A into Arlington. L. on Rte. 313 for .5 mi. L. on River Rd. to inn.
TEL. 802-375-6516
FAX 802-375-6553
Website: **www.westmountaininn.com**
E-Mail: **info@westmountaininn.com**
Box 481, Rte. 313 & River Rd.
Arlington, VT 05250

Mary Ann & Wes Carlson, Innkeepers

162

THREE MOUNTAIN INN

	14 Rooms, $80/$110 B&B $130/$170 MAP 1 Suite, $200/$230 MAP
	Amex, Visa, MC, Discov
	All Private Baths
	Closed May 1 — Mid May
	Children over 6 welcome; No Pets
	Swimming pool, Hiking, Biking on premises, Tennis, Golf, Horseback riding, XC and Downhill Skiing nearby—10 minutes away
	Breakfast & Dinner Wine & Liquor available
	No Smoking
	Conference Facilities (40)
	N/A

Jamaica is located on Rte. 30, 1/2 hr. (NW) of Brattleboro (I-91) Exit 2 and 1/2 hr. (E) of Manchester (Rte. 7N to Rt. 30/11).

TEL. 802-874-4140
FAX 802-874-4745

P.O. Box 180R
Jamaica, VT 05343

Charles & Elaine Murray,
Innkeepers

15 Capture the feeling of Vermont's past in this authentic 1790's inn where the innkeepers make the guests feel welcome. Relax, surrounded by mountain views in an unspoiled village. Rooms with canopied beds and fireplaces. Casual dining with a choice of the menu. Fireplaces in two romantic dining rooms with excellent reputation for pridefully prepared gourmet fare. Featured in *Gourmet*. Hike, bike, or x-ct ski to Jamaica State Park. Storage barn for bikes. Backroads maps available. Pub lounge. Specializing in small weddings, family gatherings and group functions. (*Traditional, Colonial, Village, Inn. Member since 1982*)

WINDHAM HILL INN

	18 Rooms, $175/$285 MAP
	Visa, MC, Amex, Discovr, DC
	All Private Baths
	Closed Xmas and April
	Appropriate for Children over 12; No Pets
	XC & Downhill Skiing, Skating, Hiking, Bicycling, Scenic Day Trip, Shopping, Golf, Tennis, Swimming
	Breakfast & Dinner
	Non-smoking Inn
	Conference Facilities (30)
	Wheelchair access (1 rm.)

I-91 (N). Exit 2 (Brattleboro Rte. 30 (N) for 21.5 mi. R. on Windham Rd. 1.5 mi. to inn.

TEL. 802-874-4080
800-944-4080

E-mail: windham@sover.net
R.R. 1, Box 44
West Townshend, VT 05359

Grigs & Pat Markham
Innkeepers

16 On 160 acres at the end of a Green Mountain hillside country road, surrounded by rock wall bordered fields and forests, and breathtaking views. Friendly innkeepers and staff welcome you to this elegant country estate with its sparkling rooms, memorable five-course gourmet meals (★★★ - *The Boston Globe*) and relaxing ambiance. Extensive onsite trail network for hiking and cross country skiing. New, dramatically sited pool and tennis facilities. Designated an "Inn of Distinction" having been judged one of the nation's ten best inns for a third year. Air-conditioned. Graphically rich web site - http://windhamhill.com
(*Elegant, Mountain, Country, Inn. Member since 1989*)

COUNTRY INN CUISINE

Webster's Dictionary defines cuisine as *1. the kitchen   2. the style or way of cooking.*   Certainly then, cuisine becomes a most essential consideration for the Inns described in this guidebook.

The approaches to cuisine among the Inns in the Independent Innkeepers' Association are as different as the Inns themselves. For some, breakfast is the primary meal presented to guests, and so no holds are barred in its design and preparation. Guests are literally awakened by the aroma of delicacies which our daily lives are too hurried to even consider. Some of these Breakfast Inns even publish their own Breakfast Cookbooks, though somehow one wonders if the items could ever smell and taste the same.

For a number of Country Inns, dining becomes the *raison detre;* the inn being established as a showcase for the chef/owner's self expression. The *"style or way of cooking"* part of the definition takes on particular meaning in these cases. At Chef-owned Inns, the diner can be assured that each meal will be an individually created masterpiece (or nearly so) prepared especially for him. Since the quality and design of the comestibles from such a kitchen carry with them the reputation and perhaps even livelihood of their creator, guests are treated to outstanding, sometimes innovative examples of what man can create for the palate. The cuisine will often be the first thing mentioned in the guest's bragging about this Inn.

Many, many people in America are "meat and potatoes" kinds of folks. They prefer comfortable, delicious everyday fare. The pot roast, recently enjoyed by this author, which was cooked on a wood burning kitchen stove at a farmhouse Inn in New Hampshire should not be missed by such a connoisseur. And the honest to goodness home cooking and farm fresh vegetables served from an abundant Lazy-Susan table on a mountain top in North Carolina is reason enough to go there.

Perhaps the more typical Country Inn cuisine for Independent Innkeepers' Association members is created by a talented chef working hand in hand with the innkeeper to complete the total hospitality experience for the guests of the Inn. Often he is well trained and widely experienced. Sometimes he has worked up through the ranks in the kitchen "learning from the school of hard knocks." Some Country Inn chefs formerly worked at larger hotels but simply do not enjoy impersonally produced cuisine. Whatever the route, Country Inn chefs usually feel they have finally found their niche.

It is the feeling of most Innkeepers that hospitality includes providing sustenance to meet their guests' needs. Whether this means hot cider in the parlor, the ever-ready coffee/hot chocolate pot, home-baked cookies, gourmet breakfast, a picnic lunch, or candlelit diner in an intimate dining room, Webster's *1. kitchen* and *2. style or way of cooking* are not lightly considered by successful innkeepers.

164

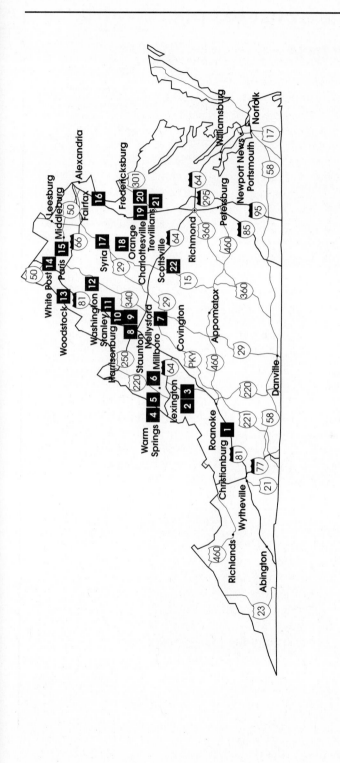

16. The Bailiwick Inn, Fairfax
17. Graves' Mountain Lodge, Syria
18. The Hidden Inn, Orange
19. Silver Thatch Inn, Charlottesville
20. Clifton—The Country Inn, Charlottesville
21. Prospect Hill, Trevilians
22. High Meadows, Scottsville

8. The Belle Grae Inn, Staunton
9. Frederick House, Staunton
10. Joshua Wilton House, Harrisonburg
11. Jordan Hollow Farm Inn, Stanley
12. Inn at Little Washington, Washington
13. Inn at Narrow Passage, Woodstock
14. L'Auberge Provencale, White Post
15. Ashby Inn, Paris

1. The Oaks Victorian Inn, Christianburg
2. Alexander Withrow House / McCampbell Inn, Lexington
3. Maple Hall, Lexington
4. Inn at Gristmill Square, Warm Springs
5. Meadow Lane Lodge, Warm Springs
6. Fort Lewis Lodge, Millboro
7. Trillium House, Nellysford

VIRGINIA
THE OAKS VICTORIAN INN

	5 rooms, $115/$150 B&B
	Visa, Mc, Amex, Disc
	All Private Baths
	Open Year-round
	No Pets; Children over 12 Garden hot tub, Sauna for two, croquet court, library, TV/VCR, etc. Mountain winery/tours, hiking, bike trails, golf, tennis, fishing, horseback riding, antiquing & Historic Sites nearby English-style breakfast Smoking outside only
	Conference Facilities (15–20)
	N/A

1 Warm hospitality, comfortable, relaxed elegance and memorable breakfasts are the hallmark of The Oaks, a century-old Queen Anne Victorian; National Register of Historic Places. Set on Christiansburg's highest hill and located in the beautiful mountain highlands of southwest Virginia, The Oaks delights and welcomes leisure and business travelers from around the world. Surrounded by lawn, perennial gardens and 300-year-old oak trees, the inn faces Main Street, once part of the Wilderness Trail blazed by Daniel Boone and Davey Crockett. Mobil ★★★; AAA ◆◆◆◆.
(Elegant Victorian, Village, Breakfast Inn. Member since 1993)

From I-81 take exit 114 (Main St.) 2 miles. From Blue Ridge Parkway, (MP165) Route 8 west 24 miles to The Oaks.
TEL. 540-381-1500
311 East Main Street
Christiansburg, VA 24073

Margaret & Tom Ray,
Owners/Innkeepers

ALEXANDER-WITHROW HOUSE/McCAMPBELL INN

	15 Rooms, $95/$125 B&B 8 Suites, $145/$165 B&B
	MC, Visa
	All Private Baths Open Year-round
	Children Welcome No Pets - Kennels Nearby
	Antiquing, Museums, College Campuses, Special Shops, Swimming, Fishing, Tennis, Carriage Rides thru Town
	Expanded Continental Breakfast for houseguests Dinner at Maple Hall nightly
	Limited Smoking
	Conference Facilities (5)
	Wheelchair Access (1 rm., dining rm. & conf. fac.)

2 In southwest Virginia, replete with impressive history and scenery, is the town of Lexington and two gracious and graceful inns, the Alexander-Withrow House, (ca. 1789) and McCampbell Inn (ca. 1809) of Historic Country Inns. Parents of VMI or W&L students as well as business or holiday travelers enjoy the comforts of these inns, within easy walking distance of all attractions. Each room interestingly furnished offers individual heating and cooling controls, TVs, phones & refreshment centers. Your needs and comfort are our main concern.
(Traditional, Town, Inn. Member since 1991)

I-81 or I-64, take either exit for Lexington and continue to town center, Main & Washington Sts. Inns across from Court House. In historic district of Lexington; 11 N Main St. which is business Rte. 11.
TEL. 540-463-2044
FAX 540-463-7262
11 No. Main Street
Lexington, VA 24450
The Peter Meredith Family, Owners;
Don Fredenburg, Innkeeper

MAPLE HALL

	16 Rooms, $100/$125 B&B 5 Suites, $145/$160 B&B
	Visa, MC
	All Private Baths
	Open Year-round
	Children Welcome; No Pets
	Tennis, Pool, Croquet, Fishing, Walking Paths, Canoeing, Hiking, Museums, Historic Sites
	Breakfast, Houseguests Dinner daily; Wine & Liquor available
	Smoking somewhat restricted
	Conference Facilities (20)
	Wheelchair Access (1 Room)

I-81 Exit 195 to Rte. 11 (N). Inn is (E) of the Interstate.

TEL. 540-463-2044
FAX 540-463-6693

Rte. 5 Box 223
Lexington, VA 24450

Peter Meredith Family,
Owners Don Fredenburg,
Innkeeper

 A member of the Historic Inns of Lexington, this 1850 plantation home on 56 rolling acres offers guests a lovely place for recreation, exploring historic sites, or just relaxing. There are walking trails, a swimming pool, tennis and fishing. The new Pond House has lovely suites and many of the attractive guest rooms have fireplaces. Historic Lexington is just a short drive away. Convenience, comfort, quiet and service attract many private and corporate groups to select Maple Hall for their small business conferences from 4 to 40.
(*Elegant, Greek Revival, Country Inn. Member since 1987*)

THE INN AT GRISTMILL SQUARE

	8 Rooms, $80/$100 B&B 7 Suites, $85/$140 B&B
	Visa, MC, Discov
	All Private Baths
	Open Year-round
	Children Welcome; Pets not allowed
	Swimming Pool, Tennis, Sauna, Golf, Horseback Riding, Hiking, Fishing, Skiing, Ice Skating
	Continental Breakfast & Dinner; Sun. Brunch; MAP Available Wine & Liquor available
	Smoking Allowed
	Conference Facilities (45)
	N/A

From (N) on Rte. U.S. 220 turn R. (W) on Rte. 619 (Small state marker) for 500 yd. to inn on R. From (S) on Rte. 220, L. (W) on Rte. 619.

TEL. (540) 839-2231
FAX: 540-839-5770

P.O. Box 359
Warm Springs, VA 24484

The McWilliams Family,
Innkeepers

 On a designated historic site, a 1771 gristmill and a blacksmith's shop are among the cluster of restored 19th-century buildings comprising this handsome inn. Guest rooms are tastefully furnished in both traditional and contemporary decor; many have working fireplaces. Exceptional dining and the many attractions of the Allegheny Mountains & spa country draw visitors from afar.
(*Traditional, Village, Inn. Member since 1977*)

167

MEADOW LANE LODGE

🛏	8 Rooms, $115/$125 B&B 2 Suites, $125/$145 B&B 4 Cottages, $115/$145 B&B
💳	Visa, MC
🛁	All Private Baths
👪	Open Year-round Children over 5 accepted in some rooms with prior approval; No Pets
🐎	Tennis, Fly Fishing, Hiking, Swimming, Mtn. Biking,
⚡R	Birding, Croquet, Camp- ing, Canoeing, Tubing, Golf, Horseback Riding, Sporting
🍽	Clays, Skiing, Ice Skating Full Breakfast daily; Picnic lunches available; Dinner Fri. & Sat. (Apr.–Oct.);
🚭	Beer & Wine available; BYOB
🏨	No smoking
	Conference Facilities (18)
♿	N/A

5 Twenty miles of hiking trails and two private miles of scenic Jackson River meander through this 1600 acre farm of mountain forests and meadows where wildflowers, wildlife, birdlife and domestic animals abound. Guests enjoy rooms and cottages with working fireplaces, sunny porches and roosters crowing wakeup calls to the kind of country breakfast you would expect on a farm. Caring for the animals and the land while preserving the past is a way of life here as this unique country inn and estate has been placed under a conservation easement guaranteeing an unspoiled refuge in perpetuity.
(*Traditional, Mountain, Retreat/Lodge. Member since 1978*)

From Staunton, Rte. 254 (W) to Buffalo Gap, Rte. 42 S. to Millboro Springs; Rte. 39 (W) to Rte. 220, continue Rte. 39 (W), 4.3 mi. to lodge entrance on right.
TEL. 540-839-5959
FAX 540-839-2135
Route 1, Box 110
Warm Springs, VA 24484
Cheryl & Steve Hooley,
Innkeepers

FORT LEWIS LODGE

🛏	9 Rooms, $135/$145 MAP 3 Family Suites, $150 MAP 2 Log Cabins, $190 MAP
💳	Visa, MC
🛁	All Private Baths
👪	Closed Nov.–Mar. Open Apr.–Oct.
🐎	Children Welcome No Pets
⚡R	3 mi. private River Fishing, Hiking, Mtn. Biking, Horseback Riding, Swimming, Golf, Deer Watching
🍽	Breakfast, Dinner, Picnic Lunch available Beer & Wine available
🚭	No Smoking in Guest Rooms
🏨	Conference Facilities (35)
♿	N/A

6 A full service country inn at the heart of a 3200 acre mountain estate. Outdoor activities abound with miles of river trout and bass fishing, swimming, extensive hiking trails, mountain biking, magnificent views and abundant wildlife. The main lodge features wildlife art and locally hand-crafted furniture. Three "in the round" silo bedrooms and two hand-hewn log cabins with stone fireplaces are perfect for a romantic getaway. Evenings are highlighted by contemporary American style cuisine served in the historic Lewis Gristmill.
(*Rustic, Mountain, Retreat/Lodge. Member since 1990*)

From Staunton, Rte. 254 (W) to Buffalo Gap; Rte. 42 to Millboro Sprgs.; Rte. 39 (W) for 0.7 mi to R. onto Rte. 678, 10.8 mi. to L. onto Rte. 625, 0.2 mi. to lodge on L.
TEL. 540-925-2314
FAX 540-925-2352
HCR 3, Box 21A
Millboro, VA 24460
John & Caryl Cowden,
Innkeepers

TRILLIUM HOUSE

  10 Rooms, $90/$110 B&B
2 Suites, $125/$160 B&B

 Visa, MC

 All Private Baths

 Closed Dec. 24 & 25
Well-behaved Children
with Responsible Parents
Welcome; No Pets

  Skiing, Golf, Tennis,
Swimming, Hiking, Fishing, Horseback Riding,
Canoeing, Antiquing

Breakfast; single entree
fixed-price Dinner Fri. &
Sat. (inquire); Reservation
required

Wine & Liquor available

Smoking Restrictions

Conference Facilities (25)

Wheelchair access (8 rms.,
dining rm. & conf. fac.)

(S) of I-64; (E) of I-81; (W) of Rte. 29.
On Rte. 664, which connects Rte. 151
with Blue Ridge Pkwy, between Mile
Posts 13 & 14.
TEL. 804-325-9126
RES. 800-325-9126
FAX 804-325-1099
Wintergreen Dr., Box 280
Nellysford, VA 22958
Ed & Betty Dinwiddie,
Innkeepers

 A country inn on Devils Knob of Wintergreen (11,000 acres high in the Blue Ridge Mountains). Trillium House was designed and built in '83 as a small self-contained 12 room country hotel. All guest rooms have private baths with individually controlled heating and cooling. Relax alone or with other guests in the great room, garden room, TV room or the outstanding library. The dining room looks out to an exceptional bird feeding exhibition as well as the 17th hole of the Devil's Knob golf course. Available to guests at preferred rates are two golf courses, swimming pools, thirty tennis courts, 25 miles of mapped hiking trails, and downhill skiing in season. The entry gate to the Wintergreen Mountain Village is one mile from the Blue Ridge Parkway, Motor cycle restrictions.

(Traditional, Mountain Resort, Inn. Member since 1985)

THE BELLE GRAE INN

  7 rooms, $79/$119 B&B
7 suites, $85/$125-$105/
$145 B&B
Visa, MC, Amex

All Private Baths

Open Year-round

Well-behaved young adults
10 and above are welcome;
No Pets

 Hiking the Mountains, Touring 5 Historic Districts, Historic Museums; Woodrow
Wilson Birthplace; Museum
of American Frontier Culture;
Statler Brothers Museum

 Breakfast daily, 7:30-9:00
A.M.; Dinner daily, 6-9
P.M.; MAP Rates Available

Wine & Liquor Available

Smoking Restrictions

 Conference Facilities (50)

Wheelchair Access (3 rms.,
dining rm. & conf. fac.)

Exit 222 off I-81. Follow 250 west to
center of Staunton. Left on Frederick
St. to 515 W. Frederick St. Circle block
for off-street parking.
TEL. 540-886-5151
FAX 540-886-6641
515 W. Frederick St.
Staunton, VA 24401

Michael Organ, Innkeeper

 This Italianate Victorian house is the centerpiece of numerous restored 1890's homes transformed into comfortable lodging rooms. All are graciously furnished, "period correct" and accented with heirlooms and keepsakes. The Inn is an easy walk to shops, museums and an easy drive to Colonial and Civil War History. Guests enjoy a truly romantic dinner in the old inn or dine casually in the garden room. The menu offers tastful American Cuisine complimented with Continental elegance and that special touch of Southern hospitality. Dinner is offered daily 6–9 P.M.

(Traditional, Victorian, In-Town, Inn. Member since 1990)

VIRGINIA
FREDERICK HOUSE

🛏	8 Rooms, $65/$110 B&B 6 Suites, $85/$165 B&B
💳	Visa, MC, Amex, Discovr, DC
🛁	All Private Baths
🏡	Open year-round
🐕	Children Welcome; No Pets
R	Convenient to Blue Ridge Pkwy., Skyline Dr., Woodrow Wilson Birthplace, Museum of American Frontier Culture, Mary Baldwin College
🍷	Breakfast
🚬	Smoking Restrictions
⊢▤▤⊣	Conference Facilities (25)
♿	N/A

9   Frederick House encompasses five restored townhomes adjacent to Mary Baldwin College in historic Staunton. For the confort and convenience of tourists or business travelers, rooms or suites are furnished with private entrance, individual comfort controls, robes, remote TV, phones, reading and writing areas. Breakfast in Chumley's tearoom includes quiches, ham and cheese pies, waffles, hot or cold cereals, homebaked breads. Restaurants, shops, museums and parks are available by easy walks through downtown Staunton.
(*Greek Revival, Inn-Town, Breakfast Inn. Member since 1997*)

From I-81 exit 222, take 250 W. 2.9 mi. Parking and entrance in rear
TEL. 540-885-4220
RES. 800-334-5575
E-mail: http://www.cfw.com/marketplace/resqid/frdpkhs.html
28 N. New Street
Staunton, VA 24401
Joe & Evy Harman, Innkeepers

JOSHUA WILTON HOUSE, INN AND RESTAURANT

🛏	5 Rooms, $95/$125 B&B
💳	Visa, MC, Amex
🛁	All Private Baths
🏡	Closed 1st wk. of Jan. only
🐕	Children 8 & over Accepted; No Pets
R	Snow skiing, Hiking, Biking, Antiquing, Golfing, Fishing all within 20 min. of inn
🍷	Breakfast & Dinner 7 days & nights per wk.
🚬	Smoking in Lounge only
⊢▤▤⊣	Conference Facilities (20)
♿	Wheelchair access (dining rm. & conf. fac.)

10   Located in an elegantly restored Victorian mansion, the Joshua Wilton House offers guests an oasis of quiet charm and gracious living in the heart of the Shenandoah Valley. The facility is within walking distance of historic downtown Harrisonburg and James Madison University. The restaurant offers a unique and extensive menu that changes with the seasons, along with an extensive list of the best wines and beers. The Cafe presents a more casual environment for dining.
(*Elegant, In-Town, Inn. Member since 1995*)

Located at 412 S. Main St. I-81, Exit 245; (W) on Port Republic Rd. to Main St. Approx. 1 mi. to Joshua Wilton House located on R.
TEL. 540-434-4464
FAX 540-432-9525
412 S. Main St.
Harrisonburg, VA 22801

Craig & Roberta Moore, Innkeepers

VIRGINIA

JORDAN HOLLOW FARM INN

	21 Rooms $110/$150 B&B
	Visa, MC, Diners, Discov, Amex
	All Private Baths 4 Whirlpools
	Open Year-round
	Well-behaved Children Welcome; No Pets
	Horseback Riding, Hiking, Bicycling, Walking Trails, nearby swimming, canoeing, fishing, caverns, historic battlefields, museums
	Full Breakfast, Dinner and Box Lunches
	Wine & Liquor available No Smoking
	Conference Facilities (35)
	Wheelchair Access (1 rm., dining rm. with help & conf. fac.)

Luray, Va. Rte. 340 Business (S) for 6 mi. to L. onto Rte. 624 L. on Rte. 689 over bridge & R. on Rte. 626 for .4 mi. to inn on R.

TEL. 540-778-2285
888-418-7000
FAX 540-778-1759
Route 2, Box 375
Stanley, VA 22851

Gail Kyle & Betsy Anderson, Innkeepers

 A cozy 200-year-old restored Colonial horse farm with walking trails and spectacular views, located in the beautiful Shenandoah Valley. Guest rooms have sun porches, and rocking chairs, some have whirlpool baths and fireplaces. The restaurant serves a "country continental" menu. The stable offers trail rides daily. Guests can bring their own horses. Located near Luray Caverns, Skyline Drive, New Market Battlefield Museum, antiquing. Two hours west of Washington, D.C.
(*Traditional, Country, Ranch. Member since 1985*)

THE INN AT LITTLE WASHINGTON

	9 Rooms, $260/$550 B&B 3 Suites, $390/$690 B&B
	MC, Visa
	All Private Baths
	Open Year-round
	Children by special arrangement; No Pets
	Blue Ridge Mtns., Shenandoah Natl. Park, Luray Caverns, 1 1/2 hr. from Washington, D.C.
	Breakfast for inn guests Dinner; Wine & Liquor available
	No Smoking
	Conference Facilities (25)
	Wheelchair Access (dining rm.)

From Wash., D.C., (1.5) hrs.) to I-66 (W) to Exit 43A (Gainesville) to Rte. 29 (S) to R. on Rte. 211 (W) (Warrenton). Continue 23 mi. to R. on Bus. Rte. 211 to Washington (W) for 0.5 mi. to inn on R.
TEL. 540-675-3800
FAX 540-675-3100
Middle and Main Streets,
Washington, VA 22747
Patrick O'Connell and
Reinhardt Lynch, Innkeepers

 In a sleepy village, America's 1st 5★ 5◆ inn offers luxurious guest rooms, lavishly furnished in imported English antiques and lush fabrics, some with balcony views of town and countryside. Chef Patrick O'Connell has captured international acclaim with his creative regional cuisine, which, along with the impeccable service, makes a visit here a memorable experience. The Inn At Little Washington has been named the nation's Restaurant of the Year by The James Beard Foundation.
(*Elegant, Victorian, Country Village, Inn. Member since 1988*)

INN AT NARROW PASSAGE

	12 Rooms, $85/$110
	Visa, MC
	10 Private Baths
	Closed Dec. 24 & 25
	Well-behaved Children welcome; No Pets
	Fishing, Canoeing, Vineyards, Antiquing, Hiking, Skiing, Historic Sites, Caverns
	Full Breakfast BYOB
	No Smoking in guest rooms
	Conference Facilities (20)
	Wheelchair Access (1 rm., dining rm. & conf. fac.)

13 This historic 1740 log inn with five acres on the Shenandoah River is a convenient place to relax and enjoy the beauty and history of the valley. In a country setting along the old Valley Pike, the inn's newer guest rooms open onto porches with views of the river and Massanutten Mountain. Early American antiques and reproductions, working fireplaces, queen-sized beds, original beams, exposed log walls, and pine floors create a comfortable Colonial atmosphere. Fine restaurants for lunch and dinner are nearby.
(*Rustic Colonial, Country, Breakfast Inn. Member since 1990*)

From Wash., D.C.; I-66 (W) to I-81 (S) to Exit 283 (Woodstock) and U.S. Rte. 11 (S) for 2 mi. The inn is at the corner of Rte. 11 and Rte. 672.

TEL. 540-459-8000
800-459-8002
FAX 540-459-8001
U.S. 11 South,
Woodstock, VA 22664

Ellen & Ed Markel, Innkeepers

L'AUBERGE PROVENÇALE

	8 Rooms, $145/$175 B&B; 3 Suites, $225 B&B
	Visa, MC, Amex, Diners, Discov
	All Private Baths
	Feb 1—Dec 31; closed Jan.
	Appropriate for Children over 10; No Pets
	Biking, Hiking, Horseback Riding, Antiquing, Canoeing, Skiing, Tennis, Museums, Golfing, Vineyard Tours, Outlet Shopping, Theatre
	Breakfast & Dinner; Picnics; Wine & Liquor available
	Smoking not allowed in guest rms. or dining rms.
	Conference Facilities (30)
	Wheelchair Access (dining rm. & conf. fac.)

14 A warm, "south of France" breath blows over this eclectic and sophisticated country inn, with its renowned "cuisine moderne Provençale" by French master- chef/owner Alain Borel, who grows his own vegetables, herbs and spices. Charming guest rooms and the bucolic setting in the hunt country of northern Virginia offer a special experience for discerning guests. 4 ◆◆◆◆ rated.
(*Elegant, Country, Inn. Member since 1988*)

On Rte. 340 (S). 1 mi. (S) of Rte. 50; 20 mi. (W) of Middleburg, 9 mi. (E) of Winchester, VA

TEL. 540-837-1375
800-638-1702
FAX 540-837-2004
Route 340, P.O. Box 119
White Post, VA 22663

Celeste & Alain Borel,
Innkeepers

THE ASHBY INN & RESTAURANT

 6 Rooms, $100/$175 B&B
4 suites, $190/$220 B&B

 Visa, MC

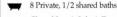 8 Private, 1/2 shared baths

 Closed Jan. 1, July 4, Dec. 24 & 25

 Appropriate for Children over 10; No Pets

 Antiquing, Vineyards, Horseback Riding, Golf, Tennis, Hiking

 Breakfast, Dinner Wed.–Sat.; Sun. Brunch
Wine & Liquor available

 No Smoking in guest rms.

Conference Facilities (20)

N/A

From Wash. D.C. Rte 66 (W) to Exit 23 — Rte. 17 (N), 7.5 mi. L. on Rte. 701 for .5 mi. Or Rte. 50 (W) thru Middleburg; 3 mi. beyond Upperville. L. just after traffic light (Rte. 759).

TEL. 540-592-3900
FAX 540-592-3781
692 Federal St.
Paris, VA 22130
John & Roma Sherman, Innkeepers

15 This 1829 inn finds its character in the small village of Paris and its heart in the kitchen. The views from guest rooms or dining patio are wonderful in every direction. The menu changes daily, ranging from home-cured salmon gravlaks or local wild mushrooms on toast to jumbo lump crabcakes or duckling with turnips.
(*Traditional, Colonial, Village, Inn. Member since 1988*)

THE BAILIWICK INN

 13 Rooms, $130/$195 B&B
1 Suite $295 B&B

 Visa, MC, Amex

 All Private Baths, 2 with Jacuzzis

 Open Year round

 Children Welcome
No Pets

 Mt. Vernon, Gunston Hall, & Woodlawn Plantations. Convenient to Washington, D.C. by metro. Civil War battlefields. Vineyard tours and Antiquing.

 Full Breakfast; Afternoon Tea; Candlelight Dinner
Wine & Beer available

 No Smoking

Conference Facilities (20)

 Wheelchair Access (1 rm.)

Route 123 (Chain Bridge Rd.) 1 mi. (S) of I-66, or via Rte. 50 from I-495 and I-95 to the (E) and (S). Midway National and Dulles International Airports.
TEL. 703-691-2266
800-366-7666
FAX 703-934-2112
4023 Chain Bridge Road
Fairfax, VA 22030

Bob & Annette Bradley, Innkeepers

16 This luxurious National Historic Register Inn is located 15 miles from Washington, D.C. with convenient access by metrorail. The rooms are patterned after those of famous Virginians featuring antiques, queen size feather beds, fireplaces and jacuzzis. Candlelight dinners are available by reservation. The inn has monthly Winemaster Dinners and Murder Mystery Weekends.
(*Elegant, In-Town, Inn. Member since 1992*)

VIRGINIA
GRAVES' MOUNTAIN LODGE

56 Rooms/Cottages
Hotel Rooms $82/$95 AP/PP
Cottages, $64/$102 PP

Visa, MC, Discovr

Private and Shared Baths

Open 3/14/97 to 11/30/97

Children Accepted; Pets Accepted in some rooms

Swimming, Tennis, Nature Walks, Hiking, Fishing, Basketball, Horseback riding, Sand-pit volleyball

Breakfast, Lunch, Dinner, Beer & Wine available

Smoking allowed in Designated areas

Conference Facilities (100)

N/A

17 A tradition for five generations, the Graves' family continues to offer their own kind of Southern hospitality at this rustic retreat complete with motel rooms, cabins and cottages. Guests eat delicious country-cooked meals, served family style, three times a day while enjoying rest and relaxation. Trout streams and farm ponds are available for fishing. Hiking trails and horseback rides through the foothills of the beautiful Blue Ridge Mountains are also available for guests during their visit. Open mid-March through November.
(*Rustic, Country, Retreat/Lodge. Member since 1972*)

From Madison, Va. U.S. Rt. 29, take Rt. 231 (N) for 7 mi. to Greystone Service Sta. Turn L. on Rt. 670. Go 4 mi. to Syria Mercantile Store. Lodge is 200 yds. past Syria on L.
TEL. 540-923-4231
FAX 540-923-4312
General Delivery
Syria, VA 22743
Jim & Rachel Graves, Innkeepers

THE HIDDEN INN

8 Rooms $79/$129 B&B
2 Cottages $139/$159 B&B

Visa, MC, Amex

All Private Baths
4 Jacuzzis

Closed Christmas

Children Accepted
No Pets

Lawn games, Wineries, Antiquing, Historic Sites, Biking, Fishing, Boating

Full Breakfast & Afternoon Tea; Optional candlelight Picnic; Wed.-Sat. fixed price Dinner; Wine & Beer available

No Smoking

Conference Facilities (20)

N/A

18 Lace and fresh-cut flowers accent this romantic Victorian farmhouse, surrounded by seven wooded acres and gardens in the heart of historic Virginia's wine country. Enjoy a cup of tea before a crackling living room fire or sip lemonade on the veranda porch swing. A full country breakfast in the sunlit dining room starts the day, packed with fascinating things to do. Guests can visit Monticello, Montpelier, tour several wineries, shop at local shops & antique stores. Bicycling, horseback riding, golf and hiking are nearby.
(*Traditional, Victorian, Village, Inn. Member since 1991*)

From Wash., DC, I-66 (W) to Rte. 29 (S) at Gainesville to Rte. 15 (S), Orange exit, to Orange; inn on L. From Richmond, I-64 (W) to Rte. 15 (N), through Gordonsville to Orange; inn on R.
TEL. 540-672-3625; 800-841-1253; FAX 540-672-5029
E-mail: **hiddeninn@ns.gemlink.com**
249 Caroline St.
Orange, VA 22960
Ray & Barbara Lonick, Innkeepers

VIRGINIA
SILVER THATCH INN

7 Rooms, $110/$150 B&B

Visa, MC, Amex, DC, CB

All Private Baths

Open Year-round exc. Dec. 24–25

Well-behaved Children over 5 welcome; No Pets

Summer Swimming. Nearby—Golf, Horse-back Riding, Jogging, Hiking, Biking, Blue Ridge Mtns., Monticello, U. of Va.

Breakfast, houseguests Dinner Tues.-Sat.

Wine & Liquor available

No Smoking

Conference Facilities (20)

N/A

From (N); U.S. Rte. 29 (S) 1 mi. (S) of Airport Rd. to L. on Rte. 1520 to inn. From(S): U.S. 250 (W) Bypass to U.S. Rte. 29 (N) 5 mi. to R. on Rte. 1520 to inn.

TEL. 804-978-4686
FAX: 804-973-6156
3001 Hollymead Dr.
Charlottesville, VA 22911
Rita & Vince Scoffone,
Innkeepers

19 This historic inn began life as a barracks built by captured Hessian soldiers during the Revolutionary War. It now provides gracious accommodations in antique-filled guest rooms and elegant candlelit dining. The restaurant features modern American cuisine, which changes with the seasons, and a wine list that won the Wine Spectator Award of Excellence. AAA ◆◆◆ for both Inn and Restaurant. (*Traditional, Country, Inn. Member since 1986*)

CLIFTON—THE COUNTRY INN

7 Rooms, $185/$245 B&B
7 Suites, $185/$245 B&B

Visa, MC

All Private Baths

Open Year-round

Well-supervised Children; No Pets

Outdoor Pool with Water-fall, Year-round Spa, Clay Tennis Court, Private Lake, Volleyball/Badminton, Croquet, Horseshoes

Continental & Full-Service Breakfast included; After-noon tea; Chef Craig Hartman's gourmet Prix-Fixe dinners served nightly

No Smoking

Meeting Facilities (25)

Wheelchair Access (1 rm., dining rm. & conf. fac.)

From I-64-exit 124; turn onto 250 (E); after 2.5 mi. R on 729 (North Milton Rd.); 2nd drive on L. From Rte. 29-take 250 (E) Bypass; R on 729 (North Milton Rd.) 2nd drive on L.

TEL. 804-971-1800
888-971-1800
FAX: 804-971-7098
1296 Clifton Inn Drive
Charlottesville, VA 22901
Craig Hartman, Innkeeper

20 Our open-kitchen policy (with self-serve cookie jar!) and personal, non-intrusive service make you feel like a familiar guest in our home. Enjoy swimming and tennis on our 40 acres or tour historic Charlottesville's wineries, Monticello (four miles away), and the University of Virginia. Chef Hartman's unforgettable dinners are served nightly and have been praised by the *Washington Post*, *Country Inns* magazine, the James Beard Foundation and many others.

(*Elegant, Country, Inn. Member since 1995*)

175

VIRGINIA
PROSPECT HILL PLANTATION INN

10 Rooms, $250/$325 MAP d/o
3 Suites, $290/$325 MAP d/o
Visa, MC, Discov
All Private Baths
8 Jacuzzi tubs
Closed Dec. 24 & 25

Children Accepted in private cottages; No Pets
Swimming Pool, Walking Paths, Hiking, Biking, Golf, Carriage Rides, Antiquing, Ballooning, Peace & quiet
Breakfast & Dinner daily
Wine & Beer available

Smoking Restrictions

Conference Facilities (26)
Wheelchair access (2 rms. & conf. fac.)

21 Prospect Hill is a 1732 plantation just 15 miles east of Charlottesville, Virginia. Lodgings are in the manor house and renovated outbuildings featuring working fireplaces, verandahs, Jacuzzis, and breakfast-in-bed. Continental candlelight dinners served daily by reservation. Please accept our invitation to arrive early enough to enjoy afternoon tea and relax before dinner. AAA◆◆◆◆; Winner Uncle Ben's Best Inn of the Year 1992–93. (*Traditional, Country, Inn. Member since 1979*)

Rte. 29 (S) to Rte. 15 (S) to Zion Crossroads & Rte. 250 (E) 1 mi. to L. on Hwy. 613 for 3 mi. to inn. (Inn is 15 mi. (E) of Charlottesville via Rte. 250; 98 mi. (SW) of D.C.)
TEL. 800-277-0844
540-967-0844
FAX 540-967-0102
E-mail: msheehan1@aol.com
2887 Poindexter Rd.
Trevilians, VA 23093
Michael & Laura Sheehan, Innkeepers

HIGH MEADOWS

9 Rooms, $79/$145 B&B
5 Suites, $110/$185 B&B
Visa, MC
All Private Baths
Closed Dec. 24 & 25 only
Appropriate for Children over 8; Prior Approval for Pets
Hiking, Wine-tasting, Croquet, Vineyard, Canoeing, Tubing, Fishing, History, Antiquing, Horseshoes, Monticello
Breakfast & Dinner; Twilight Wine-tasting; Sat. rates MAP, add $40 pp
Smoking restricted
Conference Facilities (20)
Wheelchair Access (1 rm.)

22 Choice accommodations and diversions as individual as you. Spacious and comfortable rooms & suites with fireplaces, porches, soaking and whirlpool tubs. Romantic flower gardens, relaxing walks on 50 tranquil acres of rolling meadows; spectacular mountain sunsets; European supper baskets at the pond, in the gazebo or the vineyard; Full country breakfasts on the terrace or by the fire; Fine candlelight dining after a twilight tradition of Virginia wine-tasting are a few of the pleasures that await you at this 19th-century inn (National Register of Historic Places). (*Traditional, Country, Inn. Member since 1990*)

I-64 in Charlottesville, Exit 121 to Rte. 20 (S) for 17 mi. After intersection with Rte. 726, continue .3 mi. to L. at inn sign
TEL. 804-286-2218
800-232-1832
FAX 804-286-2124
High Meadows Lane
Route 20 South
Scottsville, VA 24590
Peter Sushka and Mary Jae Abbitt, Innkeepers

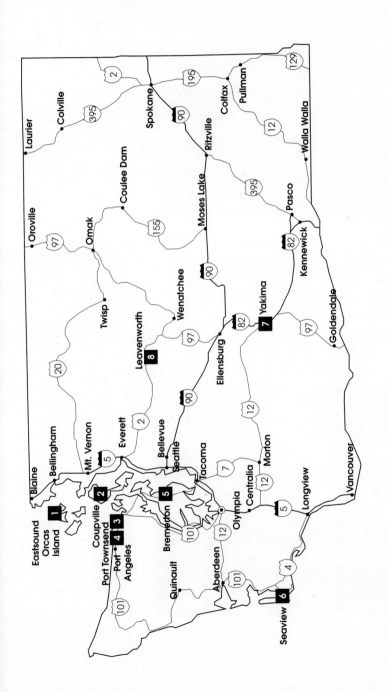

1. Turtleback Farm Inn, Eastsound
2. Captain Whidbey Inn, Coupeville
3. The James House, Port Townsend
4. Old Consulate Inn, Port Townsend

5. Willcox House Country Inn, Bremerton
6. Shelburne Inn, Seaview
7. Birchfield Manor, Yakima
8. Haus Rohrbach, Leavenworth

WASHINGTON
TURTLEBACK FARM INN

🛏	7 Rooms, $80/$160 B&B
💳	Visa, MC, Discovr
🛁	All Private Baths
🛎	Open Year-round
🐕	Appropriate for children over 8; Pets not allowed
☀R	Hiking, Salt & Fresh-water Fishing, Sea Kayaking, Golf, Bicycling, Boating, Local Crafts
🍷	Full Breakfast, Beverages any time, Sherry and Fruit BYOB
🚭	No Smoking
🏨	Conference Facilities (15)
♿	Wheelchair Access (3 Rooms)

1 A country farmhouse located on Orcas Island, the loveliest of the San Juan Islands which dot Puget Sound. This graceful and comfortable inn is considered one of the most romantic places in the country (*L.A. Times, USA Today*). Turtleback is noted for its spectacular setting, detail-perfect restoration and expansion, spotless maintenance & award-winning breakfasts. A haven for those who enjoy breathtaking scenery, varied outdoor activities, unique shopping and superb food, Turtleback Farm Inn provides a perfect destination for the discriminating traveler.
(*Traditional, Country, Inn. Member since 1991*)

From Orcas ferry landing, follow Horseshoe Hwy. (N) to first intersection (2.9 mi.). Turn L. to first R. (0.9 mi.). Continue on Crow Valley Rd. 2.4 mi. (N) to inn.
TEL 360-376-4914
FAX 360-376-5329
Orcas Island-Crow Valley Rd., Route 1, Box 650, Eastsound, **WA 98245**
William & Susan C. Fletcher, Innkeepers

THE CAPTAIN WHIDBEY INN

🛏	22 Rooms, $95/$135; 3 Suites & 7 other, $155/$120 B&B (Full)
💳	Visa, MC, Amex, Discov, Diners
🛁	Private & Shared Baths
🛎	Open Year-round
🐕	Children Welcome in some Rooms; No pets (off-premises boarding avail.)
☀R	Beach, Kayaks, 5 State Parks, Hiking, Library, Historic Town, Sailing, Charters avail.
🍷	Breakfast (Full), Lunch (avail. daily July-Sept; wknds. Oct-June); Dinner daily; Wine & Liquor available
🚭	Non-Smoking areas
🏨	Conference Facilities (30, Lagoon Lib.; 40, Cove Cottage)
♿	N/A

2 This romantic, rustic log inn dates from 1907 and overlooks the waters of Penn Cove. Feather beds, antiques and artwork in every room and superb Northwest coastal cuisine and wines are enjoyed by guests. Spot eagles and herons, or sail the cove on a day-cruise available with our innkeeper. A gracious welcome and profound relaxation await you.
(*Rustic, Country, Inn. Member since 1973*)

From north: I-5 (S) Exit 230 & Hwy. 20 to Coupeville. Turn on Madrona. From (S): I-5 (N) Exit 189, Mukilteo Ferry, Hwy. 525. Hwy. 20. From west: Keystone Ferry, Hwy. 20.
TEL. 360-678-4097
800-366-4097
FAX 360-678-4110
E-mail: captain@whidbey.net
2072 W. Captain Whidbey Inn Rd.
Coupeville, WA 98239
Don S. Stecker, Innkeeper
Captain John Colby Stone, Proprietor

THE JAMES HOUSE

8 Rooms, $75/$125 BB
3 Suites, 2 Cottages &
Bungalow, $115/$200 BB
Visa, MC, Amex

11 Private Baths

Closed Dec. 24-25

Appropriate for children over 12; No Pets

Hiking, Fishing, Kayaking, Sailing, Shelling, Biking, Antiquing, Golf, Olympic National Park nearby

Breakfast, Afternoon Sherry; Fresh baked cookies daily

No Smoking

Conference Facilities (10)

Wheelchair Access (1 rm)

From Seattle: Bainbridge Island ferry, across Hood Canal Bridge to Hwy. 19, to Hwy. 20. From points north follow Hwy. 20 to Keystone on Whidbey Island. Whidbey Keystone ferry to Port Townsend. Inn sits on the bluff overlooking the Keystone ferry.
TEL 360-385-1238
800-385-1238
Web Site: www.jameshouse.com
FAX 360-379-5551
E-mail: jameshouse@olympus.net
1238 Washington St.
Port Townsend, WA 98368
Carol McGough, Innkeeper

  This grand Victorian mansion, built in 1889, sits on the bluff with unsurpassed water and mountain views. On the National Register of Historic Places, The James House was the first bed and breakfast in the Northwest, and continues with its fine tradition of warmth and hospitality. Most rooms have expansive water views and all are furnished with period antique furniture. The James House offers the perfect setting to enjoy this quaint historic Victorian seaport village.

(Elegant, Victorian, Village, Breakfast Inn. Member since 1996)

OLD CONSULATE INN

5 Rooms, $97/$145
3 Suites, $145/$195

Visa, MC, Amex

All Private Baths

Open Year-round

Children over 12 Welcome; No pets

Sailing, wind surfing, kayaking-fresh/saltwater/ river, fishing-clamming-bicycling-antique & art galleries-tour historic homes & sites-golf-tennis-music festivals-close to national park

Breakfast, Lunch & Dinner available to group reservations. Complimentary wine, cordials & desserts

No Smoking
Conference Facilities (24)

N/A

From Seattle-N Bainbridge Ferry to Hwy 305-N to Hwy 3 to Hood Canal Bridge (cross over) to Hwy 19 to Port Townsend from Tacoma. S I-5 to 16w to Hwy 3 etc from South I-5 to Hwy 101 (off ramp 104 at Olympia) North to Hwy 20 to Port Townsend
TEL. 360-385-6753
800-300-6753
FAX 360-385-2097
E-mail: anyone@oldconsulateinn.com
313 Walker at Washington
Port Townsend, WA 98368
Rob & Joanna Jackson, Innkeepers

 Step back to a quieter more romantic time. Visit Port Townsend's award winning Founding Family Mansion-on-the-Bluff commanding sweeping views of the Bay, Mount Rainer and snow-capped Olympics. Warm hospitality greets you at every turn. Enjoy the soothing Gazebo hot-tub... afternoon tea and fresh baked cookies... evening desserts and cordials. At day's end, retire to king size beds with sweet turndowns. Awaken refreshed and join us for our renown Banquet Breakfast. AAA ◆◆◆◆

(Traditional, Victorian, Waterside, Breakfast Inn. Member since 1996)

WILLCOX HOUSE COUNTRY INN

 4 rooms, $119/$189 B&B
1 suite, $110 B&B

 Visa, MC, Discovr

 All Private Baths
(2 with Jacuzzi)

Open year-round

Children over 15; No pets

Private beach & pier,
Floating dock, Row boat &
Peddle boat, Hiking, Golf
courses in area, Antiquing

Breakfast, Lunch, Dinner
Afternoon wine & cheese
hour; breakfast included,
prix fixe; lunch and din-
ner by reservation; wine
list; Wine available

Smoking outdoors only
Conference Facilities (10)

Wheelchair access (1 rm.,
dining rm.)

5 Overlooking Hood Canal, this historic 1930's Country House Inn is situated in a forest setting between Seattle and the Olympic peninsula. The mansion estate offers park-like grounds, private saltwater beach and spectacular views. Comfortable period pieces and antiques are featured in guest rooms and the great room, billiard room, pub, library, and view dining room. *Country Inns Magazine* award: one of the top twelve inns in North America in 1993. (*Elegant, Waterside, Inn. Member since 1993*)

17 mi. east of Bremerton on Hood Canal, near Holly. Call for directions.
TEL. 360-830-4492
800-725-9477
FAX 360-830-0506
(call first)
2390 Tekiu Rd.
Bremerton, WA 98312

Cecilia & Phillip Hughes,
Innkeepers

SHELBURNE INN

13 Rooms, $99/$145 B&B
2 Suites, $169 B&B

Visa, MC, Amex

All Private Baths

Open Year-round

Quiet, well-supervised
Children; No Pets

Beachcombing, Bicycling,
Golf, Horseback Riding

Breakfast, Lunch, Dinner
Wine & Liquor available

No Smoking

Conference Facilities (35)

Wheelchair Access
(1 rm., dining rm.)

6 An unspoiled 28-mile stretch of wild Pacific seacoast is just a 10-minute walk through rolling sand dunes from this inviting country inn, built in 1896. Restoration and refurbishing of the award-winning inn has included the addition of Art Nouveau stained glass windows, along with antique furnishings and fine art. A sumptuous breakfast featuring the best of the northwest is complimentary with your room. Innovative cuisine has brought national recognition to the outstanding restaurant and pub, where lunch and dinner are served. The Shelburne has been named one of the "Top 25 inns worldwide." (*Traditional, Village, Inn. Member since 1988*)

From Seattle, I-5 (S) to Olympia Hwy. 8 & 12 to Montesano & Hwy. 101 (S) to Seaview. From OR coast, U.S. 101 across Astoria Bridge L. to Ilwaco (N) 2 mi. to Seaview.
TEL. 360-642-2442
FAX 360-642-8904
E-mail: shelinn@aone.com
Box 250, 4415 Pacific Way
Seaview, WA 98644
David Campiche & Laurie
Anderson, Innkeepers

BIRCHFIELD MANOR

 11 rooms, $80/$175 B&B

 Visa, MC, Amex, Diners

All Private Baths

Open Year-round

Not suitable for small children; No pets

Pool (in season)

Breakfast, Dinners, Banquets (including luncheons)

Smoking restrictions

Conference Facility (50)

Wheelchair Access (4 rms., dining rm. & conf. fac.)

I-82 to Yakima, Exit 34. Go (E) 2 mi.; turn R (S) onto Birchfield Rd. 1st house on R.
TEL. 509-452-1960
FAX 509-452-2334
2018 Birchfield Road
Yakima, WA 98901

Wil & Sandy Masset,
Innkeepers

 This award-winning restaurant and country inn features fine Northwest cuisine, offered by the European-trained chef/owner, in the casual relaxed atmosphere of a gracious home. Parklike grounds surround the outdoor swimming pool. Most rooms have panoramic valley views on the edge of sunny Washington wine country. Wine cellar with an extensive selection of Washington wines—and you may find your favorite winemaker at the next table! We can personalize a tour of the local wineries just for you.

(Traditional, Country, Inn. Member since 1993)

HAUS ROHRBACH PENSION

7 Rooms, $75/$125 B&B
3 Suites, $145/$160 B&B

Visa, MC, Amex, Discov, DC

8 Private Baths
Open Year-round; Closed Weekdays in Nov, Thanksgiving Day, Dec. 23-25
Children Welcome; No pets
Swimming Pool, Hot Tub, Sledding, Lawngames on site, Hiking, Biking, Skiing, Horseback Riding, Hay & Sleigh Rides, Fishing, Shopping, Art Galleries, Golf, Rafting, and museums nearby
Breakfast, other meals available for groups. Picnic or sack lunches by request, Dinner Sat. evening by request—Groups
No Smoking
Conference Facilities (12-24)
Wheelchair Access (2 rms., dining rm. and conf. fac.)

From Seattle: I-5 N to Everett; Hwy 2/Wenatchee-Stevens Pass Exit. Stay on Hwy 2 to Leavenworth. Turn L on Ski Hill Drive for 1/2 mi. Turn left on Ranger Rd to end of road.
TEL. 509-548-7024
800-548-4477
FAX 509-548-5038
12882 Ranger Rd.
Leavenworth, WA. 98826
Robert & Kathryn Harrild,
Innkeepers

Hugging a mountainside in the foothills of the Cascades, Haus Rohrbach, fashioned after the pensions of Europe, offers guests the experience of "gemutlichkeit" meaning coziness, joviality and kindness. The inn enjoys spectacular valley views. Close-up the fragrant flower boxes and well maintained gardens soothe the soul. Guests are pampered with a welcoming common area, suites designed for romance, down comforters, homemade desserts and a standard of cleanliness to put you at ease. Whatever your whim—shopping, outdoor recreation or peaceful relaxation—the richness of our four seasons makes your stay a time to remember.

(Rustic, Mountain, Breakfast Inn. Member since 1994)

THE SHINING LIGHT IN HOSPITALITY

The logo of the Independent Innkeepers' Association displays a lantern and the words "The Shining Light in Hospitality." This symbol was first established in the late 1960's by the late Norman T. Simpson, founder of the Association. It continues its omnipresent position in the Association to unite Simpson's following in a single-minded endeavor to create and protect the standards and qualities that let Independent Innkeepers "out-shine" the rest as purveyors of consistent, remarkable country inn hospitality.

The story of how Norman Simpson became "the recognized authority on country inns" has been told many times in countless articles and reviews — his travels in the 1950's and '60's throughout New England for his advertising agency business, his boredom with stays in sterile motel and hotel rooms "staring at a television set," the discovery of off-the-beaten-path inns where he felt at home and was able to relax and talk with the innkeepers and other guests, and finally, how in 1966, writing as "The Berkshire Traveler," he put together, with his wife Nancy, a little 16 page booklet containing descriptions of 12 New England inns. He called his booklet, *Country Inns and Back Roads*, and early on he began to include on the cover the image of a lantern, similar to a rusty and dented keep-sake lantern which he had in his office. He wanted the lantern to identify the properties in the booklet as "the shining light in hospitality." He told a reporter for the Associated Press in 1978 that he'd written that first issue as a lark, "I was as surprised as anyone that it became so popular." And popular it was.

At the time it was one of few such guides in America. But travelers were thirsty to learn about the new, interesting, somewhat adventuresome way to travel and really enjoy people, their heritage, and the countryside.

As the little booklet grew in size and popularity, Norman Simpson soon began to devote full time to the country inn industry which was just beginning to develop in the United States. He called his little group of innkeepers together regularly to discuss mutual problems and find solutions. He selected a name, Independent Innkeepers' Association, to identify the group's need to maintain their individuality while networking, sharing, and pursuing the highest standards of hospitality and quality.

Norman knew what he liked. He was a history buff; he was drawn to Early Americana and the gentler, friendlier, more gracious feelings of a bygone day. He found many of these values in those early inns — individuality, hominess, natural-

Continued on page 184

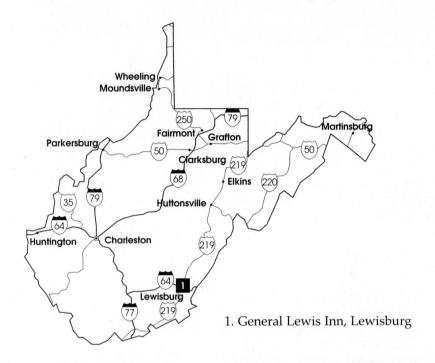

Wheeling
Moundsville
250
79
Fairmont
Grafton
Martinsburg
Parkersburg
50
Clarksburg
219
50
68
Elkins
220
35
79
Huttonsville
64
Huntington
Charleston
219
64
1
Lewisburg
77
219

1. General Lewis Inn, Lewisburg

THE GENERAL LEWIS

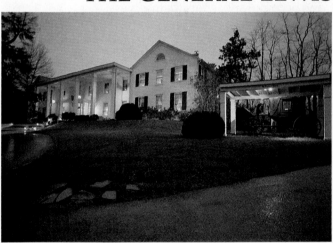

 23 Rooms, $75/$112 EP
2 Suites, $92/$112 EP

 Visa, MC, Amex, Discovr

 All Private Baths

 Open Year-round
Children Welcome
Pets Allowed

 Garden, National Historic District, Golf, Tennis (all seasons), Hiking

 Trails, Biking, Horseback Riding, Swimming (all seasons), Fishing, Canoeing, White Water Rafting, Antiquing, Theater, Caverns

Breakfast, Lunch, Dinner
Wine & Liquor available
No Smoking

 Wheelchair Access (1 rm. & dining rm.)

I-64, Lewisburg Exit 169 & Rte. 219 (S) for 1.5 mi. to Rte. 60 (E) for .3 mi. to inn on R.
TEL. 304-645-2600
FAX: 304-645-2600
301 E. Washington St.
Lewisburg, WV 24901

Mary Noel Hock &
Jim Morgan, Innkeepers

1 Come rock in a chair on the veranda of the General Lewis Inn. On chilly days dream by the fireplace, solve one of the puzzles, or play a fascinating game. Don't miss Memory Hall's display of old tools for home and farm. Antiques furnish every room, including comfortable canopy, spool and poster beds. The dining room in the 1834 wing features Southern cooking. Nestled in beautiful Greenbrier Valley, the Inn offers nearby walking tours. Explore the Lewisburg district and browse the antique shops. AAA ◆◆◆ Mobil ★★★
(Traditional, Village, Inn. Member since 1973)

ness, good home-cooked food, a slower pace, friendly and warm hospitality, and good people who cared about their guests and were involved with their communities. The buildings were interesting, often with historic backgrounds, and there were grandfather clocks and family heirlooms. They were often on back roads. These were the things he liked and looked for and wrote about.

In *Country Inns and Back Roads* he wrote simply as if he were having a conversation with his readers, telling them about his visits and what he had found. His word-pictures struck an answering chord in people. They wanted to find these places, to experience what Norman had experienced. Not only did they visit country inns, they wrote to him, sharing their own experiences; they came to see him just to talk or to ask for advice. Ultimately many began to buy inns and become innkeepers themselves - and Independent Innkeepers' Association members. That's briefly how it all started.

Norman's commitment to his book and inns and innkeepers grew stronger as his expectations and preferences grew clearer to him. He knew what he was looking for, and he was very intuitive in his assessments of whether an inn was right for his book. Norman was absolutely consistent in his message throughout the years: *"The heart and soul of an inn are people -*

people who like people. Innkeepers and inn-goers have a lot in common. They are friendly - they like to talk to each other, to share their ideas and discoveries. It's partly nostalgia, partly a desire to get out of the rat race."

At the time of Norman Simpson's untimely death in 1988, he was in the process of organizing his "collection" of innkeepers, the Independent Innkeepers' Association, into a membership-driven Association under the guidance of a Board of Regional Directors. His goal was soon realized, and the Association's guidebook became known as *The Innkeepers' Register*. The new book was sadly devoid of his appealing folksy commentary but consistently dedicated to his standards of hospitality and his own devotion to sharing information about the very best country inns with the traveling public.

Each year when the membership (now more than three hundred) gathers for its Annual Meeting, Norman Simpson's dented and rusty lantern is symbolically lighted at the first general session as a reminder to all members of the rich, dedicated heritage from which it has grown. That flame and the lantern in our logo are vivid reminders of the standards and qualities which make our Independent Innkeepers' Association *The Shining Light in Hospitality.*

1. Old Rittenhouse Inn, Bayfield
2. Canoe Bay, Chetek
3. The Creamery, Downsville
4. White Gull Inn, Fish Creek
5. Inn at Cedar Crossing, Sturgeon Bay
6. White Lace Inn, Sturgeon Bay
7. Mansion Hill Inn, Madison

OLD RITTENHOUSE INN

	17 Rooms, $99/$159 B&B 4 Suites, $119/$229 B&B 1 Cottage, $119/$229
	Visa, MC
	All Private Baths 5 Whirlpools
	Open Year-round Children Accepted
	Apostle Island's National Lakeshore; sailing, island tours, hiking, summer
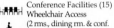	theatre, golfing, sea-kayaking, downhill & x-country skiing
	Breakfast/Lunch/Dinner/Sun. Brunch open to public Wine available
	No Smoking
	Conference Facilities (15) Wheelchair Access (2 rms., dining rm. & conf. fac.)

1 Three turn-of-the-century homes make up this Victorian inn where hospitality, superior dining, and music blend into a joyous whole. Mary and Jerry Phillips share in the creation of wonderful meals, lovely dinner concerts and other events. Guest rooms are handsomely outfitted with antiques, working fireplaces and the entire inn offers a delightful sojourn.
(*Elegant, Victorian, Village, Inn. Member since 1980*)

Duluth Hwy. 2 (E) for 60 mi. to L. on Hwy. 13 (N) (just outside Ashland) for 20 mi. to Bayfield

TEL. 715-779-5111
FAX: 715-779-5887
301 Rittenhouse Ave., P.O. Box 584
Bayfield, WI 54814

Jerry & Mary Phillips, Innkeepers

CANOE BAY

	10 Rooms, $155/$195 B&B 5 Cottages, $200/$300 B&B
	Visa, MC, Discovr
	All Private Baths & Whirlpools
	Open year-round
	No children; No Pets
	Hiking, swimming, boating, canoeing, fishing, biking, x-country skiing, snow shoeing, golfing
	Breakfast, Lunch, Dinner Extensive Wine List
	No Smoking
	Conference Facilities (25)
	Wheelchair Access (1 rm., dining rm. & conf. fac.)

2 Secluded, peaceful and distinctive, with incomparable accommodations, superb cuisine, restorative spa services, breakfast in bed and a truly spectacular setting with breathtaking lake views. This is Canoe Bay. Guest accommodations include whirlpools, fireplaces, private decks, wet bars, video/audio systems, lake views. Recreational opportunities abound. Food and wine lovers will delight in our devotion to fresh ingredients combined in unique ways for a memorable dining experience. Named one of *Top 3 Inns in the Midwest*.
(*Prairie, Waterside, Retreat, Lodge. Member since 1996*)

Hwy. 53N. to Chetek exit. N. to County Hwy. D, E. on D, 1.5 mi. to sign.

TEL. 715-924-4594
FAX 715-924-2078
W16065 Hogback Rd.
Chetek, WI 54728

Dan & Lisa Dobrowolski, Innkeepers

THE CREAMERY RESTAURANT & INN

3 Rooms, $100/$115 B&B
1 Suite, $130 B&B

Visa, MC

All Private Baths

Closed Jan.-March

Children - Yes
Pets Discouraged

Dunn Co. Pottery & Gallery, Red Cedar St. Park, Hiking, Biking, Skiing Historical Museums

Breakfast daily for guests; Lunch, Dinner Tues.-Sun., Sun. Brunch; Wine & Liquor available

Smoking Restricted

N/A

From I-94, Exit 41 at Menomonie; Hwy. 25(S) 10 mi., L. at CTH "C," 1/3 mi. on R. (75 mi. E. of St. Paul, MN.)

TEL. 715-664-8354
P.O. Box 22
Downsville, WI 54735

Richard, David, John Thomas; Jane Thomas De Florin, Innkeepers

 This remodeled turn-of-the-century creamery in the hills of western Wisconsin contains four large guest quarters with cherry woodwork, handmade tiles, pottery lamps and concealed TVs. Its sweeping views of the Red Cedar River Valley and hills along with a reputation for exceptional cuisine and fine wines has made this family-run inn well known from Chicago to Minneapolis. Dunn County Pottery studio and showrooms adjacent to the restaurant. (*Contemporary, Village, Breakfast Inn. Member since 1991*)

THE WHITE GULL INN

6 Rooms, $96/$185 EP
3 suites, $150/$250 EP
5 Cottages, $150/$250 EP

Visa, MC, Amex, Discov, Diners, CB
All Private Baths
Open Year-round exc. Thanksgiving Day, Dec. 24-25
Children Welcome in suitable rooms; No Pets

Golf, Tennis, Swimming, Sailing, Hiking, Biking, XC Skiing, Summer Stock Theatre, Music Festival, Antique Shops, Art Galleries

Breakfast, Lunch, Dinner, Wine & Beer available
No Smoking

Conference Facilities (25)
Wheelchair Access (dining rm. & conf. fac.)

Milwaukee I-43 for 98 mi. to Green Bay, then R. on Rte. 57 (N) for 39 mi. to Sturgeon Bay; (N) on Rte. 42 for 25 mi. to Fish Creek. L. at stop sign for 3 blks. to inn.

TEL. 414-868-3517
FAX 414-868-2367
4225 Main St., P.O. Box 160
Fish Creek, WI 54212

Andy & Jan Coulson, Innkeepers

 Established in 1896, this white clapboard inn is tucked away in the scenic bayside village of Fish Creek, on Wisconsin's Door Peninsula. The turn-of-the-century antiques and fireplaces give the inn rooms and surrounding cottages a warm, comfortably hospitable atmosphere. Famous for hearty breakfasts and lunches and quiet candlelight dinners, the inn is renowned for the unique, traditional Door County fish boils, featuring locally caught whitefish cooked outside over an open fire. (*Traditional, Village, Inn. Member since 1979*)

WISCONSIN
INN AT CEDAR CROSSING

🛏	9 Rooms, $85/$145 B&B
💳	Visa, MC, Discov
🛁	All Private Baths 5 Whirlpools
🏡🌳	Open Year-round exc. Dec. 25
🐕	Children-Inquire; No Pets
☀R	Sailing, Hiking, Skiing, Beaches, 5 State Parks, Galleries, Shops, Summer Theater, Golf, Tennis
☕	Breakfast, Lunch, Dinner, Evening Refreshments Wine & Liquor available No Smoking
🚭	Smoke Free Conference Facilities
⊢⊣	(26–off season)
♿	Wheelchair access (dining rm. & conf. fac.)

5 Warm hospitality, elegant antique-filled guestrooms, and creative regional cuisine are tradition at this most intimate Door County inn (National Register of Historic Places). Lovingly restored, you'll find cozy fireplaces, room service, and evening refreshments await pampered travelers. Guestrooms are exceptionally furnished—oversized canopied beds, double whirlpool tubs, private porches, inviting fireplaces. Exquisite dining features fresh ingredients, enticingly prepared entrees, sinful desserts, and casual pub, set in the beauty and culture of Wisconsin's Door Peninsula. *(Traditional, In-Town, Inn. Member since 1990)*

Hwy. 42 or 57 (N) to Sturgeon Bay. Bus. Rte. 42/57 into town across old bridge. L. on 4th Ave. 1 blk., then L. on Louisiana St. to inn.

TEL. 414-743-4200 (lodg.)
414-743-4249 (dining)
FAX 414-743-4422
336 Louisiana St.
Sturgeon Bay, WI 54235

Terry Wulf, Innkeeper

WHITE LACE INN

🛏	14 Rooms (10 with fire- places), $48/$148 B&B
	5 Suites, all with fire- places & whirlpools, $140/$190 B&B
💳	Visa, MC, Discover
🛁	All Private Baths
🏡🌳	11 Whirlpools Open Year-round
🐕	Older Children welcome No Pets
☀R	Gardens, Beaches, Sailing, Shopping, XC Skiing, Hiking, Golf
☕	Breakfast & Snacks
🚭	No smoking
⊢⊣	
♿	Wheelchair Access (1 Room)

6 Romance begins as you follow a winding garden pathway that links this charming inn's 4 historic homes. Guest rooms are furnished with exceptional comforts, period antiques, oversized whirlpool tubs, and inviting fireplaces. A warm welcome awaits as guests are greeted with lemonade or hot chocolate. Located in the resort area of Door County, the inn is close to many delights.
(Traditional, Village, Breakfast Inn. Member since 1988)

Hwy. 57 (N) to Sturgeon Bay & Bus. Rte. 42-57 into town. Cross downtown bridge to L. on 5th Ave.

TEL. 414-743-1105
16 No. 5th Ave.
Sturgeon Bay, WI 54235

Dennis & Bonnie Statz,
Innkeepers

MANSION HILL INN

 9 Rooms, $100/$290 B&B
2 Suites, $220/$250 B&B

 Visa, MC, Amex

 All Private Baths, 8
whirlpool tubs, 2 steam
showers
Open Year-around

 Children over 12 yrs.
welcome; No Pets

 Beach 2 blocks, walking
distance to downtown
shopping, theatres, res-
taurants, museum, Civic
Center, S.C., Sat. A.M.
Farmers Market on Capi-
tol Sq. several blocks to
Univ of WI
Breakfast
No Smoking

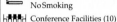 Conference Facilities (10)

 N/A

4 blocks N of state Capitol on the corner
of Gilman & Pinckney or Hwy 151 to
State Capitol, turn R. on Winconsin Ave.
go 4 blocks to Gilman, turn R., 1 block to
Pinckney, turn R.

TEL. 608-255-3999
800-798-9070
FAX 608-255-2217
424 N. Pinckney St.
Madison, WI 53703

Janna Wojtal, Innkeeper

7 Mansion Hill Inn is an 1858 Romanesque Revival Mansion located in the historic Mansion Hill district. Madison's only 4 Diamond hotel is listed on the National Register of Historic Places. Our 11 guest rooms are filled with period antiques, hand-carved marble fireplaces, and floor-to-ceiling arched windows. All rooms have private, sumptuous baths. You'll be greeted with complementary spirits and refreshments upon arrival, given evening turndown service, and, in the morning, a silver service continental plus breakfast will be delivered to your door.

(*Elegant, Victorian, Romanesque Revival, In-Town, Breakfast Inn. Member since 1997*)

Rate Definitions

In this 1996 Innkeeper's Register, rates are quoted for 2 people for 1 night and do not necessarily include service charges and state taxes. For inns offering AP and MAP, "pp" is used to indicate rates are per person. For more detailed information, ask the inns for their brochures.

AP — American Plan (3 meals included in room rate)

MAP — Modified American Plan (breakfast & dinner included in room rate)

EP — European Plan (meals not included in room rate)

B&B — Bed & Breakfast (breakfast included in room rate)

🔅R🔅 — Represents recreational facilities and diversions either on the premises of an inn or nearby

● — A dot before the inn name in the index indicates that it can be booked through a travel agent. Travel agents should contact the inns directly for specific rates and restrictions.

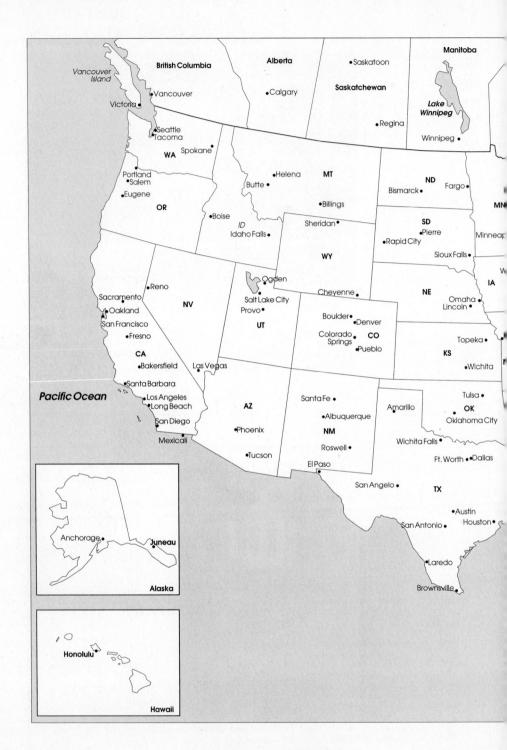

Canada

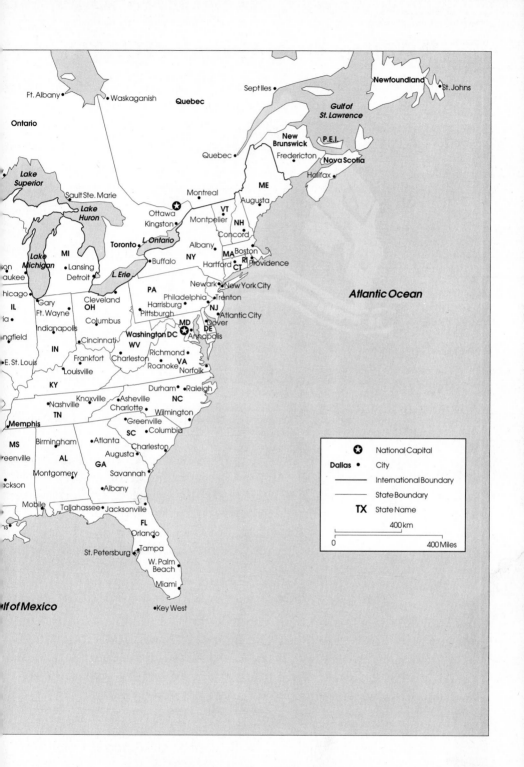

United States

INTERNATIONAL HOSPITALITY

We are proud to feature in this *Register* a fine array of accommodations in Canada and Great Britain.

Now, more than ever before, guests who enjoy IIA Inns in the United States are also traveling across the borders and across the oceans seeking similar kinds of hospitality there. Certainly international travelers who are accustomed to depending on the quality of the Independent Innkeepers' Association in the continental United States will be looking for assurance of corresponding hospitality experiences wherever they travel in other countries. Conversely, IIA member Inns in the United States would like very much to show the foreign traveler our place in the world of hospitality.

Whether in the United States, Canada, England, or Scotland the Independent Innkeepers' Association includes hospitality establishments of the finest quality. These select establishments include country house hotels, manor houses, historic homes, traditional inns, farmhouses, and small hotels. They are located in the countryside, in towns, along seashores, on mountain tops, and in other locations, all worth a visit.

To stay with any of our international number is to discover the finest innkeeper care and hospitality in comfortable, unique and well maintained facilities which you will want to brag about when you return home.

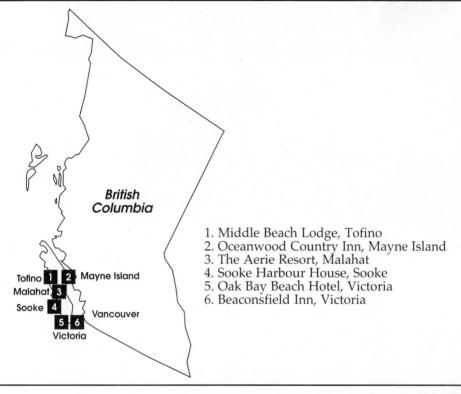

British Columbia

Tofino 1 2 Mayne Island
Malahat 3
Sooke 4
5 6 Vancouver
Victoria

1. Middle Beach Lodge, Tofino
2. Oceanwood Country Inn, Mayne Island
3. The Aerie Resort, Malahat
4. Sooke Harbour House, Sooke
5. Oak Bay Beach Hotel, Victoria
6. Beaconsfield Inn, Victoria

MIDDLE BEACH LODGE

34 Rooms, $72/$200 B&B
18 Suites, $110/$210 B&B

Visa, MC

All Private Baths

Open Year-round
Children Accepted
No Pets
Hiking, Nature Explora-
tion, Fishing, Surfing,
Kayaking, Beachcombing,
Whale Watching

Breakfast year round,
Dinner - Summer 5
nights/week, - Winter 1
night/wk

Smoking permitted out-
side only
Conference Facilities (30)
Wheelchair Access (2 bed
rms., dining rm., & Conf.
Fac. in Lounge)

5 hrs N of Victoria, 3 hrs N of Na-
naimo take the Port Alberni turn off,
A scenic drive through Cathedral
Grove, past picturesque Cameron
Lake, Middle Beach Lodge is 3 km S
of the Village of Tofino
TEL. 250-725-2900
FAX 250-725-2901
400 McKenzie Beach Rd.
P.O. Box 413
Tofino, BC V0R 2Z0
Jacqui Thomas, Innkeeper

1 Oceanfront lodges & cabins on the open Pacific; private wilderness headlands and exclusive sandy bay; two lodges—one adult oriented, one for families. Accommodations include lodge suites, rooms and private self-contained oceanfront cabins with kitchenettes and fireplaces. West Coast country dinners and barbeques served in oceanfront lounges, five nights a week during summer season and on holidays. Licensed. Corporate and group retreats welcome. Meeting rooms. All rates include daily continental breakfast in our lodges.

(Rustic, Waterside, Lodge. Member since 1996)

OCEANWOOD COUNTRY INN

	12 Rooms, $120/$295 B&B & Tea
	Visa, MC
	All Private Baths
	Open March–Nov.
	No Children under 16; No Pets
	Sauna, Hot Tub, Bicycles, Hiking, Tennis, Ocean Kayaking
	Breakfast, Dinner, Afternoon Tea; Wine & Liquor Available
	Smoking restrictions; Library & Outside only
	Conference Facilities (12) (1 rm., Dining rm. & conf. fac.)

2 On the waterfront in Canada's spectacularly beautiful Gulf Islands, Oceanwood is like a cozy and civilized English country house. Twelve individually-decorated guest rooms, all with private bath, many with fireplaces. Comfortable living room, well-stocked library, bright, plant-filled garden room and cozy games room. Charming dining room, overlooking Navy Channel, features Pacific Northwest cuisine and West Coast wines. Island activities include ocean kayaking, cycling, tennis, country walks and the infinite pleasure of peace and quiet. (*Traditional, Country, Inn. Member since 1994*)

BC Ferries from either Tsawwassen or Swartz Bay; arrive at Village Bay on Mayne Island; Turn R. out of terminal onto Dalton Dr.; R on Mariners Way; L. on Dinner Bay Road & follow it until you see Oceanwood Sign on L.—630 Dinner Bay Rd.
TEL. 250-539-5074
FAX: 250-539-3002
630 Dinner Bay Rd.
Mayne Island, B.C. V0N 2J0
Marilyn & Jonathan Chilvers, Owners

THE AERIE RESORT

	10 Rooms, $150/$260 Can. B&B 10 Suites, $250/$395 Can. B&B
	Visa, MC, Amex All Private Baths
	Open Year-round
	No Children No Pets
	Indoor Pool, Outdoor Hot Tub, Tennis Court, Walking Trails, Indoor Spa
	Breakfast, Lunch & Dinner
	Smoking Restrictions
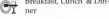	Conference Facilities (2) Wheelchair Access (dining rm.)

3 Spoil yourself in one of North America's most romantic and scenic getaways on a 5 acre parklike setting with panoramic ocean views. Relax in your luxurious suite with fireplace, jacuzzi and private terrace. Rejuvenate yourself in our spa, swim in the indoor pool, soak in the hot tub or play tennis. Explore the natural woodlands with its many attractions. Enjoy fishing, sailing or horseback riding. Soft piano and selected fine vintages from France, California and the Pacific Northwest will accompany your memorable dinner.

(*Elegant, Mountain, Resort. Member since 1995*)

From Victoria take TransCanada Hwy. #1N., turn off at Spectacle Lake exit; follow inn signs (20 mi N. of Victoria)
TEL. 250-743-7115
FAX: 250-743-4766
PO Box 108
Malahat, BC V0R 2L0
Canada
Leo & Maria Schuster, Markus Griesser, Innkeepers

SOOKE HARBOUR HOUSE INN

13 Rooms, $150/$205–$175/270 B&BL (includes lunch)

Visa, MC, Amex, Enroute

All Private Baths
7 Jacuzzis

Open Year-round; some restrictions during the week Nov-March

Children Welcome; Pets Accepted, charge of $20 per day

World Class Fishing, Golfing, Whale Watching, Gardens, Biking & Hiking Trails and Beaches, etc.

Breakfast & Lunch for Houseguests; Dinner for Public; Wine & Liquor Available

No Smoking

Conference Facilities (30)

Wheelchair Access (1 Rm., dining rm. & conf. fac.)

Victoria, B.C., Hwy. 1 (W) to Hwy. 14 & Sooke Village. Through Stoplights, 1 mi. to L. on Whiffen Spit Rd. for .5 mi. to inn.

TEL. 604-642-3421
FAX: 604-642-6988
1528 Whiffen Spit Rd.
Sooke, B.C., Canada V0S 1N0

Fredrica & Sinclair Philip, Innkeepers

4 Cozy and homelike, consistently rated one of Canada's top ten restaurants which has become known as a leader in West Coast Canadian cuisine. The restaurant uses only fresh, organic ingredients which are grown in the inn's gardens, by nearby organic farms or harvested in the wilds from around Sooke. The inn offers secluded, romantic rooms with fabulous views of the ocean and mountains. Each room features fireplaces, jacuzzi and antique furnishings and art pieces.
(*Waterside, Retreat/Inn. Member since 1988*)

OAK BAY BEACH HOTEL

48 Rooms, $109/$239 Can. B&B; 3 Suites, $199/$399 Can. B&B

Visa, MC, Amex, Diners, EnRoute

All Private Baths

Open Year-round

Children Welcome

No Pets

Yacht Excursions, Fishing, Whale Watching, Dinner Cruises, Jogging. Also: Golf, Tennis. Recreation Center and Pool nearby.

Breakfast, Lunch & Dinner; Discounts on High Tea, Dinner or Cruises Included; Dinner, High Tea Daily; Wine & Liquor avail.

Some Non-Smoking rms.

Conference Facilities (150 reception, 130 dinners)

N/A

South on Hwy. 17 Left on Hillside (E), which becomes Lansdowne. Right on Beach Dr. to Hotel.

TEL. 250-598-4556
800-668-7758
FAX 250-598-6180
1175 Beach Dr.
Victoria, B.C. Canada
V8S 2N2

Kevin & Bruce Walker, Innkeepers

5 Beautiful seaside location, warm and gracious hospitality, crackling fireplaces, first-class accommodations in an atmosphere of old world charm. This prestigious family-owned hotel in the residential area of Oak Bay is a significant part of the history and heritage of the city of Victoria. Magnificent lawns and gardens rolling to the ocean, islands, mountains in the distance, provide wonderful views. The Tudor-style architecture is complemented by antiques and period pieces. Meals, service and hospitality are the best. Rates include discount on meal or cruises. AAA ◆◆◆◆ award.
(*Victorian, Waterside, Resort. Member since 1979*)

BEACONSFIELD INN

🛏	6 Rooms, $200/$350 (Can.) B&B
	3 Suites, $350/$395 (Can.)
💳	B&B 1 Oceanfront Beach Cottage $395 (Can.)
🛁	Visa, MC
🛋	All Private Baths, 8 Jacuzzis
	Open Year-round except Dec. 24–26
🐕	Not Suitable for Children No Pets
Ⓡ	Golf, Tennis, Sailing, Beach Activities, British High Tea, Hiking Trails, Carriage Rides, Library, Antiques
☕️	Gourmet Breakfast, After-noon Tea; Evening Sherry
🚭	No Smoking
⊞	Conference Facilities (18)
♿	N/A

6 An Award-winning Heritage restoration, this 1905 Edwardian Manor set in an English cottage garden is a luxurious retreat in the residential heart of Victoria. Finely chosen amenities include original oak wainscotting and mahogany floors, English antiques, oriental carpets, stained glass windows, down comforters, eleven fireplaces, eight jacuzzi tubs. A gourmet breakfast in the Dining Room or Sunroom, Afternoon tea and evening Sherry Hour in the Library is included. Four blocks to oceanfront/downtown. (*Elegant, In-Town, Breakfast Inn. Member since 1994*)

From North: Hwy 17 to City Centre; L. on Humboldt St. From Inner Harbor: Government St. N to Humboldt St. Turn R. for 4 blocks.
TEL. 250-384-4044
FAX: 250-384-4052
Internet: http://
www.islandnet.com/beaconsfield/
998 Humboldt St.
Victoria, B.C. V8V 2Z8
Con & Judi Sollid,
Innkeepers/Owners

I WOULD LIKE TO MAKE A RESERVATION, PLEASE

Any time a place of business can accommodate only a limited number of people at a given time, some system must be worked out to schedule those people in an orderly fashion. We're all familiar with the "take a number" system at the ice cream store, and the appointment secretary at the dentist's office and the beauty parlor. Today, it seems everything from service for your car to grooming for your pet requires a reservation. And for every kind of reservation system that exists, some sort of program must be put into place to mitigate interruption of continuous service when one of the reservations can not be kept. For some systems the cancellation of a reservation causes such a minor flurry it is hardly perceivable. For others, of course, major changes in schedules, quantities, and/or physical arrangements must be made.

Various methods are employed by businesses to insure that when reservations can not be kept, the reservationist is notified. This is important especially when loss of business/income would result. Usually a cash deposit, payment in full, ticket, or credit card number is required to make sure that cancellation, should that be necessary, takes place in time to make the proper adjustments.

Businesses with limited space and capacity, such as Country Inns and their dining rooms, understand more than anyone how very important proper cancellation notification can be. Innkeepers' hospitable nature, as well as their business sense, makes them ever sensitive to the trust placed on them when a reservation is made, they must, however, maintain their individual cancellation policies for the occasions when reservations must be cancelled by the guest. Receiving and accommodating friends and strangers with kindness and fairness *is* the Country Inn business. All with proper reservations of course.

1. Sir Sam's Inn, Eagle Lake
2. Sherwood Inn, Port Carling
3. Domain of Killien, The, Haliburton
4. The Briars, Jackson Point
5. Eganridge Inn, Fenelon Falls
6. Sam Jakes Inn, Merrickville
7. Benmiller Inn, Goderich
8. Little Inn of Bayfield, The, Bayfield
9. Westover Inn, St. Marys
10. Stone Maiden Inn, Stratford
11. Jakobstettel Guest House, St. Jacobs

12. Elora Mill Inn, Elora
13. Millcroft Inn, The, Alton
14. Kettle Creek Inn, Port Stanley
15. Elm Hurst Inn, Ingersoll
16. Langdon Hall Country House, Cambridge
17 Woodlawn Terrace Inn, Cobourg
18. St. Anne's Country Inn & Spa, Grafton
19. Rosemount Inn, Kingston
20. Trinity House Inn, Gananoque

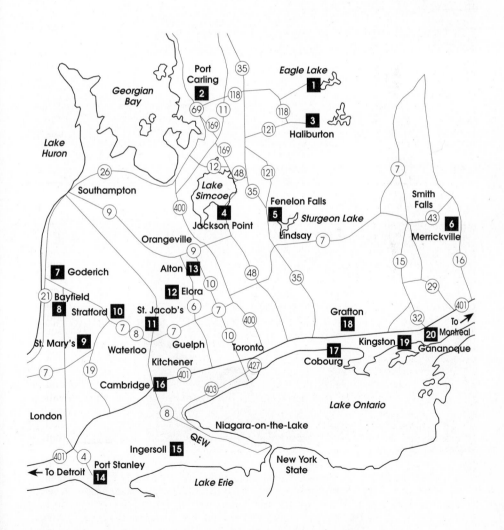

SIR SAM'S INN

21 Rooms, $98/$135 Can. MAP, PP

3 Suites, 1 Chalet, $135/$155 MAP, PP

Visa, MC, Amex, Enroute
All Private Baths

Open Year-round

Children 8 & over; No Pets

Tennis, Windsurfing, Sailing, Outdoor Pool/Whirlpool, Kayaks, Canoes, Paddleboats, Mountain Bikes, Waterskiing, Boat Cruises, Exercise Studio, Sauna in Winter, Downhill & X-Country Skiing

Breakfast, Lunch & Dinner

Smoking Restrictions

Conference Facilities (35)

N/A

1 Originally Sir Samuel Hughes' Haliburton estate, the Inn offers an historic charm and classic elegance. Magnificently situated on Eagle Lake, we celebrate nature through a host of activities—waterski, windsurf, sail, canoe or kayak. There is tennis, mountain biking, hiking and more. In winter exciting Downhill and Nordic skiing. Year round our superb candlelit dining is complemented by our unique wine cellar. Intimate rooms (most with whirlpool and fireplace). At Sir Sam's, what nature does not offer . . . we do.
(*Traditional, Waterside, Resort. Member since 1995*)

From Toronto (2 1/2 hrs) (N) on Hwy. 400 + 11 to Hwy. 118 (E) to Eagle Rd. Follow signs to Sir Sam's Road.
TEL. 705-754-2188
FAX 705-754-4262
Eagle Lake, P.O. Eagle Lake, Ont. Canada K0M 1M0

James T. Orr, Innkeeper

SHERWOOD INN

29 Rooms, $99/$209 PP
MAP - $60/$142 PP B&B

2 Suites, 9 Cottages, $146/$241 PP MAP; $99/$176 PP B&B

Visa, MC, Amex, Diners, Enroute

Private & Shared Baths
Open year-round

Children Welcome; No Pets

Tennis, Water Skiing, Windsurfing, Boating, Sailing, Canoeing, Fishing, Volleyball, Badminton, Shuffleboard, XC Skiing, Skating, Ice Fishing, Dog-Sledding, Golf nearby.

Breakfast & Lunch, Dinner available

Wine & Liquor available

Smoking Restricted

Conference Facilities (90)

Wheelchair Access (dining rm. & conf. fac.)

2 Set amongst towering pines on the edge of Lake Joseph, tranquil Sherwood Inn offers atmosphere, impeccable service and gastronomic excellence, complimented by an outstanding wine cellar. Attentive staff anticipate guests' needs with quiet efficiency and genuine friendliness. Most of all, Sherwood is a place where guests may relax and rediscover the finer qualities of life. Muskoka's only AAA Four Diamond Award recipient for dining and accommodation.
(*Elegant, Country, Inn. Member since 1992*)

Hwy. 400 N from Toronto to Foot's Bay. Turn R on Hwy. 169 S, Travel 10 km S to Sherwood Rd. Turn L on Sherwood Rd, follow to end.
TEL. 705-765-3131
800-461-4233
FAX 705-765-6668
PO Box 400, Lake Joseph
Port Carling, ONT P0B IJ0
John & Eva Heineck, Innkps.

THE DOMAIN OF KILLIEN

5 Rooms, $138/$166 Can. PP MAP
1 Suite, 6 Chalets, $130/$188 Can. PP MAP
Visa, MC, Amex
All Private Baths

Open year-round

Not suitable for children; No Pets

On Site Private Stocked Lakes, Beaches, Sailing, Canoeing, Fly Fishing, Hiking on 30 km Private Trails, Mountain Bicycling, Tennis, Nordic Skiing, Snowshoeing, Night Lit Skating Rink, Golf & Downhill Skiing nearby

Breakfast & Dinner; Picnic lunches available

Non-Smoking dining room

N/A

From Toronto, Hwy. 404 (N) to Davis, R (E) to 48; (N) to 35; L (N) to Minden; 121 R (N) to Haliburton. L (W) on 118; R (N) on Harburn Rd. 12 km to Carroll Rd.
TEL. 705-457-1100
PO Box 810
Haliburton Ontario K0M 1S0
Jean-Edouard Larcade, Innkeeper.

3 Near the southern tip of Algonquin Park, there is a small and intimate inn on the shores of a serene lake.

Set within a private 5000-acre estate of forests, hills and lakes, the Domain offers regional French cuisine and wines, quiet comfort and Hospitality, all in the tradition of the finest European inns.

Throughout the seasons, enjoy outdoor silent sports or simply, Master the Art of Doing Nothing . . . Beautifully.
(*Traditional, Lakeside, Country, Inn. Member since 1995*)

THE BRIARS

46 Rooms, $109/$195 PP Can. MAP; 4 Suites & Cott., $119/$195 pp. Can. MAP
Visa, MC, Amex, Diners
All Private Baths

Open Year-round

Fun-filled Children's program (in season)
Pet Kennels nearby

Golf, Tennis, Swimming, Boating, Summer Theatre, Nature Trails, Fireplaces, Solarium Pool, Whirlpool, Sauna & Game Rooms.

Breakfast, Lunch, Dinner Wine & Liquor available

No Smoking in dining room

Conference Facilities (75)

Wheelchair access (14 rms.)

Toronto Hwy 404 (N) to Davis; R (E) to Woodbine; L (N) 20 mi. on hwy to Sutton; L (N) on Dalton to Jackson's Pt; R (E) on Lake Drive .6 mi to Hedge Rd & Briars.
TEL 800-465-2376
FAX 905-722-9698
Website: http://www.ils.net.briars
55 Hedge Rd., R.R. #1
Jackson's Point, Ontario, Can. LOE 1LO
John & Barbara, Hugh & Andrew Sibbald & family, Innkeepers

4 This enchanting historic inn is an oasis of traditional hospitality in 200 acres of lush lawns, gardens, woods, and meadows beside sparkling Lake Simcoe. 150 year old Regency Manor with adjoining wings, dining rooms, lounges, and cottages. Country-fresh gourmet fare. Championship golf. Internationally known area attractions. One hour from Toronto. AAA recommended.
(*Traditional, Waterside, Resort. Member since 1980*)

EGANRIDGE INN & COUNTRY CLUB

	5 Cotts., $175/$200 Can. B&B; 6 Suites, $160/$175 Can. B&B
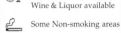	Visa, MC, Amex
	All Private Baths
	Closed Nov.–Apr.
	Children Accepted No Pets – Kennels nearby Private Golf, Tennis, Beach, Boating, Theater, Antiquing, Galleries, Shopping
	Lunch, Dinner, Room Service; MAP Rates available Wine & Liquor available
	Some Non-smoking areas
	Conference Facilities (45)
	Wheelchair Access (4 Rms.)

5 Overlooking a spectacular vista across Sturgeon Lake, in a setting of pine and stone, this inn includes Dunsford House, one of North America's finest preserved examples of 2-story, hand-hewn log home architecture, built in 1837. Challenging golf, award-winning continental cuisine, and the ultimate in luxurious accommodations fulfill guests' highest expectations.
(*Elegant, Georgian, Waterside, Inn. Member since 1991*)

From Toronto, (E) on Hwy. 401 to Exit 436. Hwy. 35. R. on Hwy. 121 to Fenelon Falls. R. on County Rd. 8 for 9 km to inn signs.
TEL. 705-738-5111
RR#3, Fenelon Falls
Ontario, Canada, K0M IN0
John & Patricia Egan,
Innkeepers

SAM JAKES INN

	18 Rooms, $88/$130 B&B 6 Suites, 6 other, $110/$150 B&B
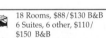	Visa, MC, Amex, EnRoute
	All Private Baths
	Open Year-round
	Children over 10; No Pets Canoeing, Bicycling, Golfing, x-country skiing, Antiqueing, Artist Tours, Historic Walking Tours, Horse & Buggy Rides
	Breakfast, Lunch & Dinner
	No Smoking
	Conference Facilities (60)
	Wheelchair Access (2 rms., dining rm. & conf. fac.)

6 Overlooking the Rideau Canal, this heritage limestone jewel is the highlight of two hundred year old Merrickville. Furnished and decorated in period style, the inn is a reflection of more tranquil days. Its fountainside garden patio, elegant verandahs, fireplace library lounge, sauna and exercise room provide ample opportunities for relaxation. Enjoy our traditional eastern Ontario cuisine while sampling Ontario wines from our award winning selection. Other indulgences include local microbrewery beers and single malt whiskies.
(*Traditional, Village, Inn. Member since 1997*)

Exit #705 off 401 (Maitland/Merrickville exit). Travel 30 km. N. to Merrickville. From Ottawa: Hwy #16 S. to Hwy #43. Travel 23 km. W. to Merrickville.
TEL. 613-269-3711
800-567-4667
FAX 613-269-3713
115 Main St. E Box 580
Merrickville, ONT. K0G1N0
Gary Clarke, Innkeeper

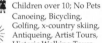

BENMILLER INN

32 Rms, $99/$265 Can. B&B

15 Suites, $179/$265 Can. B&B

Visa, MC, Amex

All Private Baths

Open Year-round

Children Welcome; No Pets

Swimming, Tennis, Golfing, Fishing, Shopping, Beaches, X-Country Skiing, Cycling, Hiking, Theatre, Spa, Museums and Galleries

Breakfast, Lunch & Dinner Wine & Liquor available

Smoking Restrictions; Non-smoking dining area

Conference Facilities (75)

Wheelchair Access (8 rms., dining rm. & conf. fac.)

From Provincial Hwy. 8 between Clinton & Goderich turn onto Huron Rd. #1 (at Benmiller Inn road sign); 3 km. to Benmiller Inn.

TEL. 800-265-1711
519-524-2191
FAX 519-524-5150
RR#4
Goderich, Ontario N7A 3Y1
Randy Stoddart & Kathy Nichol, Inkeepers

7 Housed in four strikingly restored pioneer mills, and mill owners homes. Benmiller Inn offers guests the opportunity to be pampered in a beautiful, historic setting all year round. The gentle waters of Sharpe's Creek flowing through the property and the rush of the nearby Maitland River provide an ambience of pure, unspoiled country. Guestrooms are furnished lovingly with antiques, handmade quilts; many with balconies overlooking the river. The service is excellent. The cuisine outstanding! Ask about our new spa services.
(*Rustic, Country, Inn. Member since 1995*)

THE LITTLE INN OF BAYFIELD

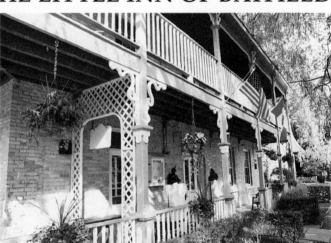

16 Rms, $95/$175 Can. B&B; 12 Sts, $100/$215 Can. B&B; 10% disc. w/theatre festival tickets

Visa, MC, Amex, EnRoute

All Private Baths

Open Year-round

Well behaved Children Welcome

Pets by prior arrangement

Summer & Winter Sports Galore, Antiquing, Heritage Village Walks, Theatre Festivals, Weekend Winetasting Dinners, Cooking Demonstration and Participation Weekends,

Hiking, Cycling and XC Country Trails

All Meals, Afternoon Tea; Sun. Brunch; MAP avail.; Wine & Liquor available Non-smoking dining area

Conference Facilities (60)

Wheelchair access (1 rm., dining rm. & conf. fac.)

From Port Huron, MI. Hwy. 402(E) to Hwy. 21(N) to Bayfield. From Toronto, Hwy. 401(W) to Hwy. 8(W) to Seaforth; follow signs to Bayfield.

TEL 519-565-2611
1-800-565-1832
FAX 519-565-5474
E-mail: littleinn@odyssey.on.ca
Main Street, Bayfield
Ontario, Canada N0M1G0
Patrick & Gayle Waters, Innkeepers

8 A famed landmark since the 1830's, this "perfect getaway" in the picturesque heritage village of Bayfield offers acclaimed regional cuisine and an extensive wine list to make dining a unique experience. Charming and comfortable bedrooms with all modern amenities, many with ensuite whirlpools and fireplaces offer a romantic setting. The four main sitting rooms have fireplaces surrounded by easy chairs and the friendly little bar is a centre for conversation. For health and recreation there is easy access to sandy beaches, golf, tennis, XC ski trails, hiking trails, cycling routes and fly fishing. The Inn is a four season stopover: Stratford and Blyth festivals in the summer, brilliant colours and wine tastings in the fall, traditional village Christmas festivities, winter sports and a marvelous selection of themed events to choose from for spring and winter weekend visits. AAA ◆◆◆◆. Wine Spectator "Award of excellence 96"

(*Colonial, Traditional, Waterside Village, Inn. Member since 1991*)

WESTOVER INN

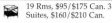	19 Rms, \$95/\$175 Can. 3 Suites, \$160/\$210 Can.
	Visa, MC, Amex, Diners, EnRoute
	All Private Baths
	Open Year-round
	Children Welcome; No Pets
	Pool, Bicycling, Tennis, Golf, X-Country Skiing, Stratford Festival, Hiking, Croquet, Antique Shops, Tube Sliding
	Breakfast, Lunch, & Dinner
	Smoking Restrictions
	Conference Facilities (40)
	Wheelchair access (2 rms., dining rm. & conf. fac.)

9 The Westover Inn began as a limestone Victorian Mansion, built in 1867 by William and Joseph Hutton. Over a century later, the Inn offers 22 charming guest rooms, two unique dining rooms and an outdoor patio serving exceptional regional cuisine. Private function facilities are available for up to 40 people. All of this set amongst 19 acres of beautifully landscaped grounds. Warm and friendly hospitality is meant to leave a lasting impression . . . it does!

(*Traditional, Village, Inn. Member since 1995*)

From Toronto—Hwy. 401 (W) to Kitchener, take Hwy. 7/8 (W), follow signs to Stratford Festival, thru the city on Ontario St. Once thru city, turn L onto Erie St. Erie St. turns into Hwy. 7, turn R on Perth Rd. 28, straight thru St. Marys, turn L on Thomas St.
TEL 519-284-2977
FAX 519-284-4043
Box 280
300 Thomas St.
St. Marys, Ontario N4X 1B1
Julie Docker & Stephen McCotter, Innkeepers

STONE MAIDEN INN

	14 rooms, \$120/\$195 Can. B&B
	Visa, MC
	All Private Baths
	Open mid-April–late Dec.
	Not suitable for young children; No pets
	Antique Shops, Book Shops, Galleries, 3 Theatres within walking distance
	Breakfast (full breakfast buffet)
	No Smoking
	Conference Facilities (20)
	Limited

10 Named after the stone maiden-heads which grace our front hallway, we offer quiet Victorian elegance with superior accommodations and the utmost in personal service. Hand-made quilts, ensuite bathrooms and handsome antiques grace our 14 air-conditioned rooms. Some rooms have canopy beds, fireplaces and whirlpool tubs. Afternoon refreshments and our generous breakfasts are complimentary. Visit Stratford during May to October for our world-renown Shakespearean Festival. Located close to city-centre and our 3 theatres. Call for theatre info. AAA ◆ ◆ ◆ ◆

(*Victorian, In-Town, Breakfast Inn. Member since 1993*)

From Detroit: Hwy. 401 E., Exit 222 N. to Stratford.From Toronto: Hwy 401 to Hwy. 8 W. to Stratford. From Buffalo: Hwy. Q.E.W. to Hwy. 403 at Hamilton; W. to Hwy. 2 at Brantford; Hwy. 403 W. to Hwy. 401 W. to Exit 222; N. to Stratford.
TEL. 519-271-7129
FAX 519-271-4615
123 Church Street
Stratford, Ontario N5A 2R3
Barb & Len Woodward, Owners/Innkeepers

JAKOBSTETTEL GUEST HOUSE INC.

 12 Rooms, $105 to $150 (Can.) B&B

 Visa, MC, Amex

 All Private Baths

 Open Year-round

 School-age Children; No pets

 Outdoor Pool, Tennis court, Horseshoe Pits, Badminton, Volleyball, Bikes & Nature Trails

 Breakfast included; Lunch & Dinner available to groups only with prior arrangement

 No Smoking

Conference Facilities (12)

N/A

From Hwy. 401, exit Hwy. 8 (W) to Kitchener, then Hwy. 86 (N) to Waterloo (stay R), follow 16 km. to lights at Rd. 17, turn L. again into village. Over bridge, then 2nd R onto Albert St. Straight ahead 2 blocks.
TEL. 519-664-2208
Fax 519-664-1326
16 Isabella St.
St. Jacobs, Ontario N0B 2N0
Ella Brubacher, Innkeeper

11 This Victorian Inn has a history as rich as its decor. There are 12 gracious guest rooms. On the 5-treed acres—an outdoor pool, tennis court, bikes, other sports, and a wooded walking trail. Renting the entire house gives groups sole access to the one attractive conference room and generous common areas. Steps away—excellent dining choices, over 80 fabulous specialty shops, maple syrup museum, and Mennonite Meetingplace.
(Victorian, Village, Breakfast Inn. Member since 1995)

ELORA MILL INN

 29 Rooms, $95/$200 Can. B&B; 3 Suites, $170/$200 Can. B&B

 Visa, MC, Amex En Route

 All Private Baths

 Open Year-round

 Children Welcome
No Pets

Golf, Tennis, Squash, Hiking, XC Skiing, Canoeing, Crafts & Antiques Shopping, Mennonite tours, Music & Highland Fest.

 All Meals
MAP Rates available

 Wine & Liquor available
Non-smoking Dining Rm.

Conference Facilities (120)

 Wheelchair Access (dining rm. & conf. fac.)

From Hwy. 401, Exit 295 (N) on Hwy. 6 (Guelph Bypass) for 2 mi. (N) of Guelph. Turn L. on Elora Rd. for 9 mi. to traffic light. Turn R. & follow signs to Elora center.
TEL. 519-846-5356
FAX 519-846-9180
77 Mill St. West
Elora, Ontario, Canada N0B 1S0
Timothy & Kathy Taylor, Innkeepers

12 This converted 19th-century grist mill is perched on the spectacular Grand River Falls in the quaint village of Elora. With heritage guest rooms and a fireside dining room and lounge, the historic country inn serves Canadian specialties with a Continental flair. Guests can enjoy the diversions of Ontario festival country or while away the hours in the inn's out-of-the-way nooks.
(Traditional, Village, Inn. Member since 1991)

THE MILLCROFT INN

	52 Rooms, $149/$225 CDN B&B includes 1 suite
	Visa, MC, Amex, Diners
	All Private Baths
	Open Year-round
	Children Welcome; No Pets
	Outdoor Pool & Hot tub, Sauna, Game Room with Billiards, Ping Pong, Darts
	Breakfast, Lunch, Dinner
	Smoking permitted
	Conference Facilities (5-50)
	Wheelchair Access (1 rm., dining rm. & conf. fac.)

13 Nestled in the Caledon Hills, The Millcroft Inn is only 40 minutes from Toronto. The Millcroft Inn's heritage setting, ambiance, 4 diamond cuisine and gracious service provide the perfect getaway and conference facility. The Inn offers 52 unique guest rooms, some with jacuzzis, fireplaces or hot tubs. The 100 acres of woodlands offer hiking, cross country skiing as well as tennis and an outdoor pool. Golf and downhill skiing are minutes away. *(Rustic, Village, Inn. Member since 1995)*

Hwy. 401 to Hwy. 410 (N). Then at King St. turn L to Hwy. 10. Hwy. 10 (N) to Coledon. At main lights turn L to Hwy. 136. Hwy. 136 turn R to village of Alton. At main stop sign turn L and follow to entrance.
TEL. 519-941-8111
1-800-383-3976 (Ontario only)
FAX 519-941-9192 guests
E-mail: milcft@flexnet.com
55 John St.
Alton, Ontario L0N 1A0
Wolfgang Stichnothe, Innkeeper

KETTLE CREEK INN

	10 Rooms, $90 B&B 5 Suites, $165/$185 B&B
	Visa, MC, Amex, Diners, EnRoute
	All Private Baths
	Open Year-round
	Children welcome; No Pets
	Hiking, Swimming, Golfing, Tennis, x-country Skiing & Snowmobiling nearby
	Breakfast, Lunch & Dinner
	Smoking Restrictions
	Conference Facilities (28)
	Wheelchair access (2 rms. & dining rm.)

14 Nestled in the heart of a small fishing village on Lake Erie, our 1849 inn offers unique accommodation and incredible dining. Cozy parlour with fireplace, intimate pub, three dining rooms.... Outside patio, gazebo, and gardens. Five luxury suites with whirlpools, gas fireplaces in living rooms, and private balconies; ten charming guest rooms. Discover sandy beaches, world class pickerel fishing, sailing and birding. Art galleries, boutiques and summer theatre.... Our tourist train. But don't forget the peace and romance of winter time. *(Traditional, Village, Inn. Member since 1997)*

Traveling E. on Hwy 401 or Hwy 3, exit at Hwy. 20; traveling W. on Hwy. 401 or Hwy. 3, exit at Hwy. 4; proceed S to Port Stanley. Inn located on L. at main intersection at the lights.
TEL. 519-782-3388
FAX 519-782-4747
E-mail: kci@webgate.net
216 Joseph St.
Port Stanley, Ont. N5L1C4
Jean Strickland & Gary Vedova, Innkeepers

ELM HURST INN

43 Rooms, $118 Can. B&B
6 Suites, $140/$165 Can.
B&B

Visa, MC, Amex, Diners,
EnRoute

All Private Baths

Open Year-round

Children and Pets welcome
Game Room, Fitness Room, Gift Shop, Walking Trail, Putting Green, Croquet, Horse Shoes, Badminton, Swimming, Golf, Skating, Volleyball, Live Theatre, Race Track
Breakfast, Lunch, & Dinner

Smoking permitted

Conference Facilities (17)
Wheelchair access (49 rms., dining rm. & conf. fac.)

One hr. W. of Tronto, Ontario and 30 min. E. of London, Ontario on Hwy. 401 at Hwy. 19, exit 218.
TEL. 519-485-5321
800-561-5321
FAX 519-485-6579
E-mail: elmhurst@oxford.net
Hwy. 19 & 401/P.O. Box 123
Ingersoll, Ont. N5O3K1

Pat Davies, Innkeeper

 Our Country Inn is nestled amongst the century old Maple trees. Our spacious guest rooms are uniquely decorated with picturesque views and some have a fireplace or a Jacuzzi. The Elm Hurst Inn also offers dining in its famous Victorian Mansion and is an ideal setting for any occasion. We are perfectly situated for great shopping, sightseeing and tourist attractions. We have an on-site putting green, skating rink, interpretive trail, woodlands, a flowing creek and a picturesque pond on our 37 acres of land.

LANGDON HALL COUNTRY HOUSE HOTEL

38 Rooms, $175/$210 Can. B&B
3 Suites, $195/$290 Can. B&B

Visa, MC, Amex, DC
All Private Baths

Open Year-round

Extra charge for Children & Pets
Tennis, Outdoor Pool, Basketball 1/2 Court, X-Country Skiing, Hiking Trails, Steamrooms, Sauna, Whirlpool, Exercise Rooms, Spa
Breakfast, Lunch, Dinner

Smoking Restrictions

Conference Facilities available
Wheelchair access (6 rms., dining rm. & conf. fac.)

Travelling (E) from London or (W) from Toronto take Hwy. 401 to Exit # 275 Fountain St/Homer Watson Blvd. Travel (S) on Fountain St. to Blair Rd., which will be 2nd St. on R. Follow the road thru the village of Blair. Langdon Drive is 4th street on the R. Langdon Hall is 1st driveway on L.
TEL. 519-740-2100
1-800-268-1898
FAX: 519-740-8161
E-mail: Langdon@golden.net
R.R. 33
Cambridge, Ontario N3H 4R8
Mary Beaton, William Bennett, Innkps.

Nestled among 200 acres of gardens and woodlands is a peaceful Country House Hotel with an atmosphere unchanged since it was first built in 1898. Each room has its own charm and most feature a sitting area with a fireplace. Please your palate with unique tastes of regional seasonal cuisine and an excellent selection of wines in the casual comfort of Wilks Bar or the elegant Garden Dining Room. Amenities include; outdoor pool, croquet, tennis court, sauna, whirlpool, exercise room, expansive trails for walking or cross-country skiing, and The Spa where a full selection of treatments is available for your indulgence. (*Elegant, Federal Revival, Country, Inn. Member since 1995*)

CANADA — ONTARIO

WOODLAWN TERRACE INN

	14 Rooms, \$92/\$165 Can. B&B 2 Suites, \$165 Can. B&B Visa, MC, Amex
	All Private Baths
	Open year-round except closed Dec. 25-26 for Xmas
	Children Welcome; No Pets
	Private garden courtyard, Inn is located close to beach, Marina, Golf course, Theatre, Antique Shops, etc.
	Full, Hot Breakfast available for guest only. Lunch & Dinner
	Smoking restrictions
	Conference Facilities (40) Wheelchair Access (2 rms., dining rm. & conf. fac.)

17 The Woodlawn offers its guests the best in contemporary dining and lodging comforts without forgetting its place in the past. Located in the heart of historic Cobourg, the Inn was built in 1835 by United Empire Loyalist Ebenezer Perry. Today, this restored residence features 14 elegant guest rooms, an internationally recognized dining room, and an intimate bar featuring the finest in wines and spirits all located close to Cobourg's renowned harbour, farmers' market and unique shops.

(Elegant, Town, Inn. Member since 1995)

1 hr. by car. (E) of Toronto. From Hwy 401, take Exit 474, go (S) on Division St. The Woodlawn is situated on the left-hand side of Division, just before the 3rd set of Lights.
TEL. 905-372-2235
1-800-573-5003
FAX 905-372-4673
E-mail: woodlawn@eagle.ca
420 Division St.
Cobourg, Ontario K9A 3R9
Gerda & Domenico Della-Casa, Innkeepers

STE. ANNE'S COUNTRY INN & SPA

	7 Rooms, 3 Suites, 2 Cottages, \$175/\$205 (Can.) AP, includes \$50 credit in the Spa Visa, MC, Amex, Enroute
	All Private Baths
	Open Year-round
	Not suitable for Children No Pets
	Tennis, Swimming Pool, Hot Tub, Walking Trails, Victoria Hall, The Northumberland Players, Antique Hunting, Full Spa
	Breakfast, Lunch & Dinner available for guests; BYOB
	No Smoking Throughout
	Conference Facilities (10)
	N/A

18 Rest, relax, rejuvenate…savor the sweet smell of fresh country air, drink pure spring water, enjoy a candle lit dinner. Pamper yourself with a massage, or maybe a facial. All this can be found in this English style "Castle" nestled on 560 acres in the hills of Northumberland County, one hour from Toronto. Exclusive spa packages mix the finest elements of a country inn ambiance with pampering and/or invigorating treatments to ensure the ultimate in relaxation and rest. Come for the day by train on the "Stress Express" from Toronto or Kingston.

(Traditional, Country, Inn. Member since 1992)

Hwy. 401 to Grafton. Exit @ 487. N towards Centreton on Aird St. for 1.5 km, to Academy Hill Rd. 1.5 km, L. to stone wall.
TEL. 905-349-2493
800-263-2663
FAX 905-349-3531
Massey Road, R.R. 1
Grafton, Ontario, Canada K0K 2G0
Jim Corcoran, Innkeeper

ROSEMOUNT INN

 8 rooms, $89/$159 Can. B&B

 Visa, MC, Amex

 All Private Baths

 Open mid-Jan.–mid-Dec.

 Suitable for children over 12; No pets

 Historic Tours, Art Galleries, Museums, Antiquing, Farmers' Market, 1000 Island Cruises, Sailing, Cycling, Boutique Shopping, Fine Dining

 Full Gourmet Breakfast

 No smoking

 Conference Facilities (16)

 N/A

U.S. Rte. 81 to 1000 Isl. Br. (W) on 1000 Isl. Pkwy. to Hwy. 2 to downtown Kingston. (R) on Brock St. 4 blocks (L) on Sydenhan. CAN: Hwy. 401—(S) at Exit 615—5 km (L) on Johnson 2 km. (R) on Sydenham.

TEL. 613-531-8844
FAX. 613-531-9722
46 Sydenham St. South
Kingston, Ontario K7L 3H1

Holly & John Edwards, Innkeepers

19 Step through the old iron gates into the quiet charm of an 1850 limestone Tuscany Villa in the heart of historic Kingston. Let us pamper you . . . your room is exquisitely appointed with Victorian antiques, fine linens and down duvets. In the morning, be awakened by the aroma of breakfast—waiting for you in the dining room—perhaps John's "Welsh Toast" with a brandied berry sauce and local maple syrup! In the afternoon— "Tea in the Parlor"! A short stroll will take you to historic sites, fine dining, specialty shops, Queen's University and the waterfront. (*Traditional, Victorian, In-Town, Breakfast Inn. Member since 1993*)

TRINITY HOUSE INN

 6 Rooms, $75/$150 Can., B&B
2 Suites, $135/$190 Can., B&B

 Visa, MC

 All Private Baths

 Open Apr.–Dec.

 One Suite suitable for young children; No Pets, Kennels Nearby

 Scenic Boat Tours, Boldt Castle, Live Theatre, Cycling, Antiquing, Historic Sites, National Parks, Spa Services, Fishing, Boat & Cycle Rentals

 Breakfast (guests) Dinner, Fully Licensed, Wine & Liquor

Smoking on Outdoor Terraces

Conference Facilities (12-16)

Wheelchair Access Partial

Hwy. 401 to Gananoque (East of Kingston) Exit 645, (S) on Hwy. 32 (Stone St) past first traffic light at King St.

TEL. 613-382-8383
(800) 265-4871 (Ontario)
FAX. 613-382-1599
90 Stone Street South
Gananoque, Ontario K7G 1Z8

Jacques O'Shea & Brad Garside, Innkeepers

20 In the heart of the famous 1000 Islands, Trinity House Inn (1859) offers award winning hospitality, superior accommodations and dining excellence, complimented with an atmosphere of casual elegance. Renowned for exceptional service and detail the Inn has been completely restored adding fine antiques, artwork and manicured Victorian waterfall gardens. Relax in our sofa lounge and sun terrace, enjoy fireside candlelit dinners or set sail aboard our 30 foot sailing yacht, 'The Lady Trinity' and savour the scenery!
(*Traditional, Victorian, In-Town, Inn. New Member since 1995*)

HOSTING YOUR SMALL GROUP

Meeting planners responsible for arranging and hosting small meetings and conferences have found that many country inns offer a new and exciting opportunity. The traditional impersonal and somewhat sterile atmosphere of many larger Conference Centers has forced the astute planner to turn to the many pleasantries found at country inns. Usually, the size of the facility ensures privacy and personal hospitality. Many larger Conference Centers must book several groups at a time to efficiently utilize their facility. Small group meetings, on the other hand, are frequently the only guests enjoying the comfortable, nicely appointed ambiance of a country inn facility.

State of the art audio-visual and facsimile equipment is now commonplace in meeting rooms at Independent Innkeepers' Association inns. The only thing missing is the often exorbitant surcharge assessed for this equipment by larger establishments. Innkeepers happily work with meeting planners to arrange local entertainment and visits to special area attractions as well as fitness and exercising opportunities for their conferee-guests. A small group meeting and personalized hospitality are a natural combination at country inns.

Food service for small group meetings is another natural for innkeepers and their chefs. The usual non-commercial orientation of inn kitchens ensures specialized menus and many "from scratch" dishes to please the appetites of business people after a full schedule of meetings. Innkeepers often tell of conferees who make arrangements to return to the inn with friends for a non-meeting visit because they wanted to share their special gastronomic discoveries.

This *1997 Innkeepers' Register* includes information about the conference facilities available at each inn. A phone call to the inn can quickly provide answers to your specific questions and access to brochures and conference information packets. As astute meeting planners have found, personal contact with an Independent Innkeepers' Association innkeeper can take the work and worry out of planning meetings.

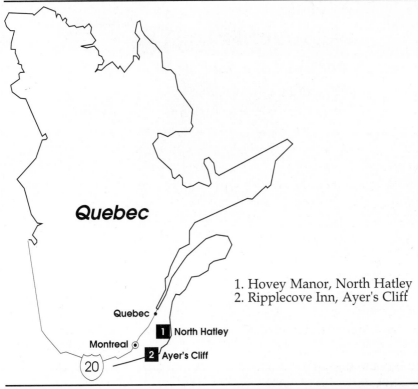

Quebec

Quebec •

Montreal ⊙

20

1 North Hatley

2 Ayer's Cliff

1. Hovey Manor, North Hatley
2. Ripplecove Inn, Ayer's Cliff

RIPPLECOVE INN

21 Rooms, $92/$155 Can.
MAP PP
5 Suites, $135/$200 Can.
MAP PP
Visa, MC, Amex

All Private Baths

Open Year-round

Not suitable for children under 5 yrs; No pets

Sailing, Beach, Boating, Heated Pool, X-Country Skiing, Skating, Ice Fishing-all on site, Golf, Alpine Skiing, Theatre, Horseback riding nearby, Breakfast, Lunch, Dinner

Smoking Restrictions

Conference Facilities (40)

N/A

From USA-I-91 (N) to Canadian border, then Rte. 55 (N) to Exit 21, turn R then follow Rte, 141 (E) for 3 mi. to Inn entrance.
TEL. 819-838-4296
RES. 800-668-4296

FAX 819-838-5541

700 Ripplecove Rd.
Ayer's Cliff, Que. J0B 1C0
Canada

Debra & Jeffrey Stafford, Innkeepers

1 Since 1945, Ripplecove Inn has been chosen by sophisticated travellers from around the world to get away from it all in an atmosphere of privacy, unsurpassed service and unending luxury. The Inn resides on a secluded 12 acre lakeside peninsula alive with English gardens, and century old pines. Choose from 26 designer decorated rooms and suites; many with fireplace, TV, lakeview, balcony and double whirlpool. Enjoy "Four Diamond Award" French cuisine with sterling service, an extensive selection of wines and the romantic ambience of our Victorian dining room and "Nag's Head" Pub. The perfect stop on route to Quebec or Montreal.
(Elegant, Victorian, Lakeside, Resort. Member since 1995)

HOVEY MANOR

	37 Rooms, $75/$150 US MAP PP (gratuities included)
	3 Suites, $75/$150 US MAP PP (gratuities included)
	Visa, MC, Amex, Diners, EnRoute
	All Private Baths, 14 Whirpools; 24 Fireplaces, 21 balconies
	Open Year-round
	Young Children and Babies Discouraged; No Pets
R	On site: Beaches, All Water Sports, Heated pool, Tennis, Touring Bikes, XC-Ski Trails, Skating Rink, Ice-Fishing, Massage Room, Games Room, and Exercise Room, nearby: Alpine Skiing, Golf, Riding, Summer Theatre.
	Breakfast, Lunch, Dinner Wine & Liquor available
	Smoking restrictions; Many non-smoking rooms
	Conference Facilities (2 rms.)
	Wheelchair Access (2 rms)

2 Formerly a private estate modeled on Mt. Vernon, this gracious manor is nestled on 1700 feet of prime lakeshore amongst spectacular English gardens. Most of the lakeside rooms offer combinations of fireplaces, whirlpool baths, canopy beds and private balconies. Acclaimed French cuisine and wine cellar (Quebec "Table de Prestige") and a full range of on site, year round recreational facilities included in our rates make this romantic inn a destination in itself. We're only 20 minutes from Vermont convenient to Montreal and Quebec City. AAA ◆◆◆◆. Canada Select ★★★★★. (*Elegant, Lakeside, Resort. Member since 1973*)

VT. I-91 (N) to border. Continue on Rte. 55N for 29 kms. to No. Hatley Exit 29 & Rte. 108 (E) for 9 kms. to No. Hatley & Hovey Manor signs.
TEL. 819-842-2421
Res. 1-800-661-2421
FAX 819-842-2248
E-mail: stafford@multimedias.ca
North Hatley, Quebec,
Canada
JOB 2CO
Steve & Kathy Stafford, Innkeepers

Hospitality

In the late '40's and early '50's as people began to explore the world of hotels and motels, the desire for sequestered namelessness and guaranteed decor during a night away from home was customary. Travelers were comforted by the assurance of not having to deal with an untested, off-brand accommodation. Certainly the last thing that concerned the traveler was the hospitality of the hotel/motel owner. For a quarter century chain hotels and motels reigned supreme. They were new, standardized, plentiful, and everyone was happy.

The needs and desires of the traveling public in the last twenty-five years, however, accompanied by the natural growth and development of the accommodations industry as a whole, have brought about a new emphasis in overnight accommodations. The '80's and 90's have brought a hue and cry for Hospitality from the now-experienced traveler, and he has discovered that this ingredient is the essence of the *Country Inn*.

Today's traveler, arriving in his late-model luxury sedan at a present day accommodation for an overnight or weekend, is looking *for an actual person whose purpose in life is to receive and entertain friends or strangers with kindness and generosity*. He wants first and foremost an *experience of Hospitality* in a quality establishment. Listen to what travelers in America brag about after their trips today. The hospitality of the innkeeper and the quality of the accommodation will always be mentioned first.

As the overnight accommodations industry has developed, *Country Inns and Hospitality*, through a natural process, have become good bedfellows: exactly what today's overnight traveler is looking for.

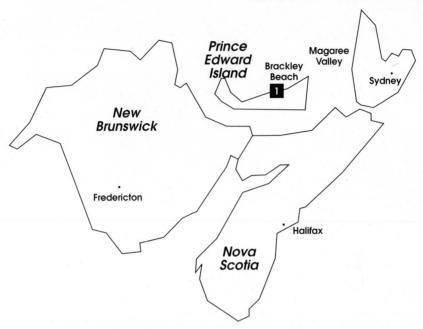

Prince Edward Island

Brackley Beach

Magaree Valley

Sydney

New Brunswick

Fredericton

Halifax

Nova Scotia

1. Shaw's Hotel, Brackley Beach

SHAW'S HOTEL

17 Rms. (6 Suites), $75/$110 PP Can. MAP;
19 Cott., $80/$130 PP Can. MAP
Visa, MC, Amex, Diners
All Private Baths
2 Jacuzzis
Open May 25–Oct. 1
Cottages open year-round
Children Welcome
Pets in Cottages only
Sailing, Canoeing, Walking Paths, Golf, Ocean Swimming, Tennis, Childrens Program
Breakfast, Dinner
Wine & Liquor available
Smoking restrictions

Conference facilities (60)
Wheelchair Access (1 rm., dining rm.)

Take ferry or plane to P.E.I. Trans Canada Hwy. (Rte.1) to Charlotte-town. Follow signs to airport and Rte. 15 for 10 mi. to Brackley Beach.
TEL. 902-672-2022
FAX 902-672-3000
Brackley Beach
Prince Edward Island,
Canada C1E 1Z3
Robbie and Pam Shaw, Innkps.

1 We are the oldest family operated Inn in Canada. The Shaw's family continues the tradition which began in 1860. Shaw's Hotel is located on a 75 acre pennisula overlooking glistening Brackley Bay. It provides an ideal setting for its 17 antique furnished rooms and suites plus its 18 charming cottages ranging in size from 1 to 4 bedrooms. Our 7 deluxe chalets featuring sauna & whirlpools are open yearly. Shaw's Hotel provides superb meals in their rates. We provide many recreational activities and are located 600 yards from Brackley Beach. (*Traditional, Ocean Side, Resort. Member since 1975*)

Great Britain

1. Philipburn House Hotel, Selkirk,
   Scottish Borders, Scotland
2. The Mill Hotel, Penrith,
   Cumbria, England
3. Cottage in the Wood, Worcester,
   Worcestershire, England
4. Petty France Hotel, Badminton,
   Avon, England
5. Royal Oak Hotel, Withypool,
   Somerset, England
6. The Crown Hotel, Exford,
   Somerset, England
7. Woolley Grange Hotel, Woolley Green,
   Wiltshire, England
8. Somerset House, Bath,
   Avon, England
9. Kennel Holt Hotel, Cranbrook,
   Kent, England
10. Maison Talbooth, Colchester, Essex
    Le Talbooth Restaurant
    Essex, England

 Members of the Independent Innkeepers' Association

The Shining Light in Hospitality

SCOTLAND

PHILIPBURN HOUSE HOTEL

 4 Rooms, £77/£90 B&B
12 Suites, £77/£99 B&B

 Visa, MC

 All Private Baths

 Open Year-round

 Children Welcome
Pets by arrangement

 Outdoor heated pool, Badminton Court, Table tennis, Games machines, Children's play area

Breakfast, Lunch, Dinner
Wine & Liquor Available

Smoking Restricted
Conference Facilities
small

Wheelchair Access (1 rm., dining rm. & conf. fac.)

SCOTLAND
45 min. from Edinburgh; less than 90 from Glasgow. If driving South A1 & M6

TEL. 0750 20747
FAX 0750 21690
Selkirk
Scottish Borders TD7 5LS
Scotland

Jim Hill & Family

1 Philipburn, built in 1751, lies within beautifully tranquil lawns and flowers. The Hill Family fell in love with Philipburn twenty one years ago, and have since sensitively fashioned Philipburn into the Border's most sought after place to stay. Charming country house bedrooms, mellow pine, flowers and chintz flow into the restaurants overlooking the gardens and pool where after a preprandial drink in the bar you can dine on the finest Border beef, fish and game.

ENGLAND

THE MILL HOTEL

 8 Rooms, £45/£65 MAP PP*
1 Suite, £50/£70 MAP PP*

 None

 7 Private Baths

 Open 1st Mar.–1st Nov.

 Children and Dogs
Welcome

 Lake District National Park, Hiking, Fishing, Horseback Riding, Golf, Canoeing, Birding, Historic Sights, Bicycling

 Breakfast, Packed Lunch & Dinner; Wine & Liquor Available

No smoking in restaurant

 N/A

NORTH COUNTRY
Exit 40 on M6. A66 8 miles toward Keswick. Take sign right to Mungrisdale Village. Hotel next door to Inn.

TEL. 01768 779659
FAX 017 687 79155
Mungrisdale, Penrith
Cumbria CA11 OXR

Richard & Eleanor Quinlan

2 At the foot of the Skiddaw Range in the Lake District is a charming white house by a stream. Here Richard & Eleanor Quinlan have established an excellent reputation for individual hospitality. Homemade bread and a mouth-watering range of puddings are featured alongside main courses which include vegetarian dishes as well as game, beef and lamb. Most people return again and again. The cluster of farms and the church nearby with the great fells towering around never cease to appeal. (*Traditional, Mountain, Hotel*)

THE COTTAGE IN THE WOOD ENGLAND

20 Rooms, £89/£135 B&B
(English) Bargain Breaks
Available; 2 Nights Min.

Visa, MC, Amex, Access,
Barclay Card

All Private Baths; 17 also
with Shower

Open Year-round

Children & pets accepted

Walking on 9-mile Malvern Hill Range. 18-hole
golf, 1 mi. Squash, 1/2 mi.
Clay pigeon shooting can
be arranged.

Breakfast, Lunch, Dinner
Wine & Liquor available

No smoking in restaurant

Conference Facilities (14)

N/A

3   A family owned and run hotel, famed for both its magnificent position high on the Malvern Hills, commanding a 30-mile view to the Cotswold Hills, and for its cuisine for which an AA red rosette has been awarded. Small Charming Hotel Guide also awarded a coveted Cèsar in 1992. The London Daily Mail entitled the view "the best view in England." An ideal touring base for the Cotswolds, Stratford upon Avon, Wye Valley, and the cathedral cities of Worcester, Gloucester, and Hereford. A.A. Courtesy and Care Award 1996.

CENTRAL

3 miles south of Great Malvern off A449 turning opposite Gulf/Rover Gas Station. Signposted from main road.
TEL. 01684 575859
FAX 01684 560662
Holywell Road, Malvern Wells, **Worcester WR14 4LG**

John and Sue Pattin, Proprietor

PETTY FRANCE HOTEL ENGLAND

20 Rooms, $90/$190 B&B

Visa, MC, Amex, DC

All Private Baths

Open Year-round

Children Welcome; Pets
in Stable Rooms

Croquet, Walking,
Riding, Golf, Biking

Breakfast, Lunch, Dinner
Wine & Liquor available

No Smoking

Conference Facilities (25)

Wheelchair Access (4 rms.,
dining rm. & conf. fac.)

4   Petty France Hotel is a small Georgian and Regency house set in extensive private gardens located at the edge of the Cotswolds and run by the owners in an informal manner. Modern French and English food is served in the light and airy Regency dining room. A large lounge and small cosy bar both with fireplaces offer guests a place to meet and relax. Twelve rooms which are built in the old stables offer unusual charm.

SOUTH/SOUTHWEST

5 mi N of M4 (Exit 18) on A46
TEL. 01454 238361
FAX 01454 238768
E=mail:
hote@pettyfrance.telme.com
Dunkirk, Badminton
**South Gloucestershire,
GL91AF**
Bill Fraser

ENGLAND

THE ROYAL OAK INN

 8 Rooms, £76 / £84 B&B; £58 MAP 1 Person

 Visa, MC, Amex, DC

 All Private Baths

 Open Year-round

 Children over 10; Pets Welcome

 Riding, Fox Hunting, Shooting, Fishing, Walking

Breakfast, Lunch, Dinner Wine & Liquor available

Smoking permitted

Wheelchair access (dining room)

WEST COUNTRY

From M5 Motorway turn off at Junction 27 and take A361 at sign for North Molton turn right go through North Molton then onto Withypool

TEL. 0164 3831506
FAX 0164 3831659
E-mail:
bradleyhotelsexmoor@easynet.co.uk
Withypool, Somerset TA247QP

5 The Royal Oak is a 17th century village inn with beamed ceilings and open log fires. The bedrooms which have private bathrooms are all individually furnished and decorated. Our chef Jill produces food with imagination and flair and has gained many awards. The village of Withypool with the River Barle running through it is steeped in Norman history. (*17 Century, Country, Village, Old Inn*)

ENGLAND

THE CROWN HOTEL

 17 Rooms, £80 / £114 B&B

 Visa, MC, Access, Amex

 All Private Baths

Open Year-round

 Children Welcome; Dogs Welcome but not in Publc Areas

 Riding, Fishing, Shooting, Walking, Fox Hunting, Stag Hunting

 Breakfast, Lunch & Dinner; Wine & Liquor available

 Smoking permitted

 Wheelchair access (dining room)

WEST COUNTRY

From M5 Motorway turn off at Junction 27 and take A361 at First Island take A396 to Wheddon Cross. Turn left at Wheddon Cross onto the B3224 for Exford.

TEL. 0164 3831554
FAX 0164 3831665
E-mail:
bradleyhotelsexmoor@easynet.co.uk
Exford, Somerset, TA247QP
Michael Bradley & John Atkin

6 The Crown is a 17th century Coaching Inn which has 20th century comforts. Elegant cosy log fired lounge and spacious relaxing dining room where our Chef Andrew serves superlative food using fresh produce mainly from the region. The bedrooms are all en Suite and furnished to a very high standard and provide comfort and warmth. To top it all the hotel is situated in the middle of the beautiful Exmoor National Park in Somerset. (*Coaching, Village*)

WOOLLEY GRANGE HOTEL

	19 Rooms, $150/$250 B&B
	3 Suites, $200/$300 B&B Visa, MC, JCB
	All Private Baths
	Open Year-round
	Children and Dogs
	Grass Tennis Courts, Croquet, Badminton, Heated Open Air Pool, Children's Playground
	All meals daily, variety of options offered for lunch & dinner
	Wine & Liquor available Smoking except in dining room
	Conference Facilities (22)
	Wheelchair Access (1 rm. & dining rm.)

7 The home of the Baskerville family for two centuries, Woolley Grange is a stone manor house built in 1610 on the rural fringe of the Saxon Hillside Wool town of Bradford-on-Avon. The hotel is renowned for the warmth of our welcome, the stylish but relaxed atmosphere, the quality of our food, much of which we grow or comes from local farms, and our genuine welcome for families. We offer the Woolley Bears Den, a staffed nursery from 10AM to 6PM every day. (*Traditional, Country, Inn*)

WEST COUNTRY

Eight miles from Bath on B3109, 1/2 mile NE of the town of Bradford-on-Avon.

TEL. 01225 864705
FAX 01225 864059
1-800-848-7721
E-Mail:
woolley@cityscape.com.uk
Woolley Green, Wiltshire
BA15 1TX England
Nigel & Heather Chapman

SOMERSET HOUSE

	10 Rooms, $64/$77 MAP, PP
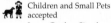	Visa, MC, Amex
	All Private Baths
	Open Year-round
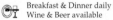	Children and Small Pets accepted
	Large Garden, Simple games for children indoors, Piano, Library
	Breakfast & Dinner daily Wine & Beer available
	No Smoking
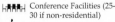	Conference Facilities (25-30 if non-residential)
	N/A

8 Somerset House is an elegant Georgian town house from which guests may enjoy views across the city of Bath as well as walks into the adjacent National Trust fields. The city centre (Abbey and Roman Baths) is only twelve minutes walk away (3/4 of a mile). To convey the emphasis we place on the food, we describe Somerset House as a restaurant with rooms. We want our guests to enjoy the freshness of the best of local produce. (*Traditional, Georgian, In-Town, Inn*)

WEST COUNTRY

Off A36 (Pulteney Rd.) at St. Mary-the-Virgin-Church. Follow signposts: for university and American Museum.

TEL. 01225 466451
FAX 01225 317188
35 Bathwick Hill,
Bath BA2 6LD
Jean, Malcolm & Jonathan Seymour

KENNEL HOLT HOTEL

 10 Rooms, £125 B&B

 Visa, MC, Amex, JCB

 All Private Baths

 Open year-round

 Children Welcome; No Pets

 Sissinghurst & many other gardens & Historic Houses, Horseback riding, Game Shooting, Good Train Service (1 hr.) from London Shopping

 Breakfast, Lunch (24 hr. notice), Dinner Tues.-Sat.; Sun. Residents only Smoking Restrictions

Conference facilities (12)

Wheelchair Access (1 Rm., dining rm. & conf. fac.)

SOUTH/SOUTHEASTERN

From M25, take junction 5-A21 (S) to Hastings, then take A262 to Goudhurst, Kennel Holt is 3 mi. from Goudhurst on A262 & 1 mi. before the A229/A262 crossroads at Cranbrook.

TEL. 01580 712032
FAX 01580 715495
Goudhurst Road,
Cranbrook Kent TN17 2PT
Sally & Neil Chalmers

9 The Weald of Kent is gardening—Sissinghurst Knole, Great Dixter, Chartwell. Neil & Sally Chalmers have made Kennel Holt the hotel to base yourselves in for a visit to this delightful area. 5 acres of gardens, individually furnished bedrooms, log fires, a panelled library, antique furniture and books. Relaxing made easy. A restaurant that specializes in fresh local ingredients and a lengthy wine list complete the arrangements for your comfort. (*Historic, Country, Inn*)

MAISON TALBOOTH & LE TALBOOTH RESTAURANT

 10 Rooms, £105/£140 B&B

 Visa, MC, Amex, Access

 All Private Baths

 Open Year-round

 Children Welcome No Pets

 Constable Country, Sailing & Golf by Arrangement

 Breakfast, Lunch, Dinner Wine & Liquor Available

 Smoking Permitted

Conference Facility (24)

 Wheelchair Access (dining rm.)

CENTRAL/EASTERN

A12 (N) of Colchester, 1st running of to Stratford St Mary Dedham, turn R on Sharp bend; Hotel 400 yards down Rd.

TEL. 01206 322367
FAX 01206 322752
Dedham
Colchester, Essex C07 6HN
England
Gerald, Diana & Paul Milsom

10 John Constable country, with this unique combination of a hotel and restaurant 10 minutes walk apart. Gerald Milsom started this business nearly 40 years ago and has achieved fame with Pride of Britain Hotels, which he started. Maison Talbooth is elegant with luxurious bedrooms, some quite glamorous. Le Talbooth is very attractive with Tudor white and black half-timbers overlooking the garden and river Stour, with an appropriate high standard of food. (*Elegant, Country, Inn*)

ENJOY EUROPE IN THE MOST INDIVIDUAL WAYS

ROMANTIK HOTELS & RESTAURANTS

INTERNATIONAL

Just like the independent and lovely hotels represented in this guide, Romantik Hotels & Restaurants International are a collection of unique individual experiences!

181 Romantik Hotels in 17 countries (including the US, Canada and The Carribean) have distinct characteristics:

- All our hotels are historic (in Europe they must be at least 100 years old, some go back to the year 1100!) - They are privately owned and managed by their owners who provide gracious and personal

service in the European tradition

- Excellent cuisine is a trademark. Many have Michelin stars or are renowned regionally for first-class dining.

We are waiting to welcome you and give you a wonderful experience of old world hospitality with today´s comforts.

For a FREE copy of our Romantik Guide´97 please write or call the Independent Innkeepers' Association.

SCOTLAND'S LEADING GROUP OF QUALITY INDEPENDENTLY OWNED HOTELS INCLUDING CASTLES, MANSION HOUSES AND FINE COUNTRY HOTELS, ALL LOCATED AMIDST SCOTLAND'S FINEST SCENERY AND CLOSE TO ALL OUR MAJOR TOURIST ATTRACTIONS AND PLACES OF INTEREST.

EACH HOTEL OFFERS THE HIGHEST STANDARD OF ACCOMMODATION, FOOD AND SERVICE COMBINED WITH ITS OWN HISTORIC OR ARCHITECTURAL INTEREST.

THE ELEGANT AND UNSPOILT INTERIORS AND SUPERB LOCATIONS OF OUR HOTELS WILL PROVIDE A TRUE TASTE OF SCOTLAND TO THE INTERNATIONAL VISITOR. SAVOUR REAL SCOTTISH CUISINE IN OUR RESTAURANTS, MANY OF THEM AWARD WINNING, AND RELAX IN THE WARM, FRIENDLY ATMOSPHERE THAT MAKES SCOTLAND'S HERITAGE HOTELS TRULY SPECIAL.

FOR OUR FREE COLOUR BROCHURE AND TARIFF PLEASE WRITE, FAX OR TELEPHONE, THE INDEPENDENT INNKEEPERS' ASSOCIATION OR OUR CENTRAL RESERVATIONS OFFICE.

CROMLIX HOUSE, PERTHSHIRE

KILDRUMMY CASTLE HOTEL, NR BALMORAL

CULLODEN HOUSE, INVERNESS

SCOTLAND'S HERITAGE HOTELS

INDEPENDENT INNKEEPERS' ASSOCIATION
PO BOX 150, MARSHALL, MI 49068.
TEL: 1-800-344-5244/1-616-789-0393
FAX: 1-616-789-0970

CENTRAL RESERVATIONS OFFICE
SUITE 2D, CHURCHILL WAY,
BISHOPBRIGGS, GLASGOW G64 2RH, SCOTLAND.
TEL: +44 141 772 6911 FAX: +44 141 772 6917

Index

The dot indicates those inns that may be booked through your travel agent. Your travel agent should contact the inn directly for specific commission rates and restrictions.

UNITED STATES

- 1661 Inn, Block Island, RI 147
  1740 House, Lumberville, PA 140
- 1842 Inn, Macon, GA 41
- Abriendo Inn, Pueblo, CO 32
- Adair, Bethlehem, NH 86
- Adams Edgeworth Inn, Monteagle, TN 150
- Adams Hilborne, The Chattanooga, TN 151
- Alexander Withrow House/McCampbell Inn, Lexington, VA 166
- Allaire Timbers Inn, Breckenridge, CO 31
- Antietam Overlook Farm, Keedysville, MD 59
- Antrim 1844, Taneytown, MD 61
- Asa Ransom House, Clarence, NY 103
  Ashby Inn & Restaurant, The, Paris, VA 173
- Babbling Brook, The, Santa Cruz, CA 23
- Bailiwick Inn, The, Fairfax, VA 173
- Ballard Inn, The, Ballard, CA 26
- Barley Sheaf Farm, Holicong, PA 141
- Barrows House, Dorset, VT 161
- Bear Creek Lodge, Victor, MT 84
- Beaumont Inn, Harrodsburg, KY 45
- Beckmann Inn & Carriage House, San Antonio, TX 152
- Bee and Thistle Inn, Old Lyme, CT 35
  Beekman Arms, Rhinebeck, NY 112
- Belle Grae Inn, The, Staunton, VA 169
- Benn Conger Inn, Groton, NY 105
- Birchfield Manor, Yakima, WA 181
- Bird and Bottle Inn, The, Garrison, NY 112
- Black Point Inn, Prouts Neck, ME 56
- Blue Hill Inn, The, Blue Hill, ME 50
- Blueberry Hill, Goshen, VT 158
- Boone's Lick Trail Inn, St. Charles, MO 83
- Boulders Inn, New Preston, CT 34
- Bramble Inn & Restaurant, The, Brewster, MA 70
  Cameron Estate Inn, Mount Joy, PA 142
- Campbell House, The, Eugene, OR 129
- Canoe Bay, Chetek, WI 186
- Canyon Villa Inn, Sedona, CA 15
- Captain Lord Mansion, Kennebunkport, ME 57
- Captain Whidbey Inn, The, Coupeville, WA 178
- Captain's House Inn, The, Chatham/Cape Cod, MA 71
- Carnegie House, State College, PA 135
- Carter House/Hotel Carter, Eureka, CA 18
- Castle Marne - A Luxury Urban Inn, Denver, CO 30
- Chalet Suzanne, Lake Wales, FL 37
- Channel House Inn, Depoe Bay, OR 128
- Charles Hinckley House, Barnstable, MA 70
- Checkerberry Inn, The, Goshen, IN 43
- Chesterfield Inn, West Chesterfield, NH 92
- Chestnut Inn at Oquaga Lake, Deposit, NY 107
- Christmas Farm Inn, Jackson, NH 87

Claremont Hotel and Cottages, Southwest Harbor, ME 51
- Cliff Park Inn & Golf Course, Milford, PA 138
- Cliffside Inn, Newport, RI 146
- Clifton - The Country Inn, Charlottesville, VA 175
- Colby Hill Inn, Henniker, NH 91
- Conover's Bay Head Inn, Bay Head, NJ 96
- Corner House Inn, Center Sandwich, NH 89
- Country Club Inn, Rangeley, ME 48
- Creamery Restaurant & Inn, The, Downsville, WI 187
- Crestmont Inn, Eagles Mere, PA 136
  Crocker House Country Inn, Hancock, ME 51
- Dan'l Webster Inn, The, Sandwich, MA 69
- Darby Field Inn, The, Conway, NH 88
- Deerfield Inn, Deerfield, MA 66
- Dexter's Inn & Tennis Club, Sunapee, NH 90
- Dockside Guest Quarters, York, ME 58
- Duff Green Mansion, The, Vicksburg, MS 79
- Dusty's English Inn, Eaton Rapids, MI 75
- Eagles Mere Inn, Eagles Mere, PA 136
- Fairview Inn, Jackson, MS 80
  Fairville Inn, Mendenhall, PA 143
- Father Ryan House Inn, Biloxi, MS 81
- Fearrington House, The, Pittsboro, NC 120
- Fort Lewis Lodge, Millboro, VA 168
- Frederick House, Staunton, VA 170
- French Manor, The, Sterling, PA 138
- Garnet Hill Lodge, North River, NY 109
- Gastonian, The, Savannah, GA 41
  Gateway Lodge, Cooksburg, PA 134
- General Lewis, The, Lewisburg, WV 183
- Genesee Country Inn, The, Mumford, NY 103
- Gideon Ridge Inn, Blowing Rock, NC 119
- Gingerbread Mansion, Ferndale, CA 18
- Glasbern, Fogelsville, PA 139
- Glen Ella Springs, Clarkesville, GA 39
- Goose Cove Lodge, Sunset, ME 52
- Governor's Inn, Ludlow, VT 159
- Grant Corner Inn, Sante Fe, NM 99
  Graves' Mountain Lodge, Syria, VA 174
- Greenville Arms 1889 Inn, Greenville, NY 111
- Grey Whale Inn, Fort Bragg, CA 19
  Greyfield Inn, Cumberland Island, GA 42
- Greystone Inn, The, Lake Toxaway, NC 116
  Griswold Inn, The, Essex, CT 35
- Groveland Hotel, Groveland, CA 22
  Hamilton House Inn, Spring Lake, NJ 95
- Hancock Inn, The, Hancock, NH 92
  Harbor House Inn by the Sea, Elk, CA 20
- Harbor Light Inn, Marblehead, MA 67
- Harmony House Inn, New Bern, NC 120
- Hartwell House, Ogunquit, ME 58
- Haus Rohrbach Pension, Leavenworth, WA 181
- Hawthorne Inn, Concord, MA 67
- Hearthstone Inn, Colorado Springs, CO 31
  Hemlock Inn, Bryson City, NC 114
  Heron Haus, Portland, OR 128
- Hickory Bridge Farm, Orrtanna, PA 144
- Hidden Inn, The, Orange, VA 174
- High Meadows, Scottsville, VA 176
- Homestead Inn, The, Greenwich, CT 36
- Hotel Manisses, Block Island, RI 146
- Inn at Buckeystown, The, Buckeystown, MD 60
- Inn at Canoe Point, The, Hulls Cove, ME 50

Index

Inn at Cedar Crossing, Sturgeon Bay, WI 188
• Inn at Cedar Falls, The, Logan, OH 124
• Inn at Crotched Mountain,
  Francestown, NH 91
• Inn at Depot Hill, The, Capitola-by-
  the-Sea, CA 23
• Inn at Gristmill Square, Warm
  Springs, VA 167
Inn at Honey Run, The, Millersburg, OH 123
Inn at Little Washington, The,
  Washington, VA 171
• Inn at Millrace Pond, The, Hope, NJ 94
Inn at Montpelier, The, Montpelier, VT 157
• Inn at Narrow Passage,
  Woodstock, VA 172
• Inn at Occidental, The, Occidental, CA 22
• Inn at Olde New Berlin, The,
  New Berlin, PA 135
• Inn at Ormsby Hill, The, Manchester
  Center, VT 162
• Inn at Starlight Lake, The, Starlight, PA 137
• Inn at Stockbridge, The, Stockbridge, MA 65
• Inn at the Taylor House, The, Valle
  Crucis, NC 118
• Inn at Weathersfield, The,
  Weathersfield, VT 160
• Inn at Webbley, Shelby, NC 117
• Inn at Zapata Ranch, Mosca, CO 32
• Inn on Summer Hill, Summerland, CA 27
• Inn on the Common, Craftsbury
  Common, VT 156
• Interlaken Inn, Lake Placid, NY 108
• Isaiah Jones Homestead, Sandwich, MA 69
• Jacksonville Inn, Jacksonville, OR 131
• James House, The, Port Townsend, WA 179
• Jared Coffin House, Nantucket, MA 73
• Jarrett Farm Country Inn, Ramona, OK 125
• John Rutledge House Inn, Charleston, SC 148
• Johnson House, The, Florence, OR 129
• Jordan Hollow Farm Inn, Stanley, VA 171
Joshua Grindle Inn, Mendocino, CA 19
• Joshua Wilton House Inn & Restaurant,
  Harrisonburg, VA 170
• King's Cottage, A Bed & Breakfast Inn,
  The, Lancaster, PA 143
• L'Auberge Provencale, White Post, VA 172
• LaCorsette Maison Inn, Newton, IA 44
• Lake Placid Lodge, lake Placid, NY 108
• Lamplight Inn B&B, The, Lake
  Luzerne, NY 109
• Landgrove Inn, The, Landgrove, VT 161
• Larchwood Inn, Wakefield, RI 145
• Lincklaen House, Cazenovia, NY 106
• Little St. Simons Island, St. Simons
  Island, GA 42
• Lodge at Moosehead Lake, The,
  Greenville, ME 48
• Lodge on the Desert, The, Tucson, AZ 16
• Longfellow's Wayside Inn, South
  Sudbury, MA 66
• Lords Proprietor's Inn, The, Edenton, NC 121
• Lovelander B&B Inn, The, Loveland, CO 30
• Lowell Inn, Stillwater, MN 77
• Madewood Plantation House,
  Napoleonville, LA 46
• Madrona Manor, Healdsburg, CA 21
• Maine Stay Inn & Cottages,
  Kennebunkport, ME 56
• Maine Stay, Camden, ME 53
• Mainstay Inn, Cape May, NJ 97

• Manor House, Cape May, NJ 97
• Manor on Golden Pond, The,
  Holderness, NH 90
• Mansion Hill Inn, Madison, WI 189
• Maple Hall, Lexington, VA 167
• Marquesa Hotel, The, Key West, FL 38
• Martine Inn, The, Pacific Grove, CA 24
• Mast Farm Inn, The, Valle Crucis, NC 119
  Meadow Lane Lodge, Warm Springs, VA 168
• Monmouth Plantation, Natchez, MS 80
  Montague Inn, Saginaw, MI 75
• Montford Inn, Norman, OK 126
• Moose Mountain Lodge, Etna, NH 89
• Morgan-Samuels B&B Inn,
  Canandaigua, NY 104
• Mountain Top Inn and Resort,
  Chittenden, VT 158
  Murphin Ridge Inn, West Union, OH 124
• National House Inn, The, Marshall, MI 76
• Newcastle Inn, The, Newcastle, ME 54
• Normandy Inn, Spring Lake, NJ 95
• Notchland Inn, The, Hart's Location, NH 87
• Oaks Victorian Inn, The,
  Christianburg,VA 166
• October Country Inn, Bridgewater
  Corners, VT 159
• Oge' House on the Riverwalk, San
  Antonio, TX 153
• Old Consulate Inn (F. W. Hastings House),
  Port Townsend, WA 179
• Old Fort Inn, Kennebunkport, ME 57
• Old Monterey Inn, Monterey, CA 24
  Old Rittenhouse Inn, Bayfield, WI 186
• Oliver Loud's Inn, Pittsford, NY 104
• Orchard Inn, The, Saluda, NC 116
• Overlook Mansion, Little Falls, NY 107
• Pentagoet Inn, The, Castine, ME 49
  Philbrook Farm Inn, Shelburne, NH 86
• Pilgrim's Inn, Deer Isle, ME 52
• Pine Crest Inn, Tryon, NC 117
• Pomegranate Inn, Portland, ME 55
• Prospect Hill Plantation Inn,
  Trevilians, VA 176
• Queen Anne Inn, The, Chatham/Cape
  Cod, MA 72
  Queen Victoria, The, Cape May, NJ 98
• Rabbit Hill Inn, Lower Waterford, VT 156
• Ralph Waldo Emerson Inn,
  Rockport, MA 68
• Rangeley Inn, Rangeley, ME 49
• Red Lion Inn, The, Stockbridge, MA 64
• Rhett House, The, Beaufort, SC 149
• Richmond Hill Inn, Asheville, NC 118
• Richmont Inn, Townsend, TN 151
• RiverSong, Estes Park, CO 29
• Robert Morris Inn, The, Oxford, MD 62
• Rose Inn, Ithaca, NY 105
  Rowell's Inn, Simonsville, VT 160
• Sandpiper Inn at the Beach,
  Carmel-by-the-Sea, CA 25
• Schumachers' Historic European Hotel,
  New Prague, MN 78
• Sea Crest by the Sea, Spring Lake, NJ 96
• Seal Beach Inn and Gardens,
  Seal Beach, CA 27
• Sedgwick Inn, The, Berlin, NY 110
• Settlers Inn, The, Hawley, PA 137
• Seven Sea Street Inn, Nantucket, MA 73
• Shelburne Inn, Seaview, WA 180
• Shellmont B&B Inn, Atlanta, GA 40

Index

Sherwood Inn, The, Skaneateles, NY 106
- Shire Inn, Chelsea, VT 157
- Silver Thatch Inn, Charlottesville, VA 175
- Simmon's Way Village Inn & Restaurant, Millerton, NY 111
- Simpson House, Santa Barbara, CA 26
- Smithton Inn, Ephrata, PA 141
Snowbird Mountain Lodge, Robbinsville, NC 114
- Southmoreland On the Plaza, Kansas City, MO 82
- Squire Tarbox Inn, The, Wiscasset, ME 54
- Stafford's Bay View Inn, Petoskey, MI 74
- Stafford's in the Field, Chocorua, NH 88
Stanford Inn by the Sea, The, Mendocino, CA 20
- Steamboat Inn, Steamboat, OR 130
- Sterling Inn, The, Sterling, PA 139
- Swag Country Inn, The, Waynesville, NC 115
- Swiss Woods B&B, Lititz, PA 142
- Tanque Verde Ranch, Tucson, AZ 16
- Tara - A Country Inn, Clark, PA 134
- Thorncroft Inn, Vineyard Haven / Martha's Vineyard, MA 72
- Three Mountain Inn, Jamaica, VT 163
- Trillium House, Nellysford, VA 169
- Tu' Tu' Tun Lodge, Gold Beach, OR 130
- Turtleback Farm Inn, Orcas Island, WA 178
- Twin Gates B&B Inn, Lutherville, MD 61
Two Meeting Street Inn, Charleston, SC 149
- Tyler Spite House, Frederick, MD 60
- Under Mountain Inn, Salisbury, CT 33
- Vagabond's House Inn, Carmel, CA 25
- Veranda, The, Senoia, GA 40
- Victorian Villa, The, Union City, MI 76
- Village Inn, The, Lenox, MA 64
- Walnut Street Inn, Springfield, MO 83
- Waterford Inne, The, Waterford, ME 55
- Waverly Inn, The, Hendersonville, NC 115
- Weathervane Inn, The, South Egremont, MA 65
- West Lane Inn, Ridgefield, CT 34
- West Mountain Inn, Arlington, VT 162
- Westchester House B&B, The, Saratoga Springs, NY 110
- Whalewalk Inn, The, Eastham, MA 71
- Whistling Swan Inn, Stanhope, NJ 93
- White Gull Inn, The, Fish Creek, WI 187
- White Inn, The, Fredonia, NY 102
White Lace Inn, Sturgeon Bay, WI 188
- White Oak Inn, Danville, OH 123
Whitehall Inn, Camden, ME 53
- Whitehall Inn, The, New Hope, PA 140
- Willcox House Country Inn, Bremerton, WA 180
- William Seward Inn, Westfield, NY 102

- Winchester Country Inn, The, Ashland, OR 131
- Windham Hill Inn, West Townsend, VT 163
- Wine Country Inn, The, St. Helena, CA 21
Wooster Inn, The, Wooster, OH 122
- Yankee Clipper Inn, Rockport, MA 68

CANADA
- Aerie Resort, The, Malahat, B.C. 194
- Beaconsfield Inn, Victoria, B.C. 196
- Benmiller Inn, Goderich, ONT 201
- Briars, The, Jackson Point, ONT 199
- Domain of Killien, Haliburton, ONT 199
- Eganridge Inn, Fenelon Falls, ONT 200
- Elm Hurst Inn, Ingersoll, ONT 205
- Elora Mill Inn, Elora, ONT 203
- Hovey Manor, North Hatley, QUE 210
- Jakobstettel Guest House Inc., St. Jacobs, ONT 203
- Kettle Creek Inn, Port Stanley, ONT 204
- Langdon Hall Country House Hotel, Cambridge, ONT 205
- Little Inn of Bayfield, The, Bayfield, ONT 201
- Middle Beach Lodge, Tofino, BC 193
- Millcroft Inn, The, Alton, ONT 204
- Oak Bay Beach Hotel, Victoria, BC 195
- Oceanwood Country Inn, Mayne Island, BC 194
- Ripplecove Inn, Ayer's Cliff, QUE 209
- Rosemount Inn, Kingston, ONT 207
- Sam Jakes Inn, Merrickville, ONT 200
- Shaw's Hotel, Brackley Beach, PEI 211
- Sherwood Inn, Port Carling, ONT 198
- Sir Sam's Inn, Eagle Lake, ONT 198
- Sooke Harbour House Inn, Sooke, BC 195
- Ste. Anne's Country Inn & Spa, Grafton, ONT 206
- Stone Maiden Inn, Stratford, ONT 202
- Trinity House Inn, Gananoque, ONT 207
- Westover Inn, St. Marys, ONT 202
- Woodlawn Terrace Inn, ONT 206

UNITED KINGDOM
- Cottage in the Wood, The, Worcester, Worcestershire 214
- Crown Hotel, The, Exford, Somerset 215
- Kennel Holt Hotel, Cranbrook, Kent 217
Maison Talbooth, Colchester, Essex 217
Mill Hotel, The, Mungrisdale, Cumbria 213
- Petty France Hotel, Badminton, Avon 214
Philipburn House Hotel, Selkirk, Scotland 213
- Somerset House, Bath, Avon 216
- The Royal Oak Hotel, Withypool, Somerset 215
- Woolley Grange Hotel, Woolley Green, Wiltshire 216

Notes

Help us help our members

. . . maintain the standards of excellence that the IIA upholds by answering the questions below and mailing the card directly to the IIA office. Your signature below is not necessary; however, we would be pleased to know who you are. Please rate each item on a scale of 1 to 5, with 1 being "least satisfactory" and 5 being "nearly perfect."

Name of the inn: _____

_____ 1) Were you greeted and served with a spirit of hospitality throughout your stay?

_____ 2) Was the guest room equipped with your comfort and safety in mind?

_____ 3) Did the inn evidence high standards of housekeeping and maintenance?

_____ 4) Was the food/service (or the area's food/service) of high quality?

_____ 5) Was the feeling of individuality in the personality or character of the inn aesthetically pleasing and consistent?

_____ 6) Did you receive value for your dollar?

_____ 7) Would you return to this inn?

Additional comments: _____

_____

Name and address of other inns you would like to recommend:

_____

_____

Your name and address (optional) _____

_____

Help us help our members

. . . maintain the standards of excellence that the IIA upholds by answering the questions below and mailing the card directly to the IIA office. Your signature below is not necessary; however, we would be pleased to know who you are. Please rate each item on a scale of 1 to 5, with 1 being "least satisfactory" and 5 being "nearly perfect."

Name of the inn: _____

_____ 1) Were you greeted and served with a spirit of hospitality throughout your stay?

_____ 2) Was the guest room equipped with your comfort and safety in mind?

_____ 3) Did the inn evidence high standards of housekeeping and maintenance?

_____ 4) Was the food/service (or the area's food/service) of high quality?

_____ 5) Was the feeling of individuality in the personality or character of the inn aesthetically pleasing and consistent?

_____ 6) Did you receive value for your dollar?

_____ 7) Would you return to this inn?

Additional comments: _____

_____

Name and address of other inns you would like to recommend:

_____

_____

Your name and address (optional) _____

_____

Independent Innkeepers' Association
P.O. Box 150
Marshall, MI 49068

Independent Innkeepers' Association
P.O. Box 150
Marshall, MI 49068